Workbook and Answer Key to Accompany Visión y voz

Second Edition

Introductory Spanish

Vicki Galloway
Angela Labarca

Prepared by Abby Kanter

WILEY
Custom Services

Printed in the United States of America.

ISBN 0-471-32382-9

WORKBOOK TO ACCOMPANY

VISIÓN Y VOZ

Introductory Spanish
SECOND EDITION

Vicki Galloway
Georgia Institute of Technology

Angela Labarca
Georgia Institute of Technology

Prepared by
Abby Kanter

John Wiley & Sons, Inc.

New York · Chichester · Weinheim
Brisbane · Singapore · Toronto

COVER PHOTO: Ronnie Kaufman / The Stock Market

REALIA CREDITS: p. 6: APRENDA INGLES, El Diario, 17 de marzo de 1997, p.8; p. 43: Xcaret, GeoMundo, vol. 13 núm. 7, p.10; p. 56: Los relojes y su historia; Geomundo, vol. 13, núm. 7, pp. 99-101; p. 65: "Sí, acepto...", Cristina, año 7, núm, 6; p.68: César Evora, Cristina, año 7, núm. 6, p. 52; p. 85: Cumpleaños de Alex Venegas, La voz, Mexicali, 10 de agosto de 1995, p. 8-C; p. 96: Desde el avión, Cristina, año 2, núm. 6, p.6; p. 109: Abuelos que cuidan niños, Tiempos del mundo, 3 de julio de 1997, News World Argentina S.A.; p. 112: Cisco Systems, 1996; p. 121: Desenmascaramos Zorro, Cristina, año 7, núm. 6, pp. 20-21; p. 124: Pollo a lo Celia Cruz, Cristina, año 7, núm. 6, pp. 30-31; p. 135: Empanadas que dan la talla, Américas, julio/agosto 1994, p.52; p. 147: Diseñando para los 90, Américas, enero/febrero, 1987, p. 32; p. 159: Tatuajes, una moda que incomoda, Tiempos del mundo, 3 de julio de 1997; p. 168: Armonía, Vogue, España, núm. 28, julio 1990, pp. 50, 52; p. 180: Laura Esquivel y una historia de novela, Nuestra Gente, vol. 4, núm. 4, p. 24; p. 192: Un alcalde diferente, Américas, abril 1997, p. 40; p. 203: Guardiana del legado silvestre, Américas, marzo/abril 1993, p. 34.

PHOTO CREDITS: p. 16: Corn Harvest (La cosecha del maíz), Diego Rivera, 1923-24, mural. Court of Fiestas, Level 1, South Wall. Secretaria de Educación Pública, Mexico City, Mexico.

ISBN 0-471-17089-5

Printed in the United States of America

10 9 8 7 6 5 4 3 2 1

Printed and bound by Bradford & Bigelow, Inc.

Contents

Preface

This Workbook accompanies the textbook *Visión y voz: Introductory Spanish, Second Edition*. The Workbook provides written activities that practice and reinforce the vocabulary and structures presented in the textbook; it also provides students with authentic readings and follow-up activities that are both thematically and culturally related to topics developed in the textbook.

Each chapter of the Workbook contains the following sections, which parallel those of the textbook: **Vocabulario: Imágenes y palabras, Gramática 1, Gramática 2** (and, in a few chapters, **Gramática 3**), **Lectura: Voces del mundo hispano**, and **Para escribir**. The activities in the Workbook offer a wide variety of learning formats, including cloze activities, dialogues, personalized questions, crossword puzzles, illustration- and realia-based activities, and so forth. The Workbook also contains **Autoevaluciones** for each unit (two chapters) of the textbook. These self-tests allow students to diagnose their needs prior to taking the instructor's unit test.

Instructors may request from their Publisher's Representative a copy of the *Visión y voz* second edition Tapescript and Answer Key supplement, which contains the answers for this Workbook.

¡Hola! ¿Qué tal?

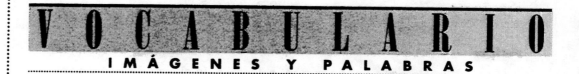

VOCABULARIO
IMÁGENES Y PALABRAS

A. ¿Qué hay...? Use **hay** + **mucho (mucha, muchos, muchas)** + object(s) to form sentences according to the following model. Make each sentence as complete as possible.

Por ejemplo: el libro
En el libro hay muchas páginas y palabras.

1. la biblioteca

   En la biblioteca hay muchos libros, muchas computadoras, muchas cintas y sillas

2. la universidad

   En la universida hay muchos alumnos, muchos profesores, muchas salas de clase, muchas residencias estudiantiles, muchos laboratorios

3. mi mochila

   En mi mochila hay lápices, muchos libros, bolígrafos, cuadernos

4. mi cuaderno

   En mi cuaderno hay muchas hojas de papel y muchos apuntes.

5. la residencia estudiantil

   En la residencia estudiantil hay muchos alumnos, muchas sillas y muchos televisores.

6. el laboratorio de idiomas (lenguas)

   En el laboratorio de idiomas hay muchas cintas y computadoras

B. Los diálogos. Completa las conversaciones.

Pablo: Hola, Viviana, ¿qué ___tal___ ?

Viviana: ___Bien___ , Pablo. Mi profesora de historia

es muy buena y la clase no es ___difícil/mala___

Y tú, Pablo, ¿cómo te ___va___ ?

Pablo: No, _____Muy_____ _____bien_____. Mi clase es muy difícil y hay

mucha _____tarea_____.

Viviana: Lo _____siento_____, Pablo.

Felipe: ¿Cómo _se_ _llama_ usted, profesora?

Sra. Pérez: _Me_ _llamo_ señora Pérez. Soy _____profesora_____ de

historia. Y tú, ¿cómo _te_ _llamas_?

Felipe: _Me_ _llamo_ Felipe y soy _____alumno_____ de historia.

Necesito ayuda con mi selección de clases. Necesito un

_____horario_____ flexible este semestre. Y necesito tomar un

_____curso_____ sin _matrícula_.
      tuition

Sra. Pérez: Sí. No hay problema.

Felipe: Muchas _gracias_, profesora Pérez

C. La universidad ideal. Completa las frases.

1. En la universidad ideal hay

a. _____

b. _____

c. _____

d. _____

2. En la universidad ideal no hay

a. _____

b. _____

c. _____

d. _____

D. Mi curso ideal. Completa las frases.

1. En mi curso ideal necesito...

a. _____

b. _____

c. _____

d. _____

2. En mi curso ideal no necesito...

a. _____

b. _____

c. _____

d. _____

1 Personas y personalidades

VOCABULARIO
IMÁGENES Y PALABRAS

A. ¿Cómo son? Completa las frases con palabras apropiadas.

Palabras útiles

sin pensar — *without thinking*

se porta — *behaves*

1. Somos trabajadores, no somos

   _____.

2. Matilde no quiere hablar frente a muchas

   personas porque ella es _____ y

   tímida.

3. Miguel es un buen amigo que escucha mis problemas con gran

   atención. Miguel es muy _____ y muy _____ al

   sufrimiento de otras personas.

4. A la profesora le gusta estar en casa con su familia. Ella es muy

   _____.

5. Algunas películas de Stephen Speilberg son cómicas o _____;

   otras, como "La lista de Schindler", son más _____.

6. Mi hermano es muy _____, siempre está en el gimnasio.

7. Carla es muy _____, hace cosas sin pensar°.

8. A Diego no le gusta descansar; es muy activo y le gusta ir a todas

   partes. Diego no es un muchacho _____.

9. Juanito siempre se porta° bien, y es muy respetuoso. Es un buen niño

y es muy _____ _____.

B. Yo no soy así. Choose four professions that you would least want to
follow, and tell why.

Por ejemplo: No quiero ser terapista porque no me gusta escuchar los
problemas de otros.

1. _____

2. _____

3. _____

4. _____

C. ¡Aprenda inglés!

Paso 1. Contesta las preguntas sobre el anuncio.

APRENDA INGLES
DE UNA MANERA RAPIDA, FACIL Y DIVERTIDA

NUESTRA GARANTIA: ¡MEJORE SUS OPORTUNIDADES Y OBTENGA UNA VIDA MEJOR EN NY!

CERTIFICADO POR EL DEPARTEMENTO DE EDUCACION DEL ESTADO DE NUEVA YORK

¡LLAME HOY!
PREGUNTE POR MARIA

1-800-INGLES-9
1-800-464-5379

PRECIOS RAZONABLES...HORAS CONVENIENTES

LUNES A VIERNES		SABADO	DOMINGO
8:00 AM A 10:00 AM	4:00 PM A 6:00 PM	8:00 AM A 12:00 PM	9:00 AM A 1:00 PM
10:00 AM A 1:00 PM		12:30 PM A 5:30 PM	1:30 PM A 5:30 PM
2:00 PM A 4:00 PM	6:00 A 9:00 (LUNES A JUEVES)	DESDE $9 SEMANALES	

8 RAZONES
PARA QUE UD. SE INSCRIBA EN EL MEJOR PROGRAMA DE INGLES EN N.Y.

1. Nos dedicamos únicamente a la enseñanza de inglés desde 1975.
2. Tenemos el método más directo de conversación que les dara resultados concretos e inmediatos: Ud. va a mejorar su conversación, gramática, vocabulario y también va a leer y escribir mucho mejor.
3. 50 profesores norteamericanos especializados en la enseñanza de inglés.
4. 4 directores para asegurar la máxima calidad de enseñanza.
5. Todos los niveles disponibles, desde principiantes hasta el más avanzado.
6. Examen de evaluacion preciso para determinar el mejor nivel de aprendizaje para cada nuevo estudiante.
7. Clases pequeñas.
8. Estudiantes dedicados y serios.

¡LAS NUEVAS CLASES COMIENZAN PRONTO!

AMERICAN LANGUAGE COMMUNICATION CENTER

• HOTEL PENNSYLVANIA • 7tma AVENIDA Y CALLE 33 (FRENTE AL MADISON SQUARE GARDEN)
UNSTED PUEDE ENCONTRAR NUESTRA ESCUELA EN EL LOBBY DEL HOTEL A LA DERECHE

1. ¿Para qué es el anuncio?
   a. libros de texto   c. clases de inglés
   b. clases de español   d. una universidad

2. ¿Cómo es el estilo (*style*) general de enseñanza (*teaching*)?

_____

3 ¿De dónde son los profesores?

_____

4. ¿Cómo son los alumnos (estudiantes)?

_____

5. En tu opinión, ¿de dónde son muchos de los alumnos?

_____

Paso 2.

1. Write the probable English cognate for the following.

   a. garantía _____

   b. oportunidades _____

   c. obtenga _____

   d. certificado _____

   e. estado _____

   f. evaluación _____

   g. avanzado _____

2. Use the context of the ad to make intelligent guesses at the meaning of the following words.

   a. vida _*life*_

   b. mejor _*better*_

   c. razones _*reasons*_

D. ¡Quiero trabajar! Lee el anuncio y contesta las preguntas.

EMPRESA IMPORTANTE SOLICITA

*Ingeniero químico industrial

REQUISITOS:

Escolaridad°: carrera° de ingeniería

Amplia experiencia en laboratorio en experimentación

Estado civil: casado° de preferencia

Hombre o mujer

*Contador

REQUISITOS:

Escolaridad: contador público

Edad: no mayor de 45 años

Estado civil: casado de preferencia

Sexo: masculino

Buena presentación

Hacer cita° al teléfono (56) 23 29

Mandar curriculum vitae
al FAX (65) 72 99 90

Presentarse a entrevista°:
Avenida Colón y Calle H #252
Colonia Nueva de 9:00 A.M. a 2:00 P.M.
Mexicali B.C. (Baja California)

Palabras útiles

la escolaridad	*education*
la carrera	*course of study*
casado	*married*
la cita	*appointment*
la entrevista	*interview*

---

1. ¿Qué profesionales necesitan?

_____

2. ¿Qué requisitos son similares a los requisitos en los E.E.U.U.?

_____

3. ¿Qué requisitos son diferentes?

a. _____

b. _____

c. _____

d. _____

4. ¿Qué hay que hacer para solicitar (*What must you do to apply for*) estos trabajos?

a. _____

b. _____

c. _____

GRAMÁTICA 1

A. Hispanos famosos. Completa la narración con las formas correctas del verbo **ser.**

El arte de Frida Kahlo (**1.**) _____ muy famoso. Ella y su esposo, Diego

Rivera, (**2.**) _____ artistas. Los dos (**3.**) _____ de México. Las

pasiones de la vida de Frida (**4.**) _____ pintar y estar con Diego.

Muchos otros hispanos (**5.**) _____ populares en los E.E.U.U. Andy

García (**6.**) _____ de Cuba pero ahora (**7.**) _____ residente de

California. (**8.**) _____ mi actor favorito. Yo (**9.**) _____ gran

aficionada (*fan*) suya. Andy no habla mucho de su vida personal.

(**10.**) _____ una persona muy privada. No le gusta vivir con mucha

publicidad; prefiere estar con su familia. ¿(**11.**) _____ tú reservado(a)

como Andy García?

Otra hispana famosa (**12.**) _____ Gloria Estefan. (**13.**) _____

cubano-americana, que ahora vive en Miami. (**14.**) _____ delgada, de

estatura mediana y muy bonita. Cantar y hacer ejercicios (**15.**) _____

sus pasiones. Ella (**16.**) _____ muy sensible, y dice, "Mis canciones

(**17.**) _____ como fotografías de mis emociones."

B. ¿Cómo son? Complete each question with the correct form of **ser**, then answer the question.

Por ejemplo: ¿**Son** los profesores listos?
  Sí, son muy listos.

1. ¿_____ (tú) impaciente a veces?

   _____

2. ¿_____ deportistas Uds.?

   _____

3. ¿De dónde _____ tus abuelos?

   _____

4. ¿Quién _____ tu escritor/a favorito(a)?

   _____

5. ¿De dónde _____ tu escritor/a favorito(a)?

   _____

C. Todo lo contrario. Complete each sentence with the appropriate form of the verb **ser**. Then write a second sentence according to the model.

Por ejemplo: Diego Rivera no es escritor. **Es artista.**

1. Jennifer Aniston y Sharon Stone no _____ pelirrojas. _____

   _____

2. Yo no _____ español/a. _____

3. Tú no _____ perezoso(a). _____

4. *Ace Ventura* no _____ una película seria. _____

   _____

5. Las figuras del artista Botero no _____ delgadas. _____

   _____

   _____

6. Stephen King y John Grisham no _____ arquitectos. _____

   _____

7. Tú y yo no _____ estúpidos. _____

8. Sean Connery no _____ joven. _____

GRAMÁTICA 2

A. Más de uno. Make the following groups of words plural, and provide the article.

Por ejemplo: contador organizado
los contadores organizados

1. lápiz rojo _____

2. alumna alegre _____

3. profesor deportista _____

4. dentista organizada _____

5. buena personalidad _____

6. persona mayor _____

B. Tal para cual. Rewrite each sentence using the new subject indicated. Make all necessary changes in number and gender.

Por ejemplo: Evita es famosa.
John y Yoko son famosos.

1. Gloria Estefan es hispana, famosa y popular.

   Andy García y Cristina _____

2. Octavio Paz es serio y trabajador.

   Frida Kahlo y Ana María Matute _____

3. Ana es pesimista.

   Ana y Carlos _____

4. Donald Trump es emprendedor y puntual.

   Oprah Winfrey _____

5. La profesora es desordenada pero responsable.

   Los alumnos _____

C. ¿Cómo es?   Select five personal characteristics and write a sentence for each, naming the person you think best represents the characteristic. The person can be real or fictional, famous or someone from your own life.

Por ejemplo: Luke Skywalker es muy aventurero.

1. _____

2. _____

3. _____

4. _____

5. _____

D. Tengo una amiga que tiene un amigo que...   You have been fixed up on a blind date. Using the indicated adjectives and **(no) soy** and **(no) me gusta**, write four facts about yourself that you would most like your date to know.

Por ejemplo: emprendedor/a   **Soy emprendedora, me gusta trabajar.**
                  tranquilo(a)   **No soy tranquila, no me gusta descansar.**

1. reservado(a) _____

2. perezoso(a) _____

3. hogareño(a) _____

4. trabajador/a _____

G R A M Á T I C A 3

A. ¡Vamos a conocernos!   Use **Quiero saber si...** (*I want to know if...*) to ask six questions about a blind date.

Por ejemplo: Quiero saber si él (ella) es optimista o pesimista. También quiero saber si le gusta bailar.

1. _____

2. _____

3. _____

4. _____

5. _____

6. _____

B. ¿Qué le gusta hacer? Tell what the people mentioned in Activity A (Gramática 1) on page 9 like, or do not like, to do.

Por ejemplo: A Andy García no le gusta hablar de su vida personal.

1. A Frida Kahlo _____

2. A Andy García _____

3. A Gloria Estefan _____

C. Gustos. Complete the following sentences with the appropriate pronoun: **me, te, le, les, nos.**

1 ¿A Uds. _les_ gusta aprender español?

2. A nosotros _nos_ gusta escuchar la música de "Las Puertas".

3. A ti _te_ gusta ir a la playa.

4. A ellos _les_ gusta leer las novelas de Gabriel García Márquez.

5. A mí _me_ gusta comer tacos.

6. A Imelda Marcos _le_ gusta ir de compras.

7. A los jóvenes _les_ gusta hablar por teléfono.

8. A nosotros _nos_ gusta salir con amigos.

D. Escríbelo tú. Form sentences based on the following groups of words, according to the models. Make any changes necessary in the number (singular or plural) or gender (masculine or feminine) of adjectives.

Por ejemplo: A ellos/estudiar/ serio
Les gusta estudiar porque son serios.

A la niña/no/trabajar/perezoso
No le gusta trabajar porque es perezosa.

1. María/trabajar/emprendedor

_____

2. Marcelo y Teresa/ir al gimnasio/deportista

_____

3. Nosotros/no/ir a fiestas/hogareño

_____

Visión y voz 2E Workbook © 1998 John Wiley & Sons

4. Diego Rivera y Frida Kahlo/pintar/artista

_____

5. El Sr. Gore/hablar/político

_____

6. Ramón/escuchar/terapista

_____

E. Personalidades y actividades. For each illustration write a
sentence based on the model.

Por ejemplo: Los niños son perezosos. Les gusta mirar la televisión.

Luis y Clara

Ana y Elena

1. _____

_____

_____

2. _____

_____

_____

Fernando

Teresa

3. _____

_____

_____

4. _____

_____

_____

F. La nueva compañera de cuarto. Complete the dialog with the following question words according to the context: **cómo, quién, quiénes, dónde, de dónde.**

Pablo:	Hola, Cristina. ¿_____ estás?
Cristina:	Bien, pero un poco distraída (*distracted*).
Pablo:	¿Por qué? ¿Qué te pasa?
Cristina:	Es que tengo una nueva compañera de habitación.
Pablo:	¿_____ es?
Cristina:	Se llama Ana. Es una alumna de ingeniería.
Pablo:	Sí. Y ¿_____ es?
Cristina:	Es de Colombia.
Pablo:	¿_____ es?
Cristina:	Es muy simpática pero muy ordenada.
Pablo:	¿Cuál es el problema? Es bueno ser ordenado.
Cristina:	Pero es que es fanática. No sé _____ están mis libros, apuntes o lápices porque Ana ordena la habitación.
Pablo:	¡Qué problema! ¿_____ vas a resolverlo?
Cristina:	Necesito hablar con Ana.

G. Preguntas. Write two or more possible questions that could evoke the following answers.

Por ejemplo: El dentista es muy reservado.
   a. ¿Quién es muy reservado?
   b. ¿Cómo es el dentista?

1. Frida y Diego son de México.

   a. _____

   b. _____

2. Andy García y Gloria Estefan están en Hollywood.

   a. _____

   b. _____

3. La enfermera es muy sensible.

   a. _____

   b. _____

Visión y voz 2E Workbook © 1998 John Wiley & Sons

4. Las personas ordenadas son puntuales también.

a. _____

b. _____

5. Gabriel García Márquez es de Colombia y es magnífico.

a. _____

b. _____

L E C T U R A
V O C E S   D E L   M U N D O   H I S P A N O

I. Diego Rivera. Lee los dos párrafos y contesta las preguntas.

Diego Rivera, el esposo de Frida Kahlo, es uno de los artistas mexicanos más populares en los E.E.U.U. Muchas de sus pinturas son de temas° sociales: las condiciones del trabajo, la pobreza°, y otros problemas de la gente común. Por lo general, las figuras de Diego Rivera son gruesas y tienen una belleza° única y rara. La mujer de este cuadro es típica de la pintura de Diego Rivera.

    La vida matrimonial de Frida y Diego es algo difícil pero muy intensa. Frida sufre mucho por el interés que Diego demuestra por otras mujeres. La pena que sufre Frida es evidente en su arte.

Palabras útiles

lel tema	*theme*
la pobreza	*poverty*
la belleza	*beauty*

1. ¿Quién es Diego Rivera? Indica dos aspectos de su identidad.

a. _____

b. _____

2. ¿De dónde es Diego Rivera?

_____

3. ¿Qué temas quiere comunicar en su arte?

_____

4. ¿Cómo son las personas que pinta?

_____

La cosecha del maíz

5. ¿Tiene un matrimonio muy tranquilo? ¿Cómo es?

_____

6. Describe el problema en el matrimonio.

_____

7. ¿Dónde se encuentra (dónde está) evidencia de la pena de Frida?

_____

II. Juan Luis Guerra. Lee los párrafos y contesta las preguntas.

Juan Luis Guerra es un artista que canta las canciones que él mismo escribe. Con sus canciones comunica los problemas de su pueblo, los dominicanos, que muchas veces arriesganº la vida para llegar a los E.E.U.U. Juan Luis Guerra canta la pena de estos inmigrantes ilegales en los clubs de Nueva York.

Palabras útiles	
arriesgan	risk
conoció	she met
dulce	sweet
el precio	price

Además de la pena de los dominicanos, Juan Luis Guerra también canta del gran amor de su vida: su esposa Nora. Nora habla de la primera vez que conocióº a Juan Luis, y dice que la atracción resultó de "su forma de ser tan dulceº y tranquila, su personalidad. Su físico, la verdad es que no me llamó la atención". Físicamente, Nora es muy diferente de Juan Luis; es de estatura pequeña, ojos claros y pelo rubio, que reflejan su ascendencia europea.

A pesar de su fama, Juan Luis quiere mantener la vida privada. Es muy tímido y prefiere estar solo. Sufre mucho cuando es el centro de atención. A Juan Luis y a Nora les gusta ir a la playa, ir de compras por la ciudad, ir a un restaurante. Pero ya no hacen estas cosas. Es el precio* de la fama.

1. ¿Quién es Juan Luis Guerra? _____

2. ¿Cómo es? _____

3. ¿Quién es Nora? _____

4. ¿Cómo es? _____

5. ¿De dónde es Juan Luis? _____

6. ¿Dónde canta Juan Luis? _____

7. ¿Qué le gusta más a Nora, el físico o la personalidad de Juan Luis?

_____

8. ¿Qué les gusta hacer a Juan Luis y a Nora?

_____

9. ¿Le gusta a Juan Luis ser el centro de atención? ¿Por qué o por qué no?

_____

PARA ESCRIBIR
Tu gran telenovela

You are a writer who wishes to submit a proposal for a new soap opera.
Present four characters. Use the vocabulary of the chapter to give a basic
description of the appearance, personality, nationality, profession, wishes,
likes, loves, and dislikes of each character.

Palabras útiles

la telenovela   _soap opera_
el/la protagonista   _main character_
el amor   _love_
querer a   _to love (someone)_
el esposo/ la esposa   _husband/wife_
el/la amante   _lover_

_____

_____

_____

_____

_____

_____

_____

_____

Capítulo 2

Metas y aficiones

VOCABULARIO
IMÁGENES Y PALABRAS

A. La familia Jiménez. Completa la narración con palabras apropiadas.

La familia de Ramiro Jiménez es muy amable. Sus familiares tienen intereses muy variados y diferentes. Ramiro tiene interés en la historia. Él puede

(**1.**) _____ nombres de gente famosa y las

(**2.**) _____ de eventos importantes. Ramiro quiere ser profesor

en un (**3.**) _____. Carlos, su hermano mayor, tiene interés en

la política. Quiere ser representante de su estado porque le gusta

(**4.**) _____ problemas y (**5.**) _____ decisiones.

Clara, su hermana, puede hablar español, inglés y francés, y quiere estudiar

otros (**6.**) _____. Ella también tiene interés en los negocios y

quiere trabajar en una (**7.**) _____ internacional. Quiere visitar

muchos (**8.**) _____ y (**9.**) _____ otra gente en

el (**10.**) _____. La Sra. Jiménez, la madre de Ramiro, tiene

interés en las finanzas. Ella trabaja en un (**11.**) _____ y gana

un (**12.**) _____ magnífico. Al Sr. Jiménez le gusta trabajar con

niños. Él es profesor en una (**13.**) _____. ¿Qué tienen en

común los Jiménez? Todos pueden (**14.**) _____ un

instrumento y tienen su propio grupo musical. Además, a todos les gusta

(**15.**) _____ ajedrez también y son muy competidores.

B. ¿Cómo eres tú? With which members of the Jiménez family do you have the most and the least in common?

Por ejemplo: Soy como... porque tengo interés en..., me gusta..., puedo... y quiero trabajar en...
No soy como... porque no tengo interés en..., no me gusta..., no puedo... y no quiero trabajar en...

1. _____

_____

_____

2. _____

_____

_____

C. La pesadilla (*nightmare*) **de Raúl.** Mira las imágenes para completar las frases.

1. Raúl no puede

_____

_____.

2. Raúl puede

_____

_____.

3. A Raúl le gusta

_____

en el futuro.

4. Ahora el monstruo no va a trabajar solo, va a trabajar en

_____ .

5. Por fin Raúl puede _____ el

problema. Él puede _____ el

violín muy bien y los monstruos están tranquilos.

D. Los tres cerditos (_little pigs_) **modernos.**   Lee la narración y contesta las preguntas con frases completas.

    Alfonso, el primer cerdito, tiene diecisiete años y es estudiante en un colegio. Tiene interés en el arte y puede pintar bien. Berto, el segundo cerdito, es diez años mayor que su hermano. Berto trabaja en una empresa de computadoras pero no está contento porque tiene interés en la música. Puede tocar el piano y cantar bien, pero los músicos no pueden ganar sueldos magníficos como los programadores de computadoras. Según Berto, Alfonso tiene que buscar empleo en los negocios porque los artistas no pueden ganar mucho. Alfonso no debe ser artista. El tercer cerdito, Carlos, es dos años mayor que Berto. Carlos es terapista y es muy inteligente. Va a resolver el problema de la carrera de Alfonso.

1. ¿Quién es el menor (el más joven)? _____

_____

2. ¿Quién es el mayor? _____

3. ¿Quién quiere ser artista? _____

4. ¿En qué tiene interés Berto? _____

5. ¿A Berto le gusta trabajar con la tecnología? _____

_____

6. ¿Quién puede tocar un instrumento? _____

_____

7. ¿Cuántos años tiene Berto? ¿Carlos? _____

_____

8. ¿Quiénes pueden ganar sueldos magníficos? _____

_____

9. ¿Quién es muy sensible? _____

_____

10. ¿Quién es más materialista? _____

_____

11. Debe probablemente quiere decir...

    a. *wants*   **c.** *should*

    b. *tries*   **d.** *needs*

E. La agenda de Gerardo. Mira la agenda de Gerardo y completa las frases.

```
3/5   examen de historia
8/5   entrevista de empleo
2/6   aniversario de papá y mamá
15/7  la playa con Virginia
12/8  película con Amelia
30/9  discoteca con Juan, Carmen y Alonso
```

Por ejemplo: Gerardo va a buscar empleo el ocho de mayo.

1. Gerardo va al cine _____ .

2. Gerardo va a estar con su familia _____ .

3. Va a bailar con sus amigos _____ .

4. Va a nadar _____ .

5. Va a estudiar mucho _____ .

F. El Banco de Costa Rica. El señor Sánchez, de San José, Costa Rica, tiene que hacer varios cheques por las siguientes cantidades. Escribe las cantidades con palabras.

1. Páguese a la orden de María Patricia Murillo C.18.090

_____

2. Páguese a la orden de Gilberto Pérez Toledo C.36.116

_____

3. Páguese a la orden de Edgar Meneses Castañeda C.26.065

_____

4. Páguese a la orden de Fernando Quesada Salom C.41.073

_____

G. Somos poetas.

Para la poeta española Gloria Fuertes, los meses del año evocan imágenes. ¿Asocias tú imágenes similares con los meses? Imita el estilo de Fuertes para escribir tu propio poema en el que cada mes represente algún aspecto de tu vida universitaria. Puedes usar sustantivos (*nouns*), verbos o adjetivos.

Por ejemplo: **Enero** es mucho estudiar.
Febrero es pensar en mi amor.
Marzo es optimista.
Abril es tomar decisiones.
Mayo es tomar exámenes.
Junio es sacar mi título...

LOS MESES*

Enero es un viejo° que viste° de blanco°.
Febrero es un loco que viste de tul°.
Marzo llorón cuerdo°.
Abril es poeta.
Mayo es invertido°.
Y junio es siesta.
Julio es arrogante.
Agosto sensual.
Septiembre es el mar°.
Octubre es un libro.
Noviembre una vela°.
Diciembre es un Niño°
que nace° y que tiembla°.

Palabras útiles	
viejo	no joven
viste	*dresses*
blanco	*white*
el tul	*net fabric*
llorón cuerdo	*sensible crybaby*
invertido	*upside down*
el mar	océano
la vela	*candle*
el Niño	Jesús
nace	*is born*
tiembla	*trembles*

GRAMÁTICA 1

A. Desordenados Anónimos.

Complete the following dialog with the correct form of **poder**, **tener**, or **tener que** according to the context.

Elena: Me llamo Elena y (**1.**) _____ un problema. (**2.**)

_____ veintidós años y soy extremadamente

desordenada. Quiero organizarme pero no (**3.**) _____ .

Mario: (terapista, jefe de "Desordenados Anónimos") ¿Dónde vives,

Elena, y con quién?

Elena: Vivo en casa con mis padres. (**4.**) _____ un hermano,

Alfredo, y una hermana, Ángela. Alfredo (**5.**) _____ su

*permission: Gloria Fuertes, Obras incompletas, p. 60.

propio dormitorio, pero Ángela y yo **(6.)** _____

compartir (*to share*) el dormitorio. Ella es desordenada también. A

veces Ángela **(7.)** _____ dormir en el sofá

¡porque no **(8.)** _____ encontrar (*to find*) la cama!

Mario: Es evidente que Uds. **(9.)** _____ un problema.

Yo **(10.)** _____ ofrecerles ayuda pero Uds.

(11.) _____ resolver el problema.

B. ¿Cómo eres tú? Contesta las preguntas.

1. ¿Tienes problemas como los de Elena? Explica.

_____

2. ¿Tienes que ordenar tu dormitorio? ¿Cuándo?

_____

3. ¿Puedes mantener el orden? ¿Cómo?

_____

4. ¿Puedes vivir con una persona totalmente desordenada? ¿Por qué sí o no?

_____

5. ¿Pueden tú y tus compañeros(as) estudiar o trabajar en un lugar totalmente desordenado? ¿Por qué?

_____

C. ¿Qué pueden hacer? Use **poder** + **infinitivo** to tell what the following people can do well.

1. Martha Stewart y el "Galloping Gourmet" _____

2. un buen diplomático _____

3. un traductor (*translator*) _____

4. Frida Khalo y Diego Rivera _____

5. Stevie Wonder _____

6. Stephen King y John Grisham _____

GRAMÁTICA 2

A. Las carreras. Completa las frases con la forma correcta de **querer** y **ir a**.

1. Juanita _____ ganar un sueldo magnífico. Por eso

_____ buscar empleo en una empresa estable.

2. Mario y Lucinda _____ estar cerca de la naturaleza.

Por eso _____ vivir en el estado de Montana.

3. Tú _____ vivir en el extranjero. Por eso

_____ trabajar en una empresa internacional.

4. Los niños _____ jugar. Por eso

_____ entrar en el gimnasio.

5. El Sr. Scrooge _____ estar cerca de su dinero. Por

eso _____ trabajar en un banco.

B. Te toca a ti. Write your own sentences, as in Activity A.

1. tú

_____

2. tu papá y/o mamá

_____

3. tu mejor amigo(a)

_____

4. el Presidente de los Estados Unidos

_____

C. Números de urgencia. Based on this directory of emergency numbers from a Spanish city, respond to each of the following situations, according to the model. Note that numbers are recited in groups of two.

AGENDA DE LA FRONDA

Teléfonos de interés		Juzgado 1 Instancia No.1	500605
Ambulancias	510909	Juzgado1 Instancia No 2	501257
Ayuntamiento	500115	Módulo de Promoción y Desarrollo	511211
Bomberos	502080	Oficina de Turismo	503005
Butano	500500	Oficina del INAEM	502479
Centro de Salud	501216	Policía Municipal	500115
Comisaría	091	Taxis	500007
Correos	501159		500002
Cruz Roja	502828		502022
Diputación	503944	Tráfico	501913
Estación Autobuses	503410	Iberdrola Atenc. al Cliente	501-702020
Guardia Civil	500502	Iberdrola Averías	590192
Hospital	502371-502372		

Por ejemplo: La familia Rodríguez busca una clínica.
Tiene que (Puede) llamar al centro de salud (*health*)**. El número es cincuenta, doce, dieciséis.**

1. Los Gutiérrez van a hacer un viaje.

_____

_____

2. El Sr. Ruiz necesita ir al hospital. ¡Es un caso de urgencia!

_____

_____

3. La Sra. Zalacaín va a visitar a su amiga pero no tiene automóvil.

_____

_____

4. ¡Ay! El Sr. Villanueva es víctima de un asalto.

_____

_____

D. ¡Vamos al cine! Read the following descriptions of movies that were being shown in Mexicali, México. Then answer the questions with complete sentences.

Una probadita

Estas son las películas que se exhiben actualmente en los cines de la localidad, aquí vemos "una probadita" de cada filme.

El Jorobado de Notre Dame

(The Hunchback of Notre Dame, 1996 EU)

Dibujos animados. La historia de la amistad entre Quasimodo, el jorobado que habita en el campanario de Notre Dame, con la bella gitana Esmeralda, quien a su vez causa el deseo ardiente del malvado Frollo.

Es una adaptación de la novela clásica del francés Víctor Hugo publicada en 1831.
Director: Gary Trousdale y Kirk Wise.
(Clasificación: AA)

Tornado

(Twister, 1996 EU)

Divertida y vertiginosa cinta de acción en la que se narra con lujo de efectos especiales la lucha de dos grupos rivales de "cazatornados" que quieren introducir valioso equipo experimental para detectar tornados a tiempo y conocer sus movimientos.
Clasificación: A
Dirige: Jan de Bont. Actúan: Helen Hunt y Bill Paxton.

Día de la Independencia

(Independence Day, 1996)

De pronto el mundo es invadido por una fuerza gigante de extraterrestres. Y cuando pareciera que los terrícolas somos impotentes para detenerlos, llega el 4 de julio que es el día de la independencia para la humanidad.
Clasificación: A
Dirige: Roland Emmerich.
Actúan: Will Smith, Bill Pullman, Jeff Coldbrum.

Misión Imposible

(Mission Impossible, EU 1996)

Mediante una operación fantasma la CIA descubre que el agente Ethan Hunt (Tom Cruise) es un traidor infiltrado en sus investigaciones secretas. Para demostrar lo contrario el protagonista tiene que atrapar al agente corrupto.
Clasificación: A
Dirige: Brian de Palma, Actúan: Tom Cruise, John Voigt y Emmenuelle Beart

Strip tease

(Strip tease, 1996)

Demi Moore es Erin Grant, una ex oficinista del FBI quien se ve en la necesidad de trabajar en un bar nudista para reunir el dinero que necesita para la custodia de su hija.
Actúan: Demi Moore y Burt Reynolds. Dirige: Andrew Bergman.
Clasificación: C

Corazón de Dragón

(Dragonheart, 1996)

Aborda el relato épico del siglo X, basado en la historia de Patrick Read Johnson y Charles Edward Pogue en donde se describe a un caballero heredero de los preceptos del Rey Arturo que es amigo de un singular dragón.
Actúan: Dennis Quaid y Sean Connery (voz).
Dirige: Rob Cohen.
Clasificación: A

El Protector

(Eraser, 1996)

Un policía se dedica a proteger la identidad de testigos de casos importantes asignándoles una personalidad nueva. Uno de sus compañeros lo traiciona y quiere matar a una de sus protegidas. Con ayuda de sus anteriores protegidos hará todo lo posible para desenmascarar al traidor.
Actúan: Arnold Schwarzenegger, James Caan y Vanessa Williams.
Dirige: Charles Rusell.
Clasificación: B

1. ¿Qué película(s) quieres ver? _____

_____

_____

Palabras útiles

la probadita	sampling
ver	to see
el campanario	bell tower

2. ¿Qué película(s) vas a ver con tus hermanitos?

_____

_____

3. ¿Qué película(s) no vas a ver con niños pequeños?

_____

_____

4. El Sr. Toledo quiere ver una película de acción. ¿Qué película va a ver?

_____

_____

5. ¿Qué película vas a ver si te gusta la ciencia ficción?

_____

_____

6. Use cognates and context clues to provide the Spanish for the following words.

a. animated feature _____

b. lives in _____

c. evil one (think of the word **malo**) _____

d. traitor _____

e. opposite _____

f. trap, catch _____

7. What U.S. movie classifications probably correspond to the following codes?

A _____   AA _____   B _____   C _____

L E C T U R A

V O C E S   D E L   M U N D O   H I S P A N O

I. Astrología: ¿verdad o ficción?

Lee el siguiente fragmento del horóscopo.

 En diciembre tenemos que buscar la felicidad. Tenemos que mantener el equilibrio entre la razón (el intelecto) y el corazón.

 Aries. 21 de marzo al 20 de abril. Este mes tienes que salir con amigos y asistir a funciones sociales. Vas a conocer a una persona que va a ser muy importante para ti. Va a ser el amor de tu vida.

 Tauro. 21 de abril al 20 de mayo. Vas a entrar en una empresa nueva. Es un negocio que puede ser muy beneficioso. Pero tienes que tener cuidado y no ser impulsivo.

 Géminis. 21 de mayo al 21 de junio. Vas a tener problemas con algunos familiares. Tienes que ser muy sensible respecto a las emociones de ellos; puedes resolver estos problemas.

 Cáncer. 22 de junio al 21 de julio. Normalmente no eres puntual ni organizado, pero este mes tienes que serlo. Si eres desorganizado este mes vas a entrar en apuros (problemas) enormes.

 Leo. 22 de julio al 21 de agosto. Eres demasiado impaciente e impulsivo. Tienes que ser más paciente y vas a aprender un secreto que te va a ayudar mucho.

 Virgo. 22 de agosto al 21 de septiembre. Vas a descubrir que tienes un talento nuevo. Tienes que ser imaginativo y trabajador.

¿Entendiste? Contesta las preguntas según las fechas de nacimiento de estas personas.

Ana   el 12 de junio
Tomás   el 6 de agosto
Clara   el 16 de abril
Guillermo el 27 de agosto
Luis   el 20 de mayo
Arturo   el 4 de julio

1. ¿Quiénes van a hacer algo nuevo?

_____

2. ¿Quiénes tienen que ser diferentes?

_____

3. ¿Quién va a ganar un sueldo mejor?

_____

4. ¿Quién va a tener una experiencia romántica?

_____

5. ¿Quién va a tener dificultades con sus padres o hermanos?

_____

II. Cómo leer tu letra

Se dice que la letra o escritura (*handwriting*) de una persona revela mucho sobre su carácter o personalidad. Mira los siguientes ejemplos y busca tu letra. Luego, lee la descripción personal correspondiente. ¿Así eres tú?

letra grande	*amigos*	Es generoso, abierto y entusiasta.
letra pequeña	*amigos*	Tiene una gran habilidad para concentrarse.
inclinada a la derecha	*Amigos*	Sentimental, romántico.
inclinada a la izquierda	*Amigos*	Es reservado. Oculta (*hides*) sus emociones.
dirección hacia arriba	*hola*	Es alegre, optimista y enérgico.
dirección hacia abajo	*hola*	Es pesimista y se siente deprimido (*depressed*).
línea derecha	*Te amo...*	Es estable.
las letras conectadas	*chico*	Es práctico y convencional.
las letras separadas	*chico*	Es intuitivo, inquieto y creativo.
algunas letras conectadas	*chico*	Perfecto equilibrio entre lo lógico, lo convencional y lo creativo.
letras largas	*Linda*	Es práctico y tiene mucha energía.
letras cortas	*Linda*	No tiene mucha imaginación, ni ambición.
letras anchas	*Linda*	Tiene muchísima imaginación.

Visión y voz 2E Workbook © 1998 John Wiley & Sons

PARA ESCRIBIR

Tus predicciones

Lee la sección astrológica del periódico de tu ciudad y escribe en español tus predicciones para los signos que siguen.

Libra. 22 de septiembre al 21 de octubre.

_____

_____

Escorpión. 22 de octubre al 21 de noviembre.

_____

_____

Sagitario. 22 de noviembre al 21 de diciembre.

_____

_____

Capricornio. 22 de diciembre al 18 de enero.

_____

_____

Acuario. 19 de enero al 18 de febrero.

_____

_____

Piscis. 19 de febrero al 20 de mayo.

_____

_____

¡Viva el finsemanismo!

VOCABULARIO
IMÁGENES Y PALABRAS

A. El campamento de verano. Completa la carta con palabras apropiadas.

Domingo, 12 de julio

Querida mamá,

Aquí estoy en el campamento de verano. Hoy no podemos nadar porque hace

(1) _____ _____. (2) _____

mucho. Pero mañana si hace (3) _____ vamos a nadar.

Aquí no hay piscina, pero podemos ir a la (4) _____ o al

(5) _____ para nadar. Hay un río, pero no es para nadar.

Vamos a (6) _____.

El martes vamos a hacer (7) _____ a las montañas. Vamos a

(8) _____ hamburguesas encima de un fuego (*campfire*).

Después vamos a (9) _____ a las montañas y

(10) _____ bajo las estrellas (*under the stars*).

El miércoles es día de deportes. A mí me gusta (11) _____

tenis, pero a mis amigos más altos les gusta el (12) _____.

Después hay deportes acuáticos y vamos a (13) _____ en

el (14) _____. Hay tantas actividades que no tengo

tiempo para (15) _____.

¡Estas (16) _____ de

verano son estupendas!

Un abrazo de tu hija que te quier e

Marisol

B. ¿Cuándo se hace? Completa las frases
según las imágenes.

Por ejemplo: A Luisa le gusta tomar el sol pero
sólo puede hacerlo en el verano
(cuando hace sol).

1. A Jorge le gusta

_____

pero sólo puede hacerlo

_____ .

2. A Teresa le gusta

_____

pero sólo puede hacerlo

_____ .

3. A Juan y a Luisa les gusta

_____

pero sólo pueden hacerlo

_____ .

4. A los jóvenes les gusta

_____

pero sólo pueden hacerlo

_____ .

5. A Carlos y a Gabriel les

gusta _____

pero sólo pueden hacerlo

_____ .

C. Amigos diferentes. Jorge es una persona tranquila y hogareña. Le gusta la naturaleza y le gusta el ocio. Su amigo Enrique es lo contrario. Es muy deportista y le gusta estar siempre activo. Escribe una lista de las actividades que a Jorge le gusta hacer, y las actividades que a Enrique le gusta hacer.

Jorge   Enrique

_____   _____

_____   _____

_____   _____

_____   _____

D. Tus vacaciones ideales. Contesta las preguntas con frases completas para describir tus vacaciones ideales.

1. ¿En que estación (*season*) del año te vas de vacaciones?

_____

_____

2. ¿Adónde vas? _____

_____

3. ¿Qué actividades puedes hacer allí?

_____

_____

4. ¿Te gusta nadar en una piscina, un lago o el mar? ¿Por qué?

_____

_____

5. ¿Cuántos días o cuántas semanas vas a pasar de vacaciones?

_____

_____

6. ¿Con quién(es) te vas? ¿Por qué?

_____

_____

GRAMÁTICA 1

A. ¿Adónde vamos? Completa la narración con la forma correcta de los verbos.

A mí me _____ (**1.** gustar) estar con mi familia pero cuando

yo _____ (**2.** ir) de vacaciones con ellos, _____

(**3.** ser) un desastre. Primero nosotros no _____ (**4.** poder)

decidir adónde _____ (**5.** querer) ir.

Mi mamá _____ (**6.** pensar) que unas buenas vacaciones

_____ (**7.** tener) que ser cerca del mar. Ella

_____ (**8.** nadar) bien y _____ (**9.** esquiar)

en el agua. Por las tardes _____ (**10.** leer) novelas y

_____ (**11.** dormir).

Mi papá _____ (**12.** querer) ir a un balneario en las

montañas donde él _____ (**13.** jugar) tenis todo el día y por

la noche _____ (**14.** escuchar) la música jazz.

Yo _____ (**15.** querer) pasar las vacaciones en una

ciudad grande porque allí _____ (**16.** conocer) a otros

jóvenes y nosotros _____ (**17.** ir) a discotecas donde los

jóvenes _____ (**18.** bailar) los bailes modernos.

A mi hermana mayor le _____ (**19.** gustar) viajar al

extranjero. Ella _____ (**20.** ir) a museos donde

_____ (**21.** ver) el gran arte del mundo. A veces nosotros

_____ (**22.** pensar) que es mejor tomar vacaciones

separadas. Yo no _____ (**23.** saber) qué hacer.

B. La rutina de Arturo. Completa la conversación con la forma correcta de los verbos.

Silvia: ¿Qué _____ (**1.** hacer) los fines de semana, Arturo?

Arturo: Bueno, siempre _____ (**2.** correr) dos millas por la mañana. Luego, si _____ (**3.** hacer) buen tiempo, mis

amigos y yo _____ (**4.** jugar) fútbol o _____

(**5.** montar) en bicicleta, o simplemente _____ (**6.** mirar) a

la gente en el parque. Si _____ (**7.** llover), o si

_____ (**8.** hacer) mal tiempo, no voy a ningún sitio; no

_____ (**9.** hacer) nada. Simplemente _____

(**10.** descansar) en casa. A veces, _____ (**11.** ver) una

película; uno de mis amigos _____ (**12.** tener) videocasetera

y siempre _____ (**13.** alquilar) muchos videos.

Silvia: ¿Y qué _____ (**14.** hacer) Uds. por la noche?

Arturo: Bueno, yo _____ (**15.** vivir) en un apartamento y,

como _____ (**16.** conocer) a mucha gente,

_____ (**17.** dar) fiestas casi todos los sábados. Mi

compañero de cuarto _____ (**18.** limpiar) el

apartamento y yo _____ (**19.** comprar) y

_____ (**20.** cocinar) la comida. Los viernes siempre

_____ (**21.** salir) con amigos.

Silvia: ¿Uds. nunca _____ (**22.** estudiar)?

Arturo: Yo, sí. _____ (**23.** hacer) mis tareas los domingos.

_____ (**24.** saber) que mis notas _____

(**25.** ser) importantes pero, como tú _____ (**26.** ver), no

_____ (**27.** trabajar) todos los días.

C. Las vacaciones. Describe las actividades de estas personas.

Raúl y Juanita

1. a. _____

   b. _____

los García

la familia Toledo

2. a. _____

b. _____

María y Daniela   los Gómez   Juan y Paulina

3. a. _____

b. _____

c. _____

Ángela   Pedro y Pablo   Pepe

Marta

4. a. _____

b. _____

c. _____

d. _____

Visión y voz 2E Workbook © 1998 John Wiley & Sons

Roberto y Raquel   Carlos y Juan

Juanita
y Raúl

5. a. _____

b. _____

c. _____

d. _____

D. Crucigrama. Para hacer este crucigrama, completa las frases.

Horizontales

1. Los hombres _____ en el río.

5. Los fines de semana nosotros _____ hasta muy tarde.

6. Juanita _____ la tele.

7. Tomás y yo _____ un paseo por la playa

10. Los niños _____ en el mar.

11. Ustedes _____ el sol en la playa.

13. Yo _____ muchas novelas en el verano.

14. Yo _____ en bote de remos.

16. Tú _____ que usar loción para el sol.

18. Yo _____ muchas películas en video.

19. Tú _____ tenis muy bien.

Verticales

1. Yo siempre lo _____ bien en el verano.

2 Tú _____ muy bien. Me gusta comer en tu casa.

3. Yo _____ en la piscina y en el lago.

4. Los Vargas _____ que agosto es el mejor mes para vacaciones.

5. Los domingos mis padres no hacen nada. _____ en casa.

8. Luis y yo _____ buenos amigos y nos gusta acampar juntos.

9. Los jóvenes _____ un paseo en el parque.

12. Los sábados mi amigo y yo _____ a caballo.

13. Uds. no _____ libros de texto en el verano.

15. Mi familia y yo _____ de vacaciones en julio.

17. Luquillo y Malibú _____ dos playas magníficas.

Visión y voz 2E Workbook © 1998 John Wiley & Sons

GRAMÁTICA 2

A. ¿Qué te gusta más? Based on each pair of drawings write a question using **gustar** and a noun. Answer the question, as in the example:

Por ejemplo: a ti

¿Te gusta más la ciudad o el campo?
Me gusta más el campo (la ciudad).

1. a Smokey el oso (*bear*)

_____

_____

2. a los niños

_____

_____

L	M	M	J	V	S	D
	1	2	3	4	5	⑥
7	8	9	10	11	12	⑬
14	15	16	17	18	19	⑳
21	22	23	24	25	26	㉗
28	29	30	31			

L	M	M	J	V	S	D
	1	2	3	4	5	6
⑦	8	9	10	11	12	13
⑭	15	16	17	18	19	20
㉑	22	23	24	25	26	27
㉘	29	30	31			

3. a ustedes

4. a tu mejor amigo(a)

_____

_____

5. a ti

_____

_____

6. a tus padres

_____

_____

7. a ustedes

_____

_____

B. ¿Qué dicen las imágenes? Según las imágenes, describe lo que les gusta hacer a estas personas. Comenta sus gustos respecto a la música, el cine, las vacaciones, los deportes, los programas de la tele, etc.

Jorge

1. _____

_____

_____

los Vásquez

2. _____

_____

_____

Arturo y
Roberto

3. _____

_____

_____

Visión y voz 2E Workbook © 1998 John Wiley & Sons

los jóvenes
de hoy

4. _____

_____

_____

Carolina

5. _____

_____

los "yuppies"

6. _____

_____

_____

C. Tus opiniones. Use **me + gusta/gustan** to name one or two things that you like at various times or in various circumstances. You may include kinds of movies, books, sports, activities, places, etc.

1. En el verano: _____

_____

2. En el otoño: _____

_____

3. En la primavera: _____

_____

4. Los domingos: _____

_____

5. Los sábados: _____

_____

6. Cuando estoy triste: _____

_____

7. Cuando estoy contento(a): _____

_____

8. Cuando estoy solo(a): _____

_____

9. En las vacaciones: _____

_____

L E C T U R A
V O C E S   D E L   M U N D O   H I S P A N O

Un lugar especial

Lee el artículo y completa las actividades que siguen.

XCARET DIMINUTO PARAÍSO DEL CARIBE MAYA

Si en el Caribe mexicano hay muchas opciones, la alternativa de Xcaret no puede descartarse. Una reducida zona arqueológica, una caleta y un cenote son los encantos que el visitante disfruta, sumado a los multicolores peces que brincan alegres an las transparentes aguas caribeñas.

El sitio arqueológico perteneció a la cultura maya, en el periodo postclásico y observa el mismo estilo que Tulum. Sólo se conservan tres templos con sus estructuras en ruinas, uno de los cuales aún exhibe restos de estuco rojo.

Para finalizar, en un terreno netamente calcáreo, una bella caleta es foco de interés para buceadores y turistas en general. Con agua templada, se extiende sobre unos 100 metros de largo y 15 de ancho aproximadamente, donde la transparencia del agua y la suavidad del oleaje fascinan al más exigente de los buceadores. Allí tienen sus dominios el pez ángel azul y el negro, dos de las especies multicolores que surcan el mar caribeño.

A. ¿Entendiste? Contesta las preguntas.

1. ¿Qué actividades o deportes hacen los turistas en Xcaret?

_____

_____

2. ¿Qué hay de interés arqueológico en Xcaret?

_____

_____

3. ¿Tienes interés en la arqueología? ¿Vas a estudiarla?

_____

_____

Palabras útiles

descartarse	to be discounted or ignored
la caleta	cove, creek, small bay
disfruta	enjoys
el pez (peces)	fish
brincan	jump
el estuco	stucco (type of building material)
el oleaje	motion of the waves
calcáreo	containing lime

4. ¿En qué deportes acuáticos puedes participar en Xcaret?

_____

5. ¿Cuál es el significado más probable de estos cognados?

a. diminuto _____

b. paraíso _____

c. alternativos _____

d. visitante _____

e. ruinas _____

f. exhibe _____

g. terreno _____

h. foco _____

i. templada _____

j. extiende _____

k. fascinan _____

6. ¿Te gustan las atracciones de Xcaret? ¿Quieres visitar esta isla algún

día? ¿Por qué?_____

_____

B. Vacaciones en Xcaret. Estás en Xcaret, donde pasas unas
vacaciones magníficas. Escríbele una tarjeta postal (_post card_) a un/a
amigo(a). Descríbele las cosas y actividades que te gustan más. Descríbele qué
haces hoy y qué vas a hacer mañana.

PARA ESCRIBIR

Tu paraíso

Inventa tu propio Paraíso de vacaciones (_Vacation Paradise_). Usa el vocabulario del Capítulo
3 para describir las vacaciones ideales. Incluye una descripción de las actividades que la
gente puede hacer y cómo es el tiempo.

_____

_____

_____

_____

_____

_____

_____

_____

_____

_____

_____

_____

Quiero escaparme de la rutina

VOCABULARIO
IMÁGENES Y PALABRAS

A. Compañeros diferentes.

Paso 1. Completa la narración con las palabras apropiadas. Algunas palabras se usan más de una vez.

Carlos y Guillermo son compañeros de cuarto en la universidad. Son

buenos amigos pero son muy diferentes. A Carlos le gusta

(1.) _____ muy temprano y siempre está muy contento

y **(2.)** _____ por la mañana. Está

(3.) _____ de energía y tiene ganas de

(4.) _____ para **(5.)** _____ a sus

clases. **(6.)** _____ de ducharse, se viste, y a la hora de

salir para las clases trata de despertar a Guillermo. Pero Guillermo no

puede **(7.)** _____ porque tiene la costumbre de **(8.)**

_____ muy tarde por la noche. Sabe que es necesario

(9.) _____, pero siempre está

(10.) _____ con Carlos por despertarlo. Cuando por fin

se levanta ya no tiene tiempo para **(11.)** _____ porque

no quiere **(12.)** _____ tarde a las clases. Guillermo

siempre se queja de sentirse **(13.)** _____. Dice que

está **(14.)** _____ de levantarse **(15.)**

_____. Quiere **(16.)** _____ en la

cama todo el día.

Visión y voz 2E Workbook © 1998 John Wiley & Sons

Paso 2. Use the expresions **me gusta...**, **me siento bien/ mal cuando...**, **(no) quiero...**, etc. to tell which roommate in Activity A you are like and why.

Por ejemplo: Soy como Guillermo porque no puedo levantarme temprano y después me siento estresada.

1. Soy como _____ porque _____

2. No soy como _____ porque _____

B. Compárate. For each adjective write a sentence comparing yourself to a friend who is different from you.

Por ejemplo: aburrido(a)
   Cuando estoy (me siento) aburrida, tengo ganas de comer.
   Cuando mi amigo está aburrido,tiene ganas de hacer deportes.

1. estresado(a)

   _____

2. contento(a)

   _____

3. aburrido(a)

   _____

4. deprimido(a)

   _____

5. nervioso(a)

   _____

6. lleno(a) de energía

   _____

7. enojado(a)

   _____

C. Mis remedios. ¿Qué haces en las siguientes circunstancias?

Por ejemplo: **Para sentirme tranquilo**, me gusta relajarme con un libro interesante y acostarme temprano. Descanso y leo un libro para olvidarme de mis estudios.

1. Para no preocuparme por los estudios

_____

2. Para estar sano(a) y lleno(a) de energía

_____

3. Cuando estoy harto(a) de la rutina

_____

4. Cuando me siento deprimido(a) o triste

_____

5. Para no morirme de aburrido(a)

_____

6. Si estoy cansado(a)

_____

7. Para despertarme temprano

_____

8. Para no tener que arreglarme mucho

_____

D. ¡Adiós, trabajo! Completa las siguientes frases para describir tus planes para unas vacaciones.

Por ejemplo: Cuando no hay clases, normalmente me quedo en casa. Pero este año, quiero irme al extranjero.

1. Cuando no hay clases, normalmente _____.

Pero para las vacaciones de _____ (_estación_), quiero

_____.

2. En _____ (_mes_), cuando hace _____ voy a

_____ porque estoy harto(a) de

_____ y me muero de ganas de

_____.

3. Puedo juntarme con _____ porque

_____. También quiero juntarme con

_____ para relajarme y _____.

4. Antes de irme, no quiero olvidarme de llamar a _____ y

comprar _____.

5. Voy a alojarme en _____.

6. Quiero quedarme _____ días allá y para divertirme en

grande quiero _____.

G R A M Á T I C A 1

A. La entrevista. You are being interviewed for a study on personal habits and their effect on performance at work. Write a question based on each group of words. Then answer the question.

Por ejemplo: ¿a qué hora?/acostarse
> **a. ¿A qué hora te acuestas?**
> **b. Me acuesto a las once.**

> levantarse / ¿triste o contento(a)?
> **a. ¿Te levantas triste o contento(a)?**
> **b. Me levanto contenta.**

1. ¿a qué hora?/ levantarse

    a. _____

    b. _____

2. levantarse / ¿lleno(a) de energía o cansado(a)?

    a. _____

    b. _____

3. bañarse o ducharse

    a. _____

    b. _____

4. vestirse / ¿bien o de una forma informal para trabajar?

a. _____

b. _____

5. arreglarse/ ¿rápido o con cuidado?

a. _____

b. _____

6. preocuparse por / hacer todo el trabajo

a. _____

b. _____

B. Lo personal. Contesta con frases completas.

1. ¿Cuándo te diviertes mucho?

_____

2. ¿Qué haces para relajarte?

_____

3. ¿De qué te quejas?

_____

4. ¿De qué se quejan tus padres?

_____

5. ¿Cuándo te sientes muy contento(a)?

_____

6. ¿Cuándo te sientes muy triste?

_____

7. ¿Puedes reírte de tus problemas o siempre te sientes estresado(a)? Explica.

_____

8. ¿Te sientes tranquilo(a) o estresado(a) cuando estudias? Explica.

_____

9. ¿Cuándo (en qué situación) te mueres de aburrido(a)?

_____

10. ¿Siempre tienes ganas de juntarte con tus amigos o a veces tienes ganas de quedarte solo(a)? ¿Por qué?

_____

C. A solas en casa. Usa los siguientes verbos para describir las imágenes. Hay un verbo que se puede usar más de una vez.

     sentirse mal   cansarse de   quejarse de   quedarse solo

Juan y Pablo

1. _____

_____

_____

Me muero de aburrido.

2. _____

_____

_____

3. _____

_____

_____

4. _____

_____

_____

5. _____

_____

_____

_____

_____

D. Mis reacciones. ¿Qué haces cuando te sientes así?

Por ejemplo: sentirse nervioso(a)

Cuando me siento nervioso, como mucho (monto en bicicleta, llamo a mi amigo, etc.)

1. morirse de aburrido(a)

_____

2. sentirse lleno(a) de energía

_____

3. preocuparse por los exámenes

_____

4. cansarse de la rutina diaria

_____

5. sentirse deprimido(a)

_____

E. Los compañeros de cuarto. Completa la siguiente narración con la forma correcta de los verbos indicados.

Todas las mañanas, (yo) _____ (**1.** levantarse)

temprano, _____ (**2.** ducharse),

_____ (**3.** vestirse) y _____

(**4.** mirarse) en el espejo.

Estoy contento y _____ (**5.** sentirse) lleno de

energía. En seguida (yo) _____ (**6.** prepararse) el

desayuno. No hay nadie en la sala, entonces _____

(**7.** divertirse) unos minutos con la televisión porque me gusta

_____ (**8.** relajarse) en la sala.

A veces, cuando mi compañero, Oscar, está en casa, (él)

_____ (**9.** despertarse) porque la tele está a todo

volumen. A él le gusta dormir más por la mañana porque siempre

_____ (**10.** acostarse) muy tarde. Oscar

_____ (**11.** quejarse) unos minutos, pero después

_____ (**12.** dormirse) otra vez. Los otros chicos de la

casa _____ (**13.** reírse) de él, porque a veces es muy

cómico cuando _____ (**14.** enojarse). Mis

compañeros y yo somos muy buenos amigos y (nosotros)

_____ (**15.** divertirse) juntos, pero todos tenemos

horarios diferentes.

Y tú, ¿_____ (**16.** preocuparse) cuando no hay

silencio en la casa y quieres _____ (**17.** dormirse)?

GRAMÁTICA 2

A. ¿Qué hora es? Indica qué hora es en cada caso.

1. _____

_____

2. _____

_____

3. _____

_____

4. _____

_____

5. _____

_____

6. _____

_____

7. _____

_____

8. _____

_____

9. _____

_____

10. _____

_____

Visión y voz 2E Workbook © 1998 John Wiley & Sons

B. Tus costumbres. Completa lo siguiente según tus hábitos y los de tu compañero(a) de cuarto.

   1. Por la mañana yo

   a. siempre _____

   b. a veces _____

   c. nunca _____

   2. Por la tarde mi compañero(a) de cuarto

   a. siempre _____

   b. a veces _____

   c. nunca _____

   3. Por la noche mi compañero(a) de cuarto y yo

   a. siempre _____

   b. a veces _____

   c. nunca _____

   4. Los domingos yo

   a. siempre _____

   b. a veces _____

   c. nunca _____

   5. Los lunes mi compañero(a)

   a. siempre _____

   b. a veces _____

   c. nunca _____

C. El orden de las actividades. Usa **antes** de y **después de** para indicar el orden de tus acciones.

Por ejemplo: comer el desayuno / vestirse
       Como el desayuno antes de vestirme.

   1. vestirse / arreglarse _____

   2. ducharse / comer el desayuno _____

   3. ducharse / arreglarse _____

   4. levantarse / arreglarse _____

Visión y voz 2E Workbook © 1998 John Wiley & Sons

LECTURA
VOCES DEL MUNDO HISPANO

EL RELOJ
Lee el artículo y completa las actividades que siguen.

Los Relojes y su historia

Primer reloj de pulsera conocido en Suiza, usado por la condesa Kocewicz en 1868.

Apresar la sucesión regular del tiempo con una máquina perfecta ha sido el perpetuo sueño cartesiano de todos los hombres

Por lo que se refiere al momento exacto de la invención del reloj tal como lo conocemos —un mecanismo dirigido por pesos y con un escape— es un asunto totalmente desconocido, así como la identidad del inventor. Por las referencias literarias podemos suponer que el reloj de engranes y contrapesos fue inventado algunos años antes de 1300.

A principios del siglo XIX se usaron estos relojes de bolsillo hechas de oro y ornados con pintura esmaltada y perlas.

Una maquinaria precisión, como la de este Rolex, trabaja con decenas de piezas que se unen requiriendo tolerancias en micrones.

Reloj de sol diseñado por J.G. Zimmer en 1750, que se conserva en Dresden.

Los modernos relojes electrónicos funcionan a base de cristales de cuarzo, económico sistema que asegura gran exactitud.

A. ¿Entendiste? Contesta las preguntas.

1. ¿Cuáles son los relojes más ornados? ¿Cuáles son los más simples?

_____

2. ¿Sabemos la fecha de la invención del reloj?

_____

3. ¿Sabemos quién es el inventor del reloj?

_____

B. Cognados. Busca los cognados en español de estas palabras en inglés.

1. paint _____

2. pearls _____

3. function _____

4. quartz _____

5. requiring _____

Palabras útiles

el reloj	máquina para decir la hora
la pulsera	*wrist*
la condesa	*countess*
diseñado	*designed*
el siglo	100 años
el bolsillo	*pocket*
ornados	decorados
el oro	metal precioso
la decena	grupo de diez
la pieza	*piece*
se unen	se juntan
dirigido	*run (directed) by*
el peso	*weight*
el asunto	*subject*
los engranes	*gears*

C. Los relojes no andan. Imagínate que mañana todos los relojes del mundo dejan de andar (*stop working*) durante seis horas. Tienes seis horas adicionales para hacer lo que quieres hacer. ¿Qué vas a hacer? ¿Te gusta la idea de un día de treinta horas? ¿Por qué o por qué no?

_____

_____

_____

_____

_____

_____

_____

_____

PARA ESCRIBIR

Tu actitud con respecto a la hora

Escribe un párrafo sobre tu actitud con respecto a la hora. Puedes usar expresiones como **Me enojo cuando...**, **Otros se enojan cuando yo...**, **Me siento estresado(a) cuando...** Puedes contestar las siguientes preguntas: ¿Siempre llegas tarde, temprano o a tiempo a ciertos eventos? ¿Te gusta tener el tiempo planeado o libre y flexible? ¿Te olvidas a veces de la hora? (Da un ejemplo.) ¿Te preocupas por no tener suficiente tiempo? ¿Tienes la misma actitud que tus compañeros o familiares (*relatives*)? Explica.

_____

_____

_____

_____

_____

_____

_____

_____

_____

_____

_____

_____

_____

_____

Asuntos de familia

V O C A B U L A R I O

IMÁGENES Y PALABRAS

A. Una reunión. Completa la narración con palabras apropiadas.

Me llamo Laura y tengo una familia grande. Este mes vamos a tener una

(1.) _____ de toda mi familia. Vamos a

(2.) _____ para celebrar el

(3.) _____ de mi **(4.)** _____

Enriqueta, (la madre de mi abuela paterna), que va a

(5.) _____ cien años. Tengo abuelos, tíos y otros

(6.) _____ viejos, pero Enriqueta es la

(7.) _____ de la familia. Tiene seis hijos y trece

(8.) _____. Es **(9.)** _____; su

marido murió hace años. Pero Enriqueta está enamorada de Carlos, un

hombre de noventa y cinco años, cinco años

(10.) _____ que ella, y este año los dos viejos van a

casarse; es decir que están **(11.)** _____.

Como todas las familias, a veces nosotros no nos

(12.) _____ bien, pero por lo general hay mucho

amor. Todos son muy amables, pero también son algo extraños. Por

ejemplo, la hermana de mi papi, mi **(13.)** _____

Amalia, siempre se queja de estar enferma y en realidad no lo está.

Pedro y Pablo, los hijos de la tía Amalia, son mis (**14.**) _____

favoritos. Son gemelos (nacieron juntos) y se (**15.**) _____ tanto

el uno al otro que son idénticos. A veces les gusta engañar a la gente fingiendo

(*pretending*) ser el otro, a veces ellos mismos no saben por seguro quién es quién.

Enriqueta tiene cinco hermanos pero cuatro son (**16.**) _____ ;

no están casados porque son hombres difíciles. El otro hermano ahora tiene

esposa, ¡acaba de (**17.**) _____ a los ochenta años!

B. La familia de Laura. Lee otra vez la actividad A y completa este resumen.

1. Amalia es la _____ de Enriqueta.

2. Pedro y Pablo son los _____ del padre de Laura.

3. Pedro va a ser el _____ de los hijos de Pablo.

4. Carlos va a ser el _____ de los hijos de Enriqueta.

5. Laura no tiene hermanos; ella es hija _____ .

C. Aspectos personales. Contesta las preguntas con frases completas.

1. ¿Quién es tu pariente más interesante y extraño(a)? ¿Cómo es? ¿Qué cosas hace?

_____

_____

2. ¿Acaba de casarse algún amigo o familiar? ¿Quién es?

_____

_____

3. ¿Te gusta compartir historias de tus parientes? ¿Por qué? ¿De qué hablas?

_____

_____

4. ¿Te pareces a otra persona de tu familia? ¿Quién es?

_____

_____

5. ¿Qué pariente influye mucho en ti? ¿De qué manera?

_____

_____

6. ¿Eres hijo(a) único(a)? ¿Piensas que es mejor ser el único o tener hermanos? ¿Por qué?

_____

_____

7. ¿Con quién te llevas bien? ¿Con quién te llevas mal? ¿Por qué?

_____

_____

D. ¿Cómo es? ¿Cómo está? Escribe una frase para describir cada imagen.

Por ejemplo: La familia está muy contenta.

Ramón tiene treinta años.

Lucinda tiene veinticinco años.

1. _____

_____

_____

_____

2. _____

_____

_____

_____

3. _____

_____

_____

_____

4. _____

_____

_____

_____

G R A M Á T I C A 1

A. Un desastre familiar. Completa las frases con la forma correcta del pretérito de los verbos.

Hace unos años yo (**1.**juntarse) _____ con mi familia

para celebrar el cumpleaños del tío Pepe. Pepe (**2.** cumplir)

_____ cincuenta años aquel día. Sus hijos, Juan y

Ramón, le (**3.** hacer) _____ una fiesta e (**4.** invitar)

_____ a toda la familia menos al primo Rodolfo. Juan

(**5.** olvidarse) _____ de invitarlo y después Rodolfo no

le (**6.** hablar) _____ nunca más en la vida. Esto

(**7.** ser) _____ el primer desastre.

La fiesta (**8.** comenzar) _____ mal y ¡(**9.** terminar)

_____ peor! El tío Raúl (**10.** pelearse)

_____ con su mujer durante la fiesta y ellos

(**11.** divorciarse) _____ unos meses después. Muchos

parientes que normalmente lo pasaban bien (**12.** llevarse)

_____ muy mal. Mi prima Ana y yo (**13.** ver)

_____ todos los problemas y (**14.** decidir)

_____ mudarnos muy lejos. Pero yo no (**15.** mudarse)

_____ porque en realidad quiero mucho a mi familia

aun cuando se llevan mal.

B. Aspectos personales. Contesta las preguntas con frases completas.

1. ¿Fuiste recientemente a una reunión con tu familia? ¿Cuándo?

_____

_____

2. ¿Se juntaron Uds. en un restaurante o en casa? ¿Por qué?

_____

_____

3. ¿Viste a parientes que no ves con frecuencia? ¿A quiénes?

_____

_____

4. ¿Compartieron Uds. historias del pasado? ¿De qué hablaron?

_____

_____

5. ¿Hablaste con muchos parientes o sólo con unos pocos? ¿Por qué?

_____

_____

6. ¿Quién hizo la fiesta? ¿Cómo fue?

_____

_____

7. ¿Conociste a alguien nuevo en la fiesta? ¿A quién? ¿Cómo es?

_____

_____

C. Bonitos recuerdos. Éstas son fotos del
álbum de la familia Gutiérrez. Escribe lo que
pasó en cada foto. Escribe las fechas con palabras.

Por ejemplo: Juan y Amelia se conocieron en
1952 (mil novecientos cincuenta y dos).

Juan y Amelia 1952

1953

1._____

_____

_____

Alicia, 1955

2._____

_____

Acapulco, 1960

3._____

_____

_____

1963

4._____

_____

_____

1972

5._____

_____

_____

D. Hoy y ayer. Escribe frases para indicar que el pasado fue diferente del presente.

Por ejemplo: Hoy estudio mucho.
               Ayer no estudié nada.

               Este año no trabajo mucho.
               El año pasado trabajé mucho.

1. Hoy me levanto temprano. _____

2. Hoy hago mi tarea. _____

3. Hoy me llevo bien con mi hermano. _____

4. Este año viajo mucho. _____

5. Esta semana mis amigos van al cine. _____

6. Esta noche me quedo en casa. _____

G R A M Á T I C A 2

A. Una boda famosa. Completa las preguntas con la forma correcta del pretérito de los verbos. Después contesta las preguntas.

Por ejemplo: ¿Quién **fue** una novia muy linda? (ser)
               Carolyn Bessette fue una novia muy linda.

SÍ, ACEPTO...

El vestido del año fue el de Carolyn Bessette, diseñado por el cubano Narciso Rodríguez de la casa Cerrutti. Esta rubia escultural llevó al altar a John John Kennedy y hoy en día se venden réplicas del traje con el lema: "pudo haber sido usted". Lo cierto es que el vestido de Carolyn impactó por su sencillez y su sensualidad. La tela abrazaba el cuerpo y la novia no sólo fue linda y envidiada... sino también muy deseada.

Visión y voz 2E Workbook © 1998 John Wiley & Sons

1. ¿Cómo _____ Carolyn? (vestirse)

_____

2. ¿Con quién _____ Carolyn? (casarse)

_____

3. ¿Quién _____ el padre famoso del novio? (ser)

_____

4. ¿Cuándo _____ este hombre famoso? (morirse)

_____

5. ¿Por qué _____ muchas mujeres a Carolyn? (envidiar [*to envy*])

_____

6. ¿_____ mucho su vestido a otros vestidos? (influir)

_____

7. En tu opinión, ¿_____ todos en esta boda elegante? (divertirse)

_____

B. Una boda singular. Completa la narración con la forma correcta del pretérito de los verbos.

Hace unos meses yo (**1.** ir) _____ a una boda muy extraña. Los dos novios (**2.** ser) _____ fanáticos de las películas viejas. Ellos (**3.** conocerse) _____ por primera vez en el cine, durante un festival de las películas de Humphrey Bogart. Aquella noche ellos (**4.** ver) _____ "Casablanca" y (**5.** sentirse) _____ muy románticos. Por eso (**6.** decidir) _____ tener la boda en el cine. El novio (**7.** conseguir) _____ todas las entradas (*tickets*) del cine y los dos (**8.** invitar) _____ a todos sus parientes y amigos. Al principio muchos (**9.** reírse) _____ de la idea, pero después nosotros (**10.** divertirse) _____ mucho. El único problema

(**11.** ser) _____ que algunas personas tienen la costumbre

de dormirse en el cine, y varios parientes (**12.** dormirse)

_____ en la oscuridad durante la ceremonia. Yo no (**13.**

dormirse) _____ porque me (**14.** encantar)

_____ tanto el espíritu romántico de los novios.

C. Bodas diferentes. Escribe los verbos en el pretérito.

1. Leo sobre varias bodas diferentes. _____

2. Una novia, fanática de la muñeca Barbie se viste como la *Barbie doll.*

_____

3. Otros novios, fanáticos de Disney, se visten de Micky y Minnie y se casan en el Mundo

de Disney. _____   _____

4. A los padres de la novia no les gusta esta idea pero todos los niños se divierten mucho

en la boda. _____   _____.

D. Crucigrama. Completa el crucigrama con la forma correcta de los
verbos en el pretérito.

Horizontales

1. Los parientes le (dar) muchos regalos a la novia.
4. Yo (leer) una revista de novias.
5. ¿Tú (dar) un paseo antes de entrar en la iglesia?
7. El ex novio (oír) de la boda.
8. Él se (quedar) en casa el día de la boda.
9. Yo (buscar) el amor de mi vida.
11. Yo (oír) que el vestido fue magnífico.
12. Yo (hacer) una fiesta en honor de los novios.

Verticales

1. El novio no (dormir) la noche antes de
la ceremonia.
2. La novia (ser) muy linda.
3. Yo la (ver) antes de la boda.
4. Sus parientes (leer) la invitación con gran alegría.
5. El novio le (dar) un anillo a la novia.
6. Yo (sacar) muchas fotos de la boda.
10. El primo de la novia (sacar) fotos también.

LECTURA

VOCES DEL MUNDO HISPANO

Con Cristina: César Evora

Lee el artículo y completa las actividades que siguen.

César Evora: "No soy un padre autoritario; soy amigo

PADRES PARECIDOS

En la fantasía de las telenovelas, ellos son los galanes guapos, fuertes, irresistiblemente románticos. Pero, ¿cómo son lejos de las cámaras, cuando en la intimidad del hogar, desempeñan el papel más importante de sus vidas?

En el caso de César Evora, el actor cubano de voz grave que estelariza la telenovela *Luz Clarita*, el argumento de la trama se confundió con un triste aspecto de su realidad...

"Yo interpreto a Mariano de la Fuente, un viudo muy serio, muy recto, que tiene una hija con problemas emocionales. Para ayudarla, lleva a su casa a una niña —Luz Clarita quien, poco a poco, lo va volviendo un hombre más tierno y humano", cuenta. "A mí esto me sirvió como una especie de catarsis, porque aunque resido en México con mi esposa Vivian y mi hija Carla, de 3 años y medio, tengo dos hijos que viven en Cuba..."

Rafael, de 11 años, y Mariana, de 10, son hijos de un primer matrimonio, y viven con su madre en La Habana, Cuba. Una vez el año — durante los meses de vacaciones escolares— visitan a su papá y hermana en Cuidad México.

"Cuando comencé a actuar en *Luz Clarita*, llevaba seis meses sin verlos, y creo que a través de mi actuación pude expresar muchos sentimientos paternales".

¿Cómo se siente ser papá a "larga distancia"?

"Es una de las pruebas más duras que me ha dado la vida". dice. "Es que mi padre fue de 'larga distancia', porque él se fue de Cuba en 1968, y no volví a verlo hasta 1988, cuando nos reunimos en Nueva York. Y aunque dicen que 'veinte años no es nada', sí es mucho tiempo para estar separados. Mi vida sin él fue durísima, porque, sobre todo al varón, el padre le hace mucha falta. Me fui formando, y llegué a la madurez buscando su imagen, agrediéndola, defendiéndola, rechazándola".

A. ¿Entendiste? Contesta las preguntas.

1. ¿Cuál es la profesión de César Evora?

_____

2. ¿Dónde vive?

_____

3. ¿Con quién vive?

_____

_____

4. ¿Cuántos hijos tiene?

_____

_____

5. ¿Quién es el mayor de los hijos?

_____

_____

6. ¿Por qué no viven todos con él?

_____

_____

7. ¿Qué memorias tristes tiene César Evora?

_____

8. ¿Cuándo ve César Evora a sus hijos?

_____

9. ¿Qué tiene César Evora en común con su propio padre?

_____

Palabras útiles	
la telenovela	soap opera
lejos	far
el hogar	donde vive una persona
el papel	role
la luz	light
el argumento de la trama	the plot
se confundió	got confused
lo va volviendo	is turning him into
tierno	cariñoso
duras	difíciles
el varón	persona del sexo masculino

B. Palabras similares. Busca los cognados en español de lo siguiente.

1. I reside _____

2. aspect _____

3. reality _____

4. catharsis (great release of emotion) _____

5. sentiments _____

6. maturity _____

C. Sinónimos. Indica el sinónimo más probable.

1. galanes
   a. niños
   b. hombres jóvenes
   c. viejos
   d. fotógrafos

2. poco a poco
   a. tristemente
   b. rápido
   c. no muy rápido
   d. sin amor

3. nos reunimos
   a. nos juntamos
   b. nos olvidamos
   c. nos casamos
   d. nos escribimos

D. Parientes a larga distancia. César Evora habla de los problemas y la tristeza de ser hijo de un padre a "larga distancia". En nuestra sociedad en movimiento, mucha veces los parientes se mudan lejos de la familia. Describe tu relación con un/a pariente a larga distancia. Usa el vocabulario del Capítulo 5 para contestar estas preguntas: ¿Quién es? (tío, primo, etc.) ¿Cuándo se mudó, adónde y por qué? ¿Cuál es su estado matrimonial? ¿Te llevas bien con este pariente? ¿Cuándo se juntan Uds.? ¿Qué haces para mantener buenas relaciones entre parientes lejanos?

_____

_____

_____

_____

_____

_____

_____

_____

_____

_____

PARA ESCRIBIR

¿Qué significa ser "viejo"?

A. Escribe un párrafo sobre cómo es ser viejo en los Estados Unidos. Describe los estereotipos de los viejos en esa cultura. ¿Qué imágenes en la televisión y las revistas contribuyen a estos estereotipos? ¿Puedes citar ejemplos de personas viejas que contradicen estos estereotipos?

_____

_____

_____

_____

_____

_____

_____

_____

_____

_____

B. Describe una experiencia que tuviste (*had*) con un/a pariente viejo(a) que contradice los estereotipos de que acabas de escribir.

_____

_____

_____

_____

_____

_____

Los hitos de la vida

VOCABULARIO

IMÁGENES Y PALABRAS

A. Según el contexto. Para completar las siguientes conversaciones, selecciona el verbo apropiado, según el contexto.

1. —Voy a dar una fiesta la semana que _____ (viene/va). ¿Quieres ir?

    —Sí, por supuesto. ¿Qué te puedo _____ (llevar/traer) para la fiesta?

2. —Mis padres _____ (vienen/dicen) a visitar este sábado y no tengo idea dónde llevarlos. ¿Me _____ (recomiendas/pides) un buen restaurante?

    —Sí, claro. Siempre _____ (recomiendo/pido) el restaurante California. Es uno de los mejores de la ciudad.

    —Pero dicen que en el California todo _____ (cuesta/paga) muy caro. No puedo _____ (gastar/costar) mucho porque no tengo mucho dinero.

3. —Mañana es el cumpleaños de mi novia y le quiero _____ (pedir/decir) "te quiero" de una manera extraordinaria.

    —¿Por qué no le _____ (llevas/traes) flores? Las chicas siempre nos _____ (regalan/piden) flores.

4. —Disculpe, señor. Me _____ (pidieron/dijeron) que en

esta calle hay un almacén muy grande.

—¿Quién le _____ (dijo/dijeron) eso? En esta calle no

hay nada.

5. —Señor, Uds. me _____ (pagaron/vendieron) este

aparato electrónico. Pero no es el que les _____

(pedí/vendí).

—Si no es el aparato que Ud. _____ (pagó/pidió), le

podemos devolver el dinero que _____ (pagó/pidió).

B. El ático de la abuela Mimi. Completa la narración con las palabras apropiadas.

En su ático la abuela Mimi tiene todos los recuerdos de una larga vida.

Las varias **(1.)** _____ que ella tiene en el ático no

cuestan mucho, es decir que no son **(2.)** _____

pero tienen gran valor sentimental. Como Mimi es viuda, muchos de los

(3.) _____ le recuerdan a su difunto marido

Jorge. En una **(4.)** _____ enorme ella tiene todos

los **(5.)** _____ que Jorge le regaló. Tiene un

(6.) _____ que siempre marca la misma hora,

pues hace años que no funciona. Jorge se lo regaló en la ocasión de su

(7.) _____ de veinte años. Tiene un libro de

poemas de Pablo Neruda y entre las páginas una

(8.) _____ seca (*dried*) que él le dio la noche que

se conocieron. También hay todas las **(9.)** _____

de amor y **(10.)** _____ de felicitaciones que su

marido le escribió, una **(11.)** _____ de música,

un par (*pair*) de (**12.**) _____ de cuero, y un súeter de (**13.**)

_____ para el invierno. En otra caja hay la (**14.**)

_____ del primer vino que compartieron, las figuritas de

encima del (**15.**) _____ de boda, una foto de una casa que fue

el primer (**16.**) _____ en que vivieron juntos, y la (**17.**)

_____ de (**18.**) _____ que Jorge usaba con su

reloj de bolsillo (*pocket*). En una bolsa de plástico está el vestido de

(**19.**) _____ que Mimi llevó el día de la boda. Hay una caja

más en el ático pero Mimi no puede abrirla (*open*) porque no tiene la

(**20.**) _____ .

C. ¿De qué es? Identifica las imágenes.

Por ejemplo: Es una billetera de cuero.

No son de oro.

1. _____
_____

2. _____
_____

3. _____
_____

4. _____
_____

5. _____
_____

D. ¿Dónde puedo comprar...? ¿Dónde puedes comprar los siguientes artículos? En cada caso menciona un artículo más.

Por ejemplo: guantes
   Puedo comprar guantes y vestidos (camisetas, etc.) en el almacén.

1. chocolate _____

_____

2. llaves _____

_____

3. libros _____

_____

4. aretes _____

_____

5. plumas _____

_____

G R A M Á T I C A 1

A. Dicho y hecho. Usa los pronombres de complemento indirecto para decir lo que se dice y lo que se hace en las siguientes situaciones.

Por ejemplo: ¿Qué le dices a un amigo que está de cumpleaños?
   Le digo "feliz cumpleaños".

1. ¿Qué le dices...?

a la gente cuando contestas el teléfono

_____

_____

a tu jefe cuando llegas al trabajo

_____

_____

2. ¿Qué le preguntas...?

al jefe en una entrevista de trabajo

_____

_____

a una persona que acabas de conocer

_____

_____

3. ¿Qué le(s) envías...?

a la empresa si quieres conseguir un puesto

_____

_____

a un/a familiar en el día de su santo

_____

_____

4. ¿Qué les venden a Uds...?

en la ferretería

_____

_____

en la dulcería

_____

_____

en la joyería

_____

_____

en la papelería

_____

_____

B. Por el amor de Marisol. Describe cada imagen según el modelo, usando los pronombres de complemento indirecto y los verbos indicados.

Por ejemplo: regalar

Ernesto le regala rosas a Marisol.

1. decir _____

_____

_____

_____

los padres de Marisol

2. llevar _____

_____

_____

_____

3. escribir, enviar _____

_____

_____

_____

4. mostrar _____

_____

_____

_____

5. escribir, leer _____

_____

_____

_____

6. decir, dar _____

_____

_____

_____

Visión y voz 2E Workbook © 1998 John Wiley & Sons

C. Aspectos personales. Contesta las preguntas con frases completas.

1. ¿Quién te hace regalos de cumpleaños?

_____

2. ¿Quién les enseña a Uds. español?

_____

3. ¿Quién te presta ropa?

_____

4. ¿Quién te pide cosas imposibles?

_____

5. ¿Quién les da a Uds. muchas tareas?

_____

D. Sentimientos. ¿Qué te evocan las siguientes emociones? Usa los pronombres de complemento indirecto para expresar por lo menos dos causas en cada caso.

Por ejemplo: Me siento nerviosa . . . cuando **les muestro** mis notas a mis padres, cuando mi jefe **me habla** y cuando mis profesores **me hacen preguntas**.

1. Me enojo cuando _____

_____

2. Me siento deprimido(a) cuando _____

_____

3. Estoy preocupado(a) cuando _____

_____

4. Me siento feliz cuando _____

_____

5. Me siento aburrido(a) cuando _____

_____

6. Estoy nervioso(a) cuando _____

_____

GRAMÁTICA 2

A. Comparaciones.   Usa las siguientes expresiones para formar tus propias comparaciones.

Por ejemplo: hablar menos cuando... que cuando...
  Hablo menos cuando me siento nervioso que cuando me siento tranquilo.

1. sacar peores notas en... que en...

_____

_____

2. prestar más atención en... que en...

_____

_____

3. pedirles a mis padres más dinero en... que en...

_____

_____

4. reírse más con... que con...

_____

_____

5. demostrarme mejor amigo(a) cuando... que cuando...

_____

_____

6. vestirme peor cuando... que cuando...

_____

_____

7. enviarles más correo electrónico a... que a...

_____

_____

8. comprar mejores regalos en... que en...

_____

_____

B. Para comparar. Escribe una comparación, usando **más** o **menos**, según el modelo. Cambia el adjetivo si es necesario. Recuerda: **bueno**, **malo**, **viejo** y **joven** son diferentes.

Por ejemplo: plata/caro/madera
La plata es más cara que la madera.

abuelo/viejo/tío
Mi abuelo es mayor que mi tío.

1. parientes/guapo/actores del cine

_____

2. aretes/caro/cadena

_____

3. montar en bici/bueno para la salud/ir en auto

_____

4. rosa/romántico/cacto

_____

5. una semana de exámenes/malo/semana de descanso

_____

6. la lana/suave(_soft_)/el cuero

_____

C. Estoy tan cansado que... Usa **tan** o **tanto** (**tanta, tantos, tantas**) para escribir frases nuevas.

Por ejemplo: Estoy cansada.
Estoy tan cansada que voy a acostarme sin comer.

Juan tiene muchos parientes.
Tiene tantos parientes que no pueden juntarse todos en una casa.

1. La cadena de oro es muy cara.

_____

2. Los jóvenes están muy enamorados.

_____

3. Mario llega muy tarde a la clase.

_____

4. Teresa tiene muchos problemas.

_____

5. Mi amigo tiene muchas cintas de música.

_____

6. El alumno está muy estresado.

_____

7. Tengo mucha tarea.

_____

G R A M Á T I C A 3

A. "Los días de nuestra vida". Completa la narración con el pretérito de los siguientes verbos (algunos se usan más de una vez) para saber lo que pasó en el último episodio de esta emocionante telenovela.

leer	saber	llamar	tener
hacer	ir	ser	venir
poder	decir	nacer	querer
preguntar	traer	parecer	cambiar
resultar			

Ayer Rodrigo (**1.**) _____ una carta de su hermano Arturo.

Rodrigo (**2.**) _____ la carta pero no

(**3.**) _____ creer lo que decía porque le

(**4.**) _____ tan imposible, y no (**5.**) _____

aceptar la información; (**6.**) _____ tan horrible. ¡Su

hermano ya no (**7.**) _____ su hermano! Cuando Arturo (**8.**)

_____, una enfermera lo (**9.**) _____ con

otro bebé. Rodrigo (**10.**) _____ a su mamá por teléfono, y le

(11.) _____ sobre este misterio. —Es verdad—, le

(12.) _____ su mamá. La enfermera me

(13.) _____ el bebé de otra mujer. Después de un año, yo

(14.) _____ la verdad pero no **(15.)** _____

decirle a nadie. Un año después, Arturo **(16.)** _____ otra

sorpresa. ¡Su pareja de veras **(17.)** _____ ser su hermana!

B. Aspectos personales.   Completa las preguntas con la forma correcta del pretérito. Después contesta las preguntas.

Por ejemplo: (venir/tú) **¿Con quién _viniste_ a la clase?**
Vine con mi amigo Carlos.

1. (estar/tú) ¿Dónde _____ anoche a las nueve?

_____

2. (saber/Uds.) ¿_____ del escándalo que pasó anoche?

_____

3. (poder/tú) ¿_____ terminar toda la tarea anoche?

_____

4. (querer) ¿_____ hacer el gran favor que te pidió tu

amigo?

_____

5. (decir) ¿Les _____ la verdad a tus padres sobre la

fiesta que hiciste en su ausencia?

_____

C. El diario de Juana.   ¿Qué le quiso decir Juana a Juan en la actividad de la página 189 de tu libro de texto? Aquí tienes su diario. Cambia los verbos de presente a pasado para resumir su historia.

15 de abril

Tengo cuatro días de descanso en Chicago. Mi amiga Lidia me muestra la ciudad y saco muchas fotos. ¡Me divierto tanto en los museos y en las tiendas encuentro cosas increíbles!

_____

_____

_____

_____

_____

_____

16 de abril
Lidia me presenta a su primo, Alfredo. ¡Pero qué chico más guapo! Los tres
vamos al cine pero yo no veo la película. Sólo pienso en Alfredo porque me da
la impresión de que se divierte mucho conmigo. Después, al llegar a casa de
Lidia, me pide mi teléfono.

_____

_____

_____

_____

_____

_____

18 de abril
Me despido de Alfredo en casa de Lidia. Me da una cadena de oro como
recuerdo del tiempo que pasamos juntos y me dice "Te quiero, Juana". ¡Qué
sorpresa! Casi me muero de emoción.

_____

_____

_____

_____

19 de abril

Ya me voy y estoy tan deprimida. Me cuesta mucho separarme de Alfredo. Alfredo no quiere ir al aeropuerto a despedirse de mí. Según Lidia, es que Alfredo no quiere sentirse triste.

_____

_____

_____

_____

_____

20 de abril

Juan me viene a visitar. Me pide las fotos del viaje a Chicago. Pero cuando le muestro las fotos, se ríe y me dice "¿Sólo sacas fotos de estatuas y edificios?" Entonces ve una foto de Alfredo y casi se muere de enojo. "¿Estás cuatro días con otro y nunca piensas en mí?". Y, con eso, se va, furioso.

_____

_____

_____

_____

_____

25 de abril

Mis padres me dicen que Juan sale con una prima de Lidia.

_____

_____

LECTURA
VOCES DEL MUNDO HISPANO

Un cumpleaños infantil

Lee el artículo y completa las actividades que siguen.

En compañía de sus padres, José Manuel y Martha Peña de Venegas, apreciamos al simpático Alejandro, protagonista del festejo.

Cumpleaños de Alex Venegas

El simpático Alejandro Venegas Peña fue objeto de una divertida fiesta para celebrar su cumpleaños número tres.

Lo más importante para Alejandro fue rodearse de tantos amiguitos y de su respectiva familia.

A la grata reunión asistieron los niños León Venegas, Venegas Tejada, Rodríguez Pulido, y muchos más que disfrutaron una estancia de lo más agradable.

Josefina Cordero de Peña y Angelita Félix de Venegas no podían faltar en la convivencia de su nieto, a quien acompañaron en todo momento y le brindaron hermosos presentes.

Los padres de Alejandro, José Manuel y Martha Peña de Venegas, no sólo se distinguieron por su labor como organizadores de la convivencia, sino también fungieron° como amables anfitriones, no descuidando ningún detalle.

Ante la insistencia de sus invitados, el cumpleañero abrió los regalitos que tuvieron el gusto de brindarle, por ello expresó las gracias con gran entusiasmo.

A. ¿Entendiste? Contesta las preguntas.

1. ¿Cuántos años cumplió Alex?

_____

_____

2. ¿Quiénes son Josefina Cordero de Peña y Angelita Félix de Venegas?

_____

3. Según el artículo, ¿por qué abrió Alex sus regalos?

_____

> **Palabras útiles**
> faltar en   *to miss*
> el anfitrión   *host*
> fungieron   *served*

B. ¿Qué significa? Escoge la mejor opción.

1. El significado más probable de **rodearse de** es
   - **a.** to be invited by
   - **b.** to be surrounded by
   - **c.** to meet
   - **d.** to ride with

2. El sinónimo más probable de **convivencia** es
   - **a.** regalo
   - **b.** familia
   - **c.** fiesta
   - **d.** grupo de amigos

3. El sinónimo más probable de **brindaron** es
   - **a.** ofrecieron
   - **b.** recibieron
   - **c.** enviaron
   - **d.** quisieron

PARA ESCRIBIR

¡Felicidades!

Usando el estilo del artículo **Un cumpleaños infantil**, escribe una descripción del cumpleaños de un/a niño(a) que conoces tú. ¿Qué recibió el/la niño(a)? ¿Quién le dio cada regalo? ¿Cuál fue el mejor/peor regalo que recibió?

_____

_____

_____

_____

_____

_____

_____

_____

Hogar, dulce hogar

VOCABULARIO

IMÁGENES Y PALABRAS

A. Rita "Relajada" y Susana "Superordenada". Completa las frases con palabras apropiadas (algunos verbos se usan más de una vez).

Rita Relajada vive en un **(1.)** _____ en un edificio alto en

la ciudad. Trabaja todo el día y de noche sale con sus amigos. No tiene

tiempo para **(2.)** _____ sus

cosas o para limpiar, y la verdad es que no le

importa mucho. Una vez ella se fue de vacaciones y

antes de irse no tuvo tiempo para

(3.) _____ el montón de

(4.) _____ en el fregadero°.

Como Rita no quería invitar a las cucarachas,

(5.) _____ todos los

(6.) _____ sucios° en la bañera°, la llenó de agua y

jabón y se fue por dos semanas. Cuando volvió, todo estaba limpio°, ¡y no

vio ni una cucaracha! Ella sólo tenía que **(7.)** _____

los platos y **(8.)** _____ los en los

(9.) _____ en la cocina. ¡Qué lista° es Rita!

Susana Superordenada, la hermana de Rita es muy

diferente. Susana vive en las **(10.)**

Palabras útiles

el fregadero *sink*

sucios *dirty*

la bañera *bathtub*

limpio *clean*

lista *inteligente*

sucio *no limpio*

la fila *row*

_____ de la ciudad, en una casa de

(**11.**) _____ rojos. Todos los días ella

(**12.**) _____ la casa y (**13.**) _____

todas las cosas en su lugar. Después (**14.**) _____ las

camas y (**15.**) _____ la aspiradora. No tiene que lavar

los platos porque hay un (**16.**) _____ en la cocina.

Susana pone la ropa sucia° en la (**17.**) _____ y luego

en la (**18.**) _____. Después de terminar los

(**19.**) _____ dentro de la casa, sale al

(**20.**) _____ donde tiene un

(**21.**) _____ de rosas, todas ordenadas perfectamente en

filas°. Entonces entra para (**22.**) _____ la mesa para

el almuerzo.

B. Quehaceres de la casa. Según las

imágenes, ¿qué tiene que hacer cada persona?

Por ejemplo: Tiene que ordenar el salón.

1._____

_____

2._____

_____

3._____

_____

4. _____

_____

5. _____

_____

6. _____

_____

7. _____

_____

8. _____

_____

9. _____

_____

C. **¿Dónde está?** Según las imágenes, indica dónde está cada animal.

Por ejemplo: El caballo grande está adentro; el caballo pequeño está afuera.

1. _____

_____

_____

_____

_____

Visión y voz 2E Workbook © 1998 John Wiley & Sons

2. _____
_____
_____
_____
_____
_____
_____

3. _____
_____
_____
_____
_____
_____
_____

4. _____
_____
_____
_____
_____
_____
_____
_____
_____

GRAMÁTICA 1

A. Un cuento de hadas: la Cenicienta. En la siguiente escena, tiene que trabajar mucho Cenicienta, un personaje bien conocido de un cuento de hadas. Trata de mejorar los párrafos sustituyendo los pronombres de complemento directo cuando sea posible. Luego, adivina: ¿Quién es la Cenicienta?

Me desperté porque una voz áspera pronunció mi nombre:

—¡¡Cenicienta!!— Era la voz de mi madrastra. Tuve que escuchar a mi madrastra.

—¡Tú, floja! Tienes que pasar la aspiradora. ¿Ya pasaste la aspiradora?

—No pude pasar la aspiradora, Madrastra. Es que... no funciona.

—Pues, tienes que reparar la aspiradora. ¡Y pronto! ¿No recuerdas que hoy viene don Felipe? Invité a don Felipe a almorzar. Tu hermanastra quiere conocer a don Felipe.

—Pero sólo son las cinco de la mañana, Madrastra.

—¿Y a mí qué me importa la hora? Mira esta planta. ¿Por qué no riegas la planta? Y los muebles, ¿por qué no sacudiste los muebles? Tiene que hacer tus quehaceres, desobediente, y ¡rápido! ¿Cuándo vas a terminar tus quehaceres?

_____

_____

_____

_____

_____

_____

_____

_____

_____

_____

_____

_____

_____

_____

_____

B. Otro cuento de hadas: una Blancanieves°
contemporánea.

¡Blancanieves ya está harta de pasar todos los días trabajando en casa! Hoy les dio una lista de quehaceres domésticos a los enanos°. Una X indica que el enano ya hizo el quehacer. Si no hay X, el enano va a hacer el quehacer después. Contesta las preguntas que siguen usando pronombres de complemento directo.

Palabras útiles

Blancanieves _Snow White_

el enano _dwarf_

Bobo	Alegre	Tímido
barrer el suelo	regar las rosas X	guardar la ropa
lavar la ropa X	ordenar la casa X	limpiar el baño X
Dormilón	**Doc**	**Blanca**
poner la mesa	hacer las camas X	preparar la comida
lavar los platos	lavar las ventanas	dirigir el trabajo de la casa X
Estornudo	**Enojado**	
cortar el césped	secar los platos	
sacar la basura X	limpiar el sótano	

Por ejemplo: ¿Quién sacó la basura?
         Estornudo la sacó.

1. ¿Lavó Doc las ventanas? _____

2. ¿Quién terminó todos sus quehaceres? _____

3. ¿Quién tiene que limpiar el sótano? _____

4. ¿Limpió Tímido el baño? _____

5. ¿Quién va a lavar los platos? _____

6. ¿Guardó Tímido la ropa? _____

7. ¿Quién tiene que secar los platos? _____

8. ¿Quién hizo las camas? _____

9. ¿Quiénes no hicieron ninguno de sus quehaceres?

_____

C. Aspectos personales. Contesta las preguntas usando los pronombres de complemento directo. Usa el presente o pretérito, según la pregunta.

1. ¿Sacaste la basura ayer? _____

2. ¿Quién limpió el baño? ¿Cuándo? _____

3. En tu hogar, ¿quién prepara la comida? _____

4. ¿Quién barre el suelo? _____

5. Algún día cuando tengas tu propia familia, ¿va a hacer una persona

todos los quehaceres? _____

G R A M Á T I C A 2

A. La visita del tío Hernando. Completa la narración con la forma correcta del pretérito o del imperfecto de los verbos.

Recuerdo la última vez que (**1.** ver) _____ a mi tío Hernando.

Aquel lunes (**2.** ser) _____ como cualquier día normal.

(**3.** ser) _____ las ocho cuando yo (**4.** despertarse)

_____ y (**5.** entrar) _____ a la cocina.

(**6.** Buscar) _____ un plato limpio pero no (**7.** haber)

_____ limpios en toda la cocina. Como siempre, la casa (**8.** estar)

_____ desordenada. A las nueve (**9.** recibir) _____

una llamada telefónica de mi prima y ella me (**10.** decir) _____

que mi tío Hernando (**11.** ir) _____ a visitarme muy pronto. Mi

tío Hernando (**12.** tener) _____ ochenta años y (**13.** ser)

_____ mi tío favorito. Pero a él le (**14.** molestar)

_____ el desorden. ¡Yo no (**15.** querer)

_____ mostrarle mi casa como (**16.** estar) _____!

Traté de ordenar la casa pero no (**17.** poder) _____ terminar. El

tío Hernando (**18.** llegar) _____ y (**19.** ver) _____ el

desorden. Pero Hernando me (**20.** conocer) _____ bien y

(**21.** decir) _____ que su sobrina favorita no (**22.** ser)

_____ una persona ordenada. Me (**23.** gustar)

_____ como soy.

B. Recuerdos de la niñez. Describe aspectos de tu niñez, según el modelo.

Por ejemplo: tu juguete favorito / ser
Mi juguete favorito era un carro pequeño.

pasar / los veranos
Pasaba los veranos en la playa.

1. en la tele/mirar

_____

_____

2. tu programa favorito/ser

_____

_____

3. jugar/los sábados

_____

_____

4. pasar/las vacaciones

_____

_____

5. para tus cumpleaños/querer

_____

_____

C. ¿Qué pasaba? Usa el imperfecto para describir todo lo que pasaba en la casa de la señora Gómez mientras ella trabajaba. Ahora todo es diferente porque ella tiene una ama de casa (*housekeeper*) muy estricta. Pero en el pasado todos hacían lo que les daba la gana.

1. Arturo _____

2. Carlos _____

3. María _____

4. Rodolfo _____

5. Diego y Carmen _____

L E C T U R A
V O C E S   D E L   M U N D O   H I S P A N O

Recuerdos de la niñez

Lee el artículo y completa las actividades
que siguen.

Marcos, el marido de la famosa Cristina, la
Oprah Winfrey cubana, escribió este tributo a
su abuelo. Los padres de Marcos se
divorciaron cuando él era muy pequeño, y su
padre lo abandonó.

"En mi mente llevo vivas imágenes de cuando era
niño y mi abuelo ponía todo su esfuerzo° en mi
crecimiento°. Yo le decía 'Papi' en vez de abuelo...
¿Cómo se me pueden olvidar esas mañanas,
cuando yo tenía apenas° cuatro años, y mi Papi me
sentaba en un banquito frente a su balance° y me
enseñaba el abecedario° docenas de veces hasta
que yo podía recitarlo como cualquier canción de
cuna? También recuerdo los paseos que dábamos todos de la mano.El me
lucía con orgullo como si yo fuera un potro que acaba de ganar una carrera
y que da una última vuelta a la pista para que todos lo admiren. ¿Y cómo me
puedo olvidar del olor de su colonia y de su áspera barba° que me pinchaba
como el beso de un gato? ¡Pero qué paz me daba cada vez que me abrazaba!

Mi abuelo. Mi 'Papi'. Mi amigo... Hace más de una década que Papá Dios se
lo llevó mientras me hablaba mirándome a los ojos, dejándome en los labios
las únicas palabras que hubiera querido que él oyera:

    TE QUIERO MUCHO, MI VIEJO.

    Feliz día de los padres.

A. ¿Entendiste? Contesta las preguntas.

1. ¿Cómo llamaba Marcos a su abuelo?

_____

2. ¿Qué hacían juntos Marcos y su abuelo?

_____

3. ¿Qué memorias de los sentidos (*senses*) físicos asocia Marcos con su abuelo?

_____

4. ¿Qué día festivo fue la ocasión de este tributo?

_____

Palabras útiles	
el fregadero	*sink*
el esfuerzo	*effort*
el crecimiento	*growth*
apenas	*barely, hardly*
el balance	*rocking chair*
el abecedario	*la recitación del alfabeto*
la áspera barba	*rough beard*

B. ¿Qué significa? Selecciona la mejor respuesta.

1. Según el contexto, el significado más probable de **en vez de** es
   a. in addition to   **c.** instead of
   b. because of   **d.** on behalf of

2. Según el contexto, el sinónimo más probable de **Dios se lo llevó** es
   a. fue de viaje   **c.** pasó tiempo en la iglesia
   b. murió   **d.** era un cura (*priest*)

C. Tus recuerdos. Marcos describe sus recuerdos felices de cuando era muy joven y estaba con su abuelo. Describe los recuerdos más felices de tu niñez. ¿Qué te gustaba hacer? ¿A qué jugabas y con quiénes? ¿Adónde te gustaba ir? ¿Cuántos años tenías en la memoria más temprana que puedes recordar? Descríbela.

_____

_____

_____

_____

_____

_____

_____

_____

_____

_____

_____

PARA ESCRIBIR

Recuerdos de tu niñez

Escribe una carta a un/a pariente o amigo(a) de tu niñez. Describe las cosas que hacían juntos. Recuerda que para describir costumbres del pasado tienes que usar el imperfecto.

_____

_____

_____

_____

_____

_____

_____

_____

_____

Historias de mi niñez

V O C A B U L A R I O
IMÁGENES Y PALABRAS

A. La niñez triste. Completa las frases con palabras apropiadas del vocabulario.

Ana María Matute es una escritora española que suele escribir sobre la niñez. Pero los niños de esta autora casi siempre tienen una niñez triste. Mientras la niña típica estadounidense juega con su "Barbie", las niñas de sus cuentos no tienen

(1.) _____. Una niña pobre pone un trapo° en una rama° y

(2.) _____ que esta rama es una muñeca. Los niños no tienen

(3.) _____ como perros o gatos. Juegan con los insectos o con las

(4.) _____ o **(5.)** _____ que viven cerca en su **(6.)** _____. A un niño le gusta imaginarse un **(7.)** _____ que vuela° por el aire, hasta que un día se

(8.) _____ de un árbol y se muere. Algunos niños son tan tristes que no tienen

Palabras útiles	
el trapo	*rag*
la rama	*twig*
vuela	*flies*
el fuego	*fire*

(9.) _____ de morir porque la muerte representa una

forma de escape. A veces estos niños se hacen

(10.) _____ porque juegan con el fuegoº o hacen otras

cosas **(11.)** _____ . Parecen crueles cuando les

(12.) _____ piedras a los animales, pero la verdad es

que no entienden lo que hacen. Los verdaderos crueles en los cuentos de

Matute son los adultos que a veces **(13.)** _____ a los

niños cuando no hacen nada malo. Los pobres niños de Matute... cuando

tienen **(14.)** _____ nadie les da comida; cuando

tienen **(15.)** _____ nadie les da agua, y cuando

tienen **(16.)** _____ nadie los abraza hasta que se

duermen. Estos niños viven solos y sin amor y sólo

(17.) _____ con tener el cariño que necesitan.

B. Los juegos infantiles. Describe cada imagen.

1._____
_____

2._____
_____

3._____
_____

4._____

_____

5._____

_____

6._____

_____

C. Pero ¿qué te pasa? ¿Por qué llora cada uno de estos niños?

Por ejemplo: Luis llora porque se cayó.

Laura

Guillermo

1._____

_____

2._____

_____

3._____

_____

Visión y voz 2E Workbook © 1998 John Wiley & Sons

Federico y Luisa

Enrique

4. _____

_____

5. _____

_____

G R A M Á T I C A 1

A. Una gran novela española. Completa las frases con la forma correcta del pretérito o del imperfecto de los verbos.

El Lazarillo de Tormes es una famosa novela española.

Un autor anónimo la _____ (**1.** escribir)

en 1554. Lazarillo _____ (**2.** ser) un

chico muy pobre, que _____ (**3.** nacer),

literalmente, en el río Tormes. Lazarillo

_____ (**4.** perder) a su padre cuando

sólo _____ (**5.** tener) ocho años, y su pobre madre no

_____ (**6.** poder) cuidarlo bien. Un día un ciego°

_____ (**7.** llegar) a la venta° donde _____

(**8.** trabajar) la madre de Lazarillo. El ciego le _____ (**9.** decir)

que _____ (**10.** querer) emplear a Lazarillo como guía y que

_____ (**11.** ir) a cuidarlo bien. Así Lazarillo

_____ (**12.** irse) con el ciego. Pero después de poco el niño

Palabras útiles	
ciego	*blind*
la venta	*inn*
el golpe	*hit, blow*
durar	*to last*

_____ (**13.** saber) que en realidad el

ciego_____ (**14.** ser) un hombre muy cruel. Siempre le

_____ (**15.** hacer) cosas crueles a Lazarillo, y por lo general

no lo _____ (**16.** cuidar) bien. Un día el ciego le

_____ (**17.** dar) un golpe° en la cabeza tan duro que, según

Lazarillo, "más de tres días me _____ (**18.** durar°) el dolor".

La vida con el ciego _____ (**19.** ser) muy difícil para Lazarillo,

pero por fin el niño _____ (**20.** poder) escaparse.

B. ¿Qué quería ser? Según las imágenes, indica con qué soñaba ser cada persona de niño(a) y lo que hace ahora en realidad.

Por ejemplo: María tiene veinticinco años y trabaja en una guardería (es maestra de niños). Cuando tenía cinco años quería (soñaba con) ser actriz.

María, 25 años   María, 5 años

Rafael, 37 años   Rafael, 9 años

Luisa, 41 años   Luisa, 13 años

1._____

_____

_____

_____

2._____

_____

_____

_____

Jóvenes

Ramón, 15 años   pequeño

3. _____

_____

_____

_____

4. _____

_____

_____

_____

Julia, 29 años   Julia, 10 años

5. _____

_____

_____

C. ¿Cómo eran? Usa los siguientes adjetivos para describir cómo eran los niños de las imágenes y después escribe por qué. Sigue el modelo.

Jorgito

travieso	inteligente	desordenado
emprendedor	perezoso	tímido
divertido	amable	

Por ejemplo: Jorgito era emprendedor porque en los veranos tenía una empresa en el vecindario.

Juan

Rosita y Diego

Teresa

1. _____

_____

_____

2. _____

_____

_____

3. _____

_____

_____

Gerardo

Sarita

Pablo

4. _____

_____

_____

5. _____

_____

_____

6. _____

_____

_____

Guadalupe

7. _____

_____

_____

Visión y voz 2E Workbook © 1998 John Wiley & Sons

D. Mis padres y yo. Escribe comparaciones entre tus padres cuando eran jóvenes y tú, según el modelo.

Por ejemplo: quejarse de
> **Mi papá (mamá) se quejaba de no tener un televisor en color. Yo me quejo de no tener una imprensora (*printer*) en colores para mi computdora.**

1. quejarse de

_____

_____

_____

2. llevar (*to wear*)

_____

_____

_____

3. jugar con

_____

_____

_____

4. tener miedo de

_____

_____

_____

5. usar... para escribir composiciones

_____

_____

_____

6. soñar con

_____

_____

_____

7. tener que

_____

_____

_____

G R A M Á T I C A 2

A. Recuerdos de la niñez. Completa las siguientes narraciones con los verbos indicados, usando el pretérito o el imperfecto según el contexto.

gustar traer haber venir

1. Siempre me _____ mis fiestas de cumpleaños, pero la

fiesta de hace diez años no me _____ nada. Mis

abuelos, que por lo general me _____ muñecas

preciosas, ese año sólo me _____ una lámpara feísima.

Antes de ese año, siempre _____ una gran fiesta en

casa y todos mis amigos y familiares _____, pero esa

vez no _____ fiestas y no _____

nadie a visitarme.

ser leer estar dormir saber ir

2. _____ las dos de la mañana. Mientras mi hermano y

yo _____ tranquilamente arriba, mis padres

conversaban en la cocina. Mi papá _____

preocupado y esa noche sólo _____ dos horas. Al día

siguiente, yo _____ lo que mis padres ya

_____ , que íbamos a mudarnos a otra ciudad.

| vestirse | ver | morirse | empezar | reírse | pedir |

3. Para la noche de brujas, doña Clara siempre _____ de

princesa para saludar a los niños. Pero un año, _____ de

horrible vampira. Cuando los niños la _____ de repente, casi

_____ de miedo y _____ a correr, pero luego, al

reconocer a doña Clara, _____ muchísimo. Todos los niños le

_____ vestirse de princesa el próximo año.

B. El Centro de Serenidad. Completa el anuncio con la forma correcta del pretérito o del imperfecto de los verbos, según el contexto.

EL SECRETO DE MI TRANQUILIDAD INTERIOR LO TIENE EL CENTRO DE SERENIDAD

Cuando yo _____ (**1.** ir) por

primera vez al Centro de Serenidad

_____ (**2.** estar) nervioso,

desanimado y _____

(**3.** parecer) mucho más viejo de lo que soy

en realidad. _____

(**4.** sentirse) siempre estresado y mis

amigos _____

(**5.** preocuparse) por mi salud. En una

semana los profesores de meditación me

_____ (**6.** enseñar) a

descansar. Yo _____

(**7.** empezar) a sentir esa tranquilidad

interna que siempre _____

(**8.** desear).

¡_____

(**9.** nacer) de

nuevo! Antes

_____ (**10.** perder) el

control de los nervios dos veces al día. Pero

una semana de instrucción en El Centro

me _____ (**11.** regalar) la

libertad del estrés.

Llame al **Centro de Serenidad** y pida una cita sin compromiso.
625-9027 o 238-8809
Carrera 12, No. 32-28
Santafé de Bogotá, D.C.

LECTURA
VOCES DEL MUNDO HISPANO

I. ABUELOS QUE CUIDAN NIÑOS

Lee el artículo y completa las actividades que siguen.

En el complejo "Casa Grande" de Longchamps, un grupo de jubilados regala afecto, ternura y atenciones a veinticuatro niños que por problemas de maltrato o abuso sexual han sido separados de su familia.

L a abuela Lucía, la abuela Chola, el abuelo Bernabé, el abuelo Angel, son jubilados y tienen más de 70 años. Jesica es una bebé de algo más de 1 año, Hugo tiene 12, Marina aparenta alrededor de 5. Los reunió el azar y los unió el amor, y la historia de todos cambió de golpe. Allí, en el complejo "Casa Grande" de Longchamps, en la provincia de Buenos Aires, Argentina, estos abuelos y otros —que son parte de la Asociación de Jubilados local— han vuelto a sentirse útiles y necesitados. Y con infinito afecto y ternura tratan de curar las heridas del alma de esos 24 niños que la Justicia decidió separar de sus padres, de los cuales han padecido maltrato o abuso sexual.

Todo comenzó cuando la presidenta del Consejo del Menor de la provincia de Buenos Aires, la doctora Marta Pascual, (docente universitaria y ex jueza de Menores) pidió ayuda a la Asociación de Jubilados Amigos de Longchamps, a pocos kilómetros de la capital. El aumento de la violencia doméstica en la provincia se traduce en cifras contundentes: en la oficina de Registro y reubicación de menores abandonados, abusados y maltratados llegan 70 casos nuevos por semana.

"Podíamos tener una institución donde ubicarlos, un equipo, pero nos faltaba ese contacto diario, acompañar a los niños. Cuando uno recorre los Hogares de Menores a la tardecita ve esa tristeza, la falta de una familia, la añoranza de una madre, de un papá que los escuche o los acaricie... Aquí las entidades de la tercera edad están muy bien organizadas, muchos abuelos son todavía jóvenes, tienen tiempo y mucha riqueza para transmitir. Quienes venimos de una generación que se ha criado al lado de nuestros abuelos y nos han transmitido tantos valores, pensamos que debíamos convocarlos a nuestro proyecto. Y así nació Casa Grande."

A. ¿Entendiste? Contesta las preguntas.

1. Los abuelos del artículo ¿son los abuelos biológicos de los niños? ¿Por qué se llaman "abuelos"?

_____

_____

2. El programa de "Casa Grande" ¿qué beneficios ofrece a los viejos? ¿A los niños?

_____

_____

3. ¿Quién empezó este programa?

_____

_____

4. ¿Qué problema quería curar?

_____

_____

Palabras útiles	
el jubilado	persona vieja que ya no trabaja
el afecto y la ternura	cariño, amor
la herida	*wound*
padecido	*suffered*
el Consejo	*Counsel*
ubicar	poner
el equipo	grupo
recorrer	andar por
la falta	*lack*
convocar	invitar

B. ¿Qué significa? Escoge la mejor opción.

1. Según el contexto, el sinónimo más probable de **aparenta** es:

    a. siente   **b.** parece

    c. quiere   **d.** nace

2. Según el contexto, el significado más probable de **maltrato** es:

    a. care   **b.** loss

    c. mistreatment   **d.** poverty

3. Según el contexto, el significado más probable de **aumento** es:

    a. elimination   **b.** hearing

    c. decrease   **d.** increase

C. Una vida mejor. Contesta las preguntas.

1. Describe la vida de los "abuelos" antes de entrar en Casa Grande. ¿Cómo se sentían? ¿Qué necesitaban?

_____

_____

2. Describe la vida de los niños antes de entrar en Casa Grande. ¿Con quiénes vivían? ¿De qué sufrían a veces? ¿Qué necesitaban?

_____

_____

3. Usa **más** o **menos** para escribir una comparación entre la vida de los "abuelos" antes y después de Casa Grande.

_____

_____

4. Usa **más** o **menos** para escribir una comparación entre la vida de los niños antes y después de Casa Grande.

_____

_____

II. LA DINÁMICA DE LOS IDIOMAS

Los idiomas son sistemas de comunicación abiertos y dinámicos. En español, como en inglés, muchas palabras y expresiones que se usan hoy no se usaban en la época de nuestros abuelos o bisabuelos. Algunas palabras mueren o pasan de moda, pero otras nacen para reflejar la sociedad actual (del presente). Además, como ahora hay más intercambio de ideas e información entre la gente del mundo (piensa en los viajes, la televisión por satélite y el correo electrónico), los idiomas se acomodan y se prestan muchas palabras. Lee el anuncio de la siguiente página y completa las actividades que siguen.

A. La jerga de la red (_Net jargon_). Mira el anuncio y descubre tres palabras tomadas del inglés.

B. Palabras importadas. El español, como el inglés o cualquier otro idioma, adopta palabras de otros idiomas. Sin embargo, cuando una palabra pasa de un idioma a otro, ciertos cambios son necesarios. Mira la siguiente lista de palabras importadas del inglés al español y trata de pronunciarlas. Verifica la pronunciación con tu profesor/a. En cada caso, indica cuál de estos métodos se usa para adaptar la palabra al español.

    a. la palabra inglesa se traduce (_is translated_)

    b. la palabra se escribe igual aunque se pronuncia de manera diferente

    c. la palabra se escribe de manera diferente aunque se pronuncia de manera similar

Por ejemplo: hobby
           La palabra se escribe igual aunque se pronuncia de manera diferente.

___ **1.** el navegante de la red	___ **4.** el surfing	___ **7.** cliquear
___ **2.** la telaraña mundial	___ **5.** el rockero	___ **8.** los blue jeans
___ **3.** el software	___ **6.** el frisbi	___ **9.** la home page

PRESENTANDO EL SERVIDOR MAS PODEROSO Y MEJOR GUARDADO DEL MUNDO.

¿Sabe usted todo lo que podría lograr si tuviera acceso a su mainframe? Lo fundamental, aprovechar toda su capacidad y poder para competir y colocarse en la cima del mundo empresarial actual.

Ahora, Cisco Systems le ayuda a aprovechar esa capacidad y a distribuirla a través de su organización y a nivel internacional, convirtiendo su mainframe en el servidor más poderoso del mundo.

Cisco conecta su mainframe a la red cliente servidor, convirtiéndolo en un servidor de Internet. ¿No es esto genial? Su mainframe le da el poder de procesamiento y los ruteadores y switches de Cisco se encargan de que la información llegue rápida y segura a su destino, ya sea dentro o fuera de su compañía.

No olvide que, cuando se trata de networking, Cisco le ofrece la mayor cantidad de opciones. Todo esto, unido a nuestra trayectoria de proveer consistentemente lo último en tecnología de redes para la integración de SNA/LAN, demuestra el por qué más compañías Fortune 500 confían en las soluciones de internetworking de Cisco.

Para mayor información llámenos o visítenos en nuestra página del Web.

¿No cree que es hora de que su mainframe salga a la luz?

CISCO SYSTEMS

UNA RED QUE TRABAJA SIN EXCUSAS™

DESTAPE SU MAINFRAME Y CONVIERTALO EN EL SERVIDOR MAS PODEROSO

Infórmese sobre la más reciente estrategia de CiscoBlue en el: www.cisco.com/warp/public/731/cblue/index.html o llamando a su oficina de Cisco local. Como líder global en software de internetworking, Cisco le ofrece un sinnúmero de opciones para redes. Para saber más acerca de nuestros seminarios, servicio/apoyo y productos, llámenos o visite nuestra página del web (www.cisco.com).

VISITENOS EN FELABAN. CARTAGENA. COLOMBIA. 26 – 29 DE NOVIEMBRE

C. ¿Qué quiere decir?   Aquí tienes algunas palabras inglesas que se asocian con la adolescencia en la cultura estadounidense. ¿Puedes explicarles a tus amigos hispanos lo que significan?

1. curfew _____

_____

2. to be grounded

_____

3. allowance _____

_____

4. cheerleader _____

_____

5. mall rat _____

_____

6. sleepover _____

_____

7. prom _____

_____

8. homecoming _____

_____

PARA ESCRIBIR

Recuerdos de la niñez

Describe tus recuerdos infantiles de tiempos que pasabas con un/a abuelo(a) o con otro(a) pariente viejo(a). Describe cómo era esta persona, qué hacían juntos, adónde iban, etc. Luego, describe una ocasión en particular que pasaste con tu pariente.

_____

_____

_____

_____

_____

_____

_____

_____

_____

_____

_____

_____

_____

_____

9

¡Buen provecho!

IMÁGENES Y PALABRAS

A. Una cocinera fatal. La pobre de Ana no cocina bien, y las cenas que ella organiza son siempre un desastre. Hace unas semanas invitó a sus amigos a cenar y ellos aceptaron con un poco de miedo. Completa la narración seleccionando las palabras apropiadas.

No supo (**1.** quemar, cocer, tostar) _____ el cerdo en su

punto ¡y quedó tan duro! La ensalada tenía demasiado vinagre y por eso

estuvo muy (**2.** agria, verde, rellena) _____. Cocinó la

trucha tanto que quedó totalmente (**3.** blanca, quemada, revuelta)

_____, mientras la carne de res, al contrario, quedó casi

(**4.** asada, cruda, caliente) _____. También sirvió una pizza

muy rara. Tenía (**5.** helado, queso, pan) _____ mozzarela y

salsa de (**6.** cebolla, langosta, tomate) _____ como una

pizza normal, pero ¡también tenía (**7.** carne, cebolla, piña)

_____! El peor plato fue un pollo con una salsa tan

(**8.** asada, picante, tinta) _____ que no se podía comer sin

tomar mucha agua. Para el postre sirvió (**9.** fresas, papas, gambas)

_____ fritas. No me parece buena idea (**10.** freír, servir,

encantar) _____ esa fruta.

B. Recuerdos de una cubanoamericana. Completa la narración de Gloria con las palabras apropiadas.

Muchos de mis recuerdos de mi niñez se asocian con la comida. Por la

mañana mi mamá siempre me preparaba un (**1.**) _____

enorme. Empezaba con (**2.**) _____ revueltos y

(**3.**) _____, con (**4.**) _____ tostado cubierto de

(**5.**) _____. Y para beber, un vaso de (**6.**) _____

de naranja. Cuando estaba enferma siempre me traía una

(**7.**) _____ de pollo riquísima. Los días festivos como, por

ejemplo, El Día de Acción de Gracias, siempre servía un

(**8.**) _____ relleno, con arroz blanco y frijoles negros. A mi

padre le gusta la (**9.**) _____ de res pero en los últimos años

comemos más (**10.**) _____ o pollo que carne por razones de

salud. En los picnics del verano siempre llevábamos el

(**11.**) _____ frito y las (**12.**) _____ de lechuga y

tomate. En el otoño mamá siempre preparaba una (**13.**) _____

de manzanas, que se servía con (**14.**) _____ de vainilla. Era el

(**15.**) _____ perfecto para una cena magnífica.

C. Aspectos personales. Completa las siguientes frases.

1. La comida que prefiero comer cuando estoy solo(a) es

_____ .

2. La comida ideal para una ocasión festiva es

_____ .

3. La comida que les gusta a los niños es

_____ .

4. La comida ideal para un picnic es

_____ .

5. En un restaurante elegante siempre pido

_____.

6. Cuando estudio me gusta comer

_____.

7. Cuando estoy deprimido(a) o nervioso(a)

_____.

8. Para una cena romántica prefiero servir

_____.

G R A M Á T I C A 1

A. ¿Cómo está hecho? Vuelve a escribir cada frase según el modelo.

Por ejemplo: Martha Stewart prepara bien la cena.
Sus cenas están bien preparadas.

1. Diego Rivera pinta cuadros con colores vivos.

_____

2. Mi mamá siempre quema los frijoles.

_____

3. Tú siempre haces las tareas con cuidado.

_____

4. Gabriel García Márquez escribe novelas con un sentido mágico.

_____

5. El profesor enseña las lecciones con imaginación.

_____

6. Mi papá siempre cuece el pollo con demasiada sal.

_____

7. El cocinero cubre la carne de res con cebollas.

_____

B. ¡Mil gracias! Describe lo que una persona hizo en cada imagen. También expresa las gracias que dieron la gente, según el modelo.

Por ejemplo:

a. El cocinero les sirvió una magnífica cena.

b. —Gracias por habernos preparado (servido) esta magnífica cena.

1. a. _____

_____

b. _____

_____

espina

Quitar: to remove

2. a. _____

_____

b. _____

_____

Cenicienta

hada madrina

3. a. _____

_____

b. _____

_____

4. a. _____

_____

b. _____

_____

5. a. _____

_____

b. _____

_____

6. a. _____

_____

b. _____

_____

GRAMÁTICA 2

A. La gran fiesta. Marta, Luisa y Dolores son compañeras de cuarto. Van a hacer una gran fiesta para todos los estudiantes en su residencia estudiantil. Han hecho una lista de todos sus quehaceres. Una marca indica que el quehacer ya está hecho. Indica lo que ya ha hecho cada joven y lo que todavía no ha hecho.

Por ejemplo: Marta ya ha comprado el queso pero todavía no ha barrido el suelo.

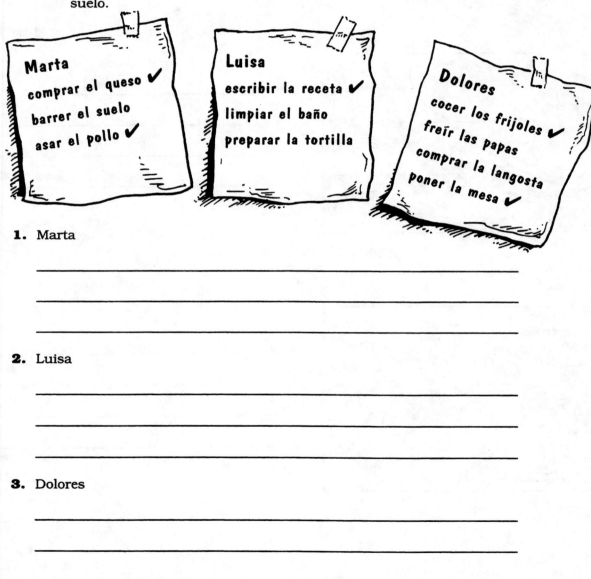

Marta
comprar el queso ✔
barrer el suelo
asar el pollo ✔

Luisa
escribir la receta ✔
limpiar el baño
preparar la tortilla

Dolores
cocer los frijoles ✔
freír las papas
comprar la langosta
poner la mesa ✔

1. Marta

_____

_____

_____

2. Luisa

_____

_____

_____

3. Dolores

_____

_____

_____

B. Una entrevista con Antonio Banderas.

Paso 1. Lo que sigue es parte de una entrevista entre Cristina y el actor español Antonio Banderas. Cristina le entrevistó durante la filmación de "El Zorro" en México. Completa las frases con la forma correcta del presente perfecto de los verbos.

Cristina: Antonio, ¿cómo te _____ (**1.** ir) en México?

Antonio: Estoy encantado. Me siento como en mi casa. Ya son tres meses y medio que estoy acá y la gente me _____

(**2.** tratar *to treat*) muy bien. Me encuentro muy a gusto con la gente, las tradiciones y la cultura. Hay muchas conexiones con mi país. Paseando por las calles de México _____

(**3.** quedar) alucinado al reconocer edificios y monumentos.

Lamentablemente _____ (**4.** salir) poco

porque _____ (**5.** estar) grabando en el estado de Puebla. Empiezo a las dos de la tarde y termino a las seis de la madrugada. El resto del tiempo es para descansar y estar con mi familia.

* * *

Después Cristina le pregunta a Antonio sobre el gran placer de trabajar con el famoso actor Anthony Hopkins.

Cristina: Soñabas trabajar con Anthony Hopkins y se te dio...

Antonio: Sólo _____ (**6.** hacer, nosotros) un par de escenas juntos y

_____ (**7.** ser) un

placer. El primer día me temblaban un poco las piernas.

Paso 2. Contesta estas preguntas.

1. ¿Qué aspectos de México le han gustado a Antonio Banderas?

   _____

2. ¿Por qué no ha podido ver más de la región?

   _____

3. ¿Has visto películas de Antonio Banderas? ¿Cuáles?

   _____

4. ¿Sabes con quién se ha casado Antonio Banderas?

   _____

C. Aspectos personales.
Usa las palabras dadas y añade otras para escribir preguntas. Después contéstalas, según los modelos. Usa las palabras **ya, todavía, alguna vez, muchas veces**

Por ejemplo: perder / tus llaves

   **a. ¿Cuántas veces has perdido tus llaves? o
   ¿Has perdido alguna vez tus llaves?**

   b. Las he perdido muchas veces.

   aprender mucho / en este curso

   a. ¿Has aprendido mucho en este curso?

   b. Sí, ya he aprendido mucho en este curso.

1. ver / una película fantástica

   a. _____

   b. _____

2. oír / tu conjunto de rock favorito

   a. _____

   b. _____

3. encontrar / el gran amor de tu vida

   a. _____

   b. _____

4. comer / platos de otra cultura

    a. _____

    b. _____

5. comer / pescado crudo

    a. _____

    b. _____

6. pasar / una noche sin dormir

    a. _____

    b. _____

7. romper / algo de mucho valor

    a. _____

    b. _____

8. olvidarse / el cumpleaños de una persona querida

    a. _____

    b. _____

9. hacer / algo que después has sentido

    a. _____

    b. _____

10. escribir / una carta de "Querido Juan" o "Querida Juana"?

    a. _____

    b. _____

L E C T U R A

VOCES DEL MUNDO HISPANO

POLLO A LA CELIA CRUZ

Lee el artículo y completa las actividades.

Celia Cruz es una cantante cubana muy popular.

Pollo a lo Celia Cruz

"Yo no sabía cocinar.

Pedro, mi esposo, es quien me ha ido enseñando. Hoy en día, cada vez que llego a mi casa, desués de una gira, me gusta meterme a la cocina y preparar algunos platillos. Una de las cositas que me gusta hacer es la sopa con azafrán porque me huele a hogar. De hecho, cada vez que voy a España, le traigo a mis amigos azafrán. Mi especialidad en la cocina es un pollito que ya hemos bautizado como Pollo a la Celia Cruz. Es facilísimo de hacer y sabe delicioso. Además, puede servir como platillo de dieta porque no tiene nada de grasa".

INGREDIENTES

1 Pollo
10 Limones
Orégano al gusto

PREPARACION:

La preparación es muy sencilla.

• Tomo el pollo y le quito la grasa.

• Lo meto en una ollita viejísima que tengo, pero que parece acabada de comprar, y le echo bastante limón. Yo diría que el jugo de 10 limones.

• Después le pongo orégano porque a Pedro no le gusta el comino.

• Después, tapo la olla viejita y lo pongo a fuego lento. Ese pollo va soltando un jugo delicioso y se va cocinando en él. Queda como si fuera un delicioso pollo asado.

A. ¿Entendiste. Contesta las preguntas.

1. ¿Quién ha sido el profesor de cocina de Celia Cruz?

   _____

2. ¿Cuándo le gusta más a Celia cocinar?

   _____

3. Según lo que se implica, ¿dónde se cultiva mucho azafrán?

   _____

4. Según Celia, ¿cuáles son las tres ventajas (beneficios) de este plato?

   _____

5. ¿Cuál es el cognado en inglés de **bautizado**?

   _____

6. El significado más probable de **comino** es...
   a. flour   b. cumin
   c. applesauce   d. liver

Palabras útiles	
la gira	viaje
el azafrán	saffron, a bright yellow spice
huele	smells
bautizado	nombrado
sabe	aquí significa que tiene el sabor
la grasa	fat
la ollita	recipiente que se usa para cocer
el fuego	fire
lento	no rápido

B. Memorias culinarias. Contesta las preguntas.

1. Describe la mejor cena que has comido. ¿Qué comiste? ¿Dónde? ¿Con quién?

   _____

   _____

   _____

2. Describe la peor cena que has comido. ¿Qué comiste? ¿Dónde? ¿Con quién? ¿Por qué fue la peor—por la comida o por las circunstancias?

   _____

   _____

   _____

   _____

PARA ESCRIBIR

Tu propia receta

Escribe un párrafo sobre tus habilidades culinarias (o la falta de ellas).
Contesta las siguientes preguntas.

1. ¿Cuándo te gusta cocinar?

2. ¿Por qué no te gusta cocinar?

3. ¿Para quiénes cocinas?

4. ¿Qué te gusta cocinar?

5. ¿Cómo lo haces?

_____

_____

_____

_____

_____

_____

Si eres un/a gran cocinero(a), escribe una receta al estilo de la de Celia Cruz
de un plato tuyo. Si no te gusta cocinar, adivina la receta del plato favorito de
tu niñez.

_____

_____

_____

_____

_____

_____

La buena mesa

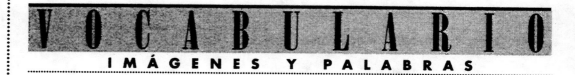

A. Usos clásicos, raros o folclóricos de la comida. Completa las frases con las palabras apropiadas.

1. Se usa el _____ para

protegerse de los vampiros.

2. La bruja del cuento de Hansel y Gretel

construyó su casa de dulces,

_____ y otras

_____.

> **Palabras útiles**
>
> Ricitos de Oro   *Goldilocks*
>
> el oso   *bear*
>
> dar golpes   *to hit*
>
> la mosca   *fly*

3. Por lo general las brujas usan las _____ exóticas para

hacer sus pociones mágicas. Las ponen un una _____

grande con agua muy caliente y las _____ mientras

recitan palabras mágicas.

4. Ricitos de Oroº comió la _____ que iba a ser el desayuno

de los tres ososº.

5. Tradicionalmente comemos las _____ de

_____ en el cine, mientras las _____

_____ se comen en un picnic.

6. Para freír comidas se usa una _____ pero en las tiras

cómicas ese utensilio se usa para darle golpesº a la cabeza de la gente.

7. Para hacer el "BLT", un sandwich clásico norteamericano, hay que tener

dos _____ de pan, una de tomate y unos trozos de

_____ .

8. Según un refrán popular, se puede atraer más moscas° con

_____ que con _____ .

9. Todo el mundo sabe que comer una barra de _____ puede

curar la depresión.

10. La _____ es un condimento que se pone en los perritos

calientes pero también se aplica a la piel para curar ciertas enfermedades.

B. La salsa de tomate italiana. Completa la receta con las palabras
apropiadas.

Palabras útiles	
el diente	*clove*
el fuego	*fire, heat*
la albahaca	*basil*

Primero hay que (**1.**) _____ todos los ingredientes que vas a

necesitar. Hay que (**2.**) _____ y picar una cebolla y unos dientes°

de (**3.**) _____ . Después hay que (**4.**) _____ estos

ingredientes al aceite en una (**5.**) _____ al fuego°. Luego hay que

echarle hojas de albahaca° picadas y (**6.**) _____ y dos

(**7.**) _____ de tomates pelados y (**8.**) _____ .

Entonces hay que (**9.**) _____ dos cucharaditas de sal y

agregarlas a la salsa. Ahora el único ingrediente que le (**10.**) _____

es media cucharadita de pimienta. Tienes que (**11.**) _____ estos

ingredientes y dejarlos cocer por dos horas o más. Mientras se está cociendo, el (**12.**) rico _____ de la salsa te va a perfumar la casa. Se puede

(**13.**) _____ por todas partes. Por fin hay que servir la salsa

sobre (**14.**) _____ cocinados "al dente".

C. ¿Cómo se pesa? ¿Cómo se vende? Para cada comida, indica cómo se
pesa o cómo se vende. También haz un comentario sobre cómo o cuándo tú la
comes.

Por ejemplo: los chiles verdes

> **Los chiles verdes se pesan por libras (o se venden en latas). Yo
> los como con carne.**

> el pollo

> **El pollo se pesa por libras o kilos. Yo lo como con arroz y
> frijoles (o yo lo como como plato principal).**

1. el tocino _____

2. las papitas fritas _____

3. las galletas _____

4. las palomitas de maíz _____

5. la mermelada _____

6. la mostaza _____

![GRAMÁTICA 1]

A. ¿Quién lo hizo? Contesta las preguntas según las imágenes. Usa los
pronombres de complemento directo e indirecto.

Carlos

1. ¿Quién le dio brócoli al perro?

_____

_____

_____

_____

La bruja

2. ¿Quién les ofreció golosinas a los niños?

_____

_____

_____

_____

Diablito

3. ¿Quién le agregó chiles verdes a la torta?

_____

_____

_____

_____

4. ¿Quién le quitó la barra de chocolate al bebé?

_____

_____

_____

_____

Tienes que mantenerte en dieta. Tres comidas al día, sin antojitos

5. ¿Quién le prohibió los antojitos a Enrique?

_____

_____

_____

_____

Jack   Gigante

6. ¿Quién le dio los frijoles mágicos a Jack?

_____

_____

_____

_____

Dioses   Pandora

7. ¿Quiénes le dieron la caja a Pandora?

_____

_____

_____

_____

B. Aspectos personales. Usa pronombres de complemento directo e indirecto para contestar las preguntas.

1. ¿Quién te preparó la mejor comida de tu vida?

_____

2. ¿Quién te sirvió el plato más raro de tu vida?

_____

3. ¿Les has servido a tus amigos tu propia "especialidad de la casa"?

_____

4. Cuando sales con tus amigos, ¿qué restaurante les prepara a Uds. los platos más ricos?

_____

5. ¿Quién te enseñó el arte de cocinar?

_____

6. ¿Quién te preparaba la comida cuando eras niño(a)?

_____

7. ¿Vas a prepararle un pastel de cumpleaños a tu mejor amigo(a) este año?

_____

C. ¡Los regalos peligrosos! Lee el siguiente relato y luego contesta las preguntas.

Normalmente un regalo es un símbolo del cariño, pero la historia y la ficción nos ofrecen algunas excepciones. Por ejemplo, los antiguos griegos les regalaron un caballo enorme a sus enemigos, pero adentro estaban los guerreros griegos. La caja que los dioses griegos le dieron a Pandora contenía todos los males del mundo. Además, la manzana que la vieja malvada le ofreció a Blancanieves la hizo dormir por muchos años. En _La Odisea_, los habitantes de una isla extraña les sirvieron la fruta del loto a los compañeros de Ulises. A causa de esta fruta mágica los hombres perdieron el deseo de volver a su hogar y quisieron quedarse en la isla.

1. ¿Quiénes le dieron una colección de problemas a una joven?

_____

2. ¿Quiénes le sirvieron a un grupo una comida que produce el olvido?

_____

3. ¿Quién le dio una fruta peligrosa a una joven?

_____

4. ¿Quiénes le dieron un regalo peligroso a sus enemigos?

_____

G R A M Á T I C A 2

A. Espero que... Escribe frases según el modelo.

Por ejemplo: Los niños no se sienten bien. ¿Comieron demasiadas golosinas?
Espero que no hayan comido demasiadas golosinas.

1. Ofelia no cocina bien. ¿Preparó ella la cena esta noche?

_____

2. Ese mesero parece estar enojado. ¿Me olvidé de dejarle propina?

_____

3. Pero... ¿dónde está mi tarjeta de crédito? ¿La dejé en el restaurante?

_____

4. Esta sopa se ve muy mal... ¿La quemé?

_____

5. La cocina huele mal. ¿Dejé una cebolla podrida (_rotten_) por alguna parte?

_____

6. El microondas no funciona. ¿Lo rompí yo?

_____

B. ¿Qué crees tú? Completa cada frase con el presente perfecto del verbo. Después responde a cada frase según el modelo.

Por ejemplo: El mesero dice que nos ha servido (servir) los platos bien calientes.
Creo que nos los ha servido bien calientes. (No creo que nos los haya servido bien calientes.)

1. Los políticos dicen que siempre _____ (decir) la verdad.

_____

2. Mi mamá dice que siempre nos _____ (cocinar) las comidas con mucho cariño.

_____

3. En los cuentos del Dr. Seuss, el "Grinch" dice que siempre

_____ (tener) cariño por los "Who".

_____

4. El Sr. Scrooge dice que siempre _____ (ser) generoso con los pobres.

_____

5. Evita Perón dice que siempre _____ (querer) al pueblo argentino.

_____

6. La artista estadounidense Madonna dice que siempre

_____ (desear) una vida más tranquila.

_____

7. El artista mexicano Diego Rivera dice que siempre _____
(tener) ganas de pintar.

_____

C. Nora la "neurótica". Mientras Nora y su esposo Tomás el
"tranquilo" estaban de vacaciones, sus hijos, Laura, de 17 años y Esteban, de
19 años, se han quedado en casa. Poco antes de volver a casa, Nora presiente
un desastre y le expresa sus preocupaciones a Tomás. Él trata de calmarla.
Completa su conversación según el modelo.

Por ejemplo: **Nora:** Sé que Laura y Esteban hicieron una fiesta y que no
ordenaron la casa después.
Tomás: No creo que hayan hecho una fiesta.
Nora: Espero que hayan ordenado la casa.

1. Nora: Probablemente se olvidaron de darle de comer al gato y el
pobrecito se murió.

Tomás: _____

Nora: _____

2. Nora: Estoy segura de que Laura dejó encendida la estufa y la casa se
quemó.

Tomás: _____

Nora: _____

3. Nora: Y Esteban es tan perezoso. Sé que no regó las flores del jardín y
mis rosas murieron.

Tomás: _____

Nora: _____

4. Nora: Y olvidaron de cerrar la puerta con llave y un ladrón entró y nos
robó.

Tomás: _____

Nora: _____

Tomás: Una pregunta, mi amor. ¿Crees que el ladrón nos haya robado
antes o después del incendio?

L E C T U R A

V O C E S   D E L   M U N D O   H I S P A N O

LAS EMPANADAS

Lee el artículo y completa las actividades que siguen.

GASTRONOMIA

EMPANADAS QUE DAN LA TALLA

POR JACK ROBERTIELLO

A PRIMERA VISTA, una empanada parece ser una propuesta simple: alguna sabrosa mezcla envuelta en una masa. Pero nada es previsible con estas empanaditas que constituyen el bocado favorito de América del Sur. Distintas versiones de este plato son populares en casi todos los países de América Central y del Sur. Las diversas variaciones del básico tema casero de masa y relleno abre cauce a una multidad de empanadas, pasteles, pastelería. Sean fritas o al horno son tantas las combinaciones que es imposible catalogarlas todas; habrá que entrevistar a todos los cocineros de las Américas. La informalidad de este plato hace de él un festín adaptable y movedizo. Algo tan informal como la empanada no necesita cuantificación.

Las distintas versiones de la empanada incluyen, entre otras, pequeñas almohaditas rellenas con carne de cangrejo y servidas con cocteles; empanadas rellenas con carne de cerdo y papas que se comen en picnics o se venden en la calle; bollos de masa frita rellenos con queso blanco; o pasteles de manzana o pera, cubiertos de azúcar y canela. Rellenos con un sinfín de combinaciones de puerco, langostino, pollo, verduras, queso o fruta, las posibles combinaciones están sólo limitadas por el contenido de la despensa o el refrigerador y el deseo de improvisar del cocinero.

Palabras útiles

dan la talla	son superiores
la masa	*dough*
la empanada	pan relleno de carne, frijoles, vegetales u otras cosas
la cuantificación	la acción de expresar en números o de estudiar formalmente
la almohadita	*little pillow*
el cangrejo	*crab*
la canela	*cinnamon*

A. ¿Entendiste? Completa las frases.

1. Según el contexto, el significado más probable de **envuelto** es...

   a. instead of   **b.** flavored by

   c. wrapped up in   **d.** mixed with

2. El autor nos dice la siguiente información sobre las empanadas excepto . . .

   a. su efecto sobre la salud   **b.** sus variaciones

   c. su popularidad   **d.** dos metódos posibles de cocinarlas

3. La variedad más grande de empanadas resulta de los(las) diferentes . . .

   a. maneras de prepararlas   **b.** masas

   c. especias   **d.** rellenos

B. El plato favorito. Según al artículo, las empanadas son el plato más popular de América del Sur. Descríbele a un amigo latinamericano el plato más popular de los Estados Unidos. Describe el plato: ¿se prepara con variaciones como la empanada? ¿por qué es tan popular? ¿en qué ocasiones se sirve? ¿dónde se sirve?

_____

_____

_____

_____

_____

_____

Para escribir

El buen comer

Hay una multitud de libros de cocina que se publican hoy en día. Escoge uno de los siguentes libros de cocina (o inventa tu propio libro) y descríbelo en términos generales. Tambien incluye una receta ejemplar.

- Recetas para gente que no tiene tiempo para cocinar
- Platos tradicionales de mi familia (mi cultura)
- Cocinar para los enamorados
- Cocinar con poco dinero
- Recetas para los que no les gusta cocinar
- Cocinar para los niños

_____

_____

_____

_____

_____

_____

_____

_____

_____

_____

_____

¿Qué me pongo?

V O C A B U L A R I O
I M Á G E N E S   Y   P A L A B R A S

A. ¿Qué llevan? Describe lo que llevan las siguientes personas.

1. Carlos "chévere"

_____

_____

_____

_____

2. Alicia "atleta"

_____

_____

_____

_____

3. Tomás "tienelotodo"

_____

_____

4. Teresa "tienelotodo"

_____

_____

Visión y voz 2E Workbook © 1998 John Wiley & Sons

5. Eduardo el "escolar"

_____
_____
_____
_____

6. Norberto "del norte"

_____
_____
_____
_____

7. Paula "preparada"

_____
_____
_____
_____

8. Sonia "salvavidas"

_____
_____
_____
_____

B. Aspectos personales. Contesta las preguntas con frases completas.

1. En alguna ocasión, ¿te has olvidado de poner en la maleta alguna prenda de ropa importante al salir de viaje? ¿Cuál? ¿Qué pasó?

_____

_____

2. ¿Un/a amigo(a) se ha puesto ropa inapropiada para la ocasión alguna vez? Explica.

_____

_____

3. ¿Te has puesto tú ropa inapropiada alguna vez? ¿Cuándo? ¿Qué te pusiste?

_____

_____

4. ¿Qué telas prefieres cuando compras ropa? ¿Para qué estación y qué ocasión?

_____

_____

5. ¿Qué color asocias con la envidia? ¿el peligro? ¿la tristeza? ¿la naturaleza?

_____

_____

C. Crucigrama. Completa el crucigrama.

Horizontales

1. Es mejor _____ los pantalones antes de comprarlos.

6. Llevo un _____ de baño para nadar.

7. Los pantalones de _____ son buenos para el invierno.

10. Matilde llevaba una falda, blusa y chaqueta del mismo color; era un _____ muy atractivo.

11. A veces mi amiga _____ de compras cuando está deprimida.

12. _____ es sinónimo del color café.

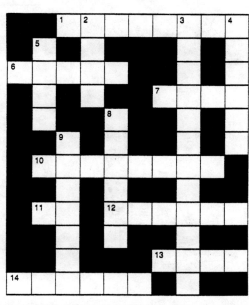

13. No quiero llevar el traje de mi padre; es pasado de _____.

14. Esta blusa es _____ de moda; es de un estilo muy antiguo.

Verticales

2. Ramón conduce un carro _____ para llamar la atención a las chicas.

3. La _____ (dos palabras) se lleva por adentro.

4. Muchos vestidos de boda están hechos de seda y _____.

5. _____ es una mezcla de blanco y negro.

8. El niño se pone el _____ para acostarse.

9. Algunas uvas son verdes, otras son _____.

GRAMÁTICA 1

A. La ropa nueva del emperador. Completa esta versión moderna de una antigua leyenda con la forma correcta de los verbos. Según el contexto, usa el infinitivo, el presente del indicativo o el presente del subjuntivo.

El emperador _____ (**1.** sufrir) de una falta de autoestima.

Quiere que todos lo _____ (**2.** admirar) pero él no se

_____ (**3.** respetar) a sí mismo. Durante un viaje a Los

Ángeles, nota que hay mucha gente bien respetada que no parece

_____ (**4.** tener) otras virtudes que su ropa espléndida de

marcas famosas. Así nuestro emperador, un poco tonto, _____

(**5.** visitar) el taller del famoso diseñador Cristián de Plata. El señor de Plata

le _____ (**6.** decir) —Si Ud. quiere que todo el mundo lo

_____ (**7.** mirar) con admiración, es necesario que

_____ (**8.** vestirse) a la última moda. Además, le recomiendo

que _____ (**9.** hacerse) un nuevo "look". Le aconsejo que

_____ (**10.** olvidarse) de ese traje tradicional tan pasado de

moda. Es mejor que _____ (**11.** ponerse) esta camiseta y este saco de cuero que es uno de Plata original. Y las canas ¡hay que

_____las (**12.** cambiar)! El pelo negro le hace lucir

más joven.

El emperador decide _____ (**13.** seguir) todos los consejos

del señor de Plata. Después _____ (**14.** mirarse) y le gusta

mucho lo que _____ (**15.** ver). Una semana después lo invitan

a aparecer en el programa de "Cristina" sobre "Hombres cuya vida ha

cambiado como resultado del nuevo look". Todos lo _____

(**16.** recibir) con grandes aplausos. Sólo un niño del público

_____ (**17.** pensar) de una forma independiente.

—Mira, mamá,— _____ (**18.** decir) el niño. —¡Qué bobo! ¡Un

hombre de 50 años que _____ (**19.** querer) parecer un joven

de 20 años!

B. El hermano protector.
Jacinto y Marisa son hermanos. Como Jacinto es mayor, tiene una actitud muy protectora hacia su hermana. Pero hay contradicciones entre su actitud hacia ella y otras chicas que conoce. Escribe frases según el modelo.

Por ejemplo: Otras chicas llevan ropa muy ajustada (*tight*).
A Jacinto le gusta que otras chicas lleven ropa ajustada pero no quiere que Marisa la lleve.

1. Otras chicas llevan faldas cortas.

_____

_____

2. Otras chicas compran blusas de encaje.

_____

_____

3. Otras chicas salen con sus amigos hasta muy tarde.

_____

_____

4. Otras chicas escogen vestidos muy llamativos (que llaman la atención).

_____

_____

5. Otras chicas tienen tatuajes.

_____

_____

6. Otras chicas se ponen trajes de baño mínimos.

_____

_____

C. Aspectos personales. Completa las frases.

1. Mis padres no quieren que yo _____

_____ .

2. Es mejor que mis padres _____

_____ .

3. Es muy importante que los líderes políticos _____

4. No me gusta que los jóvenes _____

_____ .

5. Los profesores me piden que _____

_____ .

6. Tengo una amiga que está enamorada de un chico. Le aconsejo que

_____ .

7. Para ser feliz es necesario que yo _____

_____ .

8. Mi amigo quiere ser más organizado. Le recomiendo que

_____ .

9. Mi amiga dice que no tiene nada que ponerse. Le recomiendo que

_____ .

GRAMÁTICA 2

A. La Cenicienta: después del baile. Completa la narración con una forma de **ser** o **estar**. Usa el infinitivo, el presente de indicativo o el presente de subjuntivo, según el contexto.

(**1.**) _____ la una de la mañana. El baile ha terminado y el

príncipe (**2.**) _____ deprimido porque no sabe dónde

(**3.**) _____ la mujer de sus sueños. Entonces encuentra un

zapato. El zapato (**4.**) _____ muy raro porque

(**5.**) _____ de cristal. Cree que (**6.**) _____ de la

mujer misteriosa con quien bailaba. El príncipe (**7.**) _____

muy confuso y consulta con su papá, el rey, que (**8.**) _____

mayor y por eso (**9.**) _____ más sabio (*wise*).

Príncipe: Padre, ¿qué clase de mujer lleva zapatos de cristal?

Rey: Los zapatos de cristal pueden (**10.**) _____ muy

peligrosos. Si se rompen la mujer puede hacerse daño a los

pies. Es posible que esos zapatos (**11.**) _____ de una

mujer loca, a quien le gusta el peligro. Es mejor que te olvides

de ella.

Príncipe: Pero, padre, ella (**12.**) _____ muy bella y me gusta

(**13.**) _____ con ella.

Rey: Además, los zapatos de cristal no (**14.**) _____ muy

prácticos. (**15.**) _____ caros y se rompen fácilmente.

Seguramente esa mujer no (**16.**) _____ muy práctica.

Es mejor que tu mujer (**17.**) _____ prudente. Te

recomiendo que busques otra.

B. Entrevista del diseñador del año. Trabajas para una revista de modas y tienes una entrevista con Cristián de Plata, el diseñador del año. Usa la forma correcta de **ser** o **estar** para completar las preguntas y las respuestas. Usa el infinitivo, el presente de indicativo o el presente de subjuntivo según el contexto.

Tú: Sr. de Plata, su nombre (**1.**) _____ muy exótico,

pero ¿de dónde (**2.**) _____ Ud.?

Sr. de Plata: (**3.**) _____ de Hackensack, New Jersey. Pero es

mejor que el nombre de un diseñador (**4.**) _____

europeo, y por eso lo cambié.

Tú: Todos dicen que este año las faldas van a (**5.**)

_____ más cortas. ¿(**6.**) _____ verdad?

Sr. de Plata: Sí. Uso menos tela para las faldas cortas y así no

(**7.**) _____ tan caras para fabricar.

Tú: Pero, a muchas mujeres les gustan las faldas más largas. La

mujer de hoy (**8.**) _____ más cómoda en una falda

larga. La mujer moderna, que (**9.**) _____ en su

oficina o un laboratorio, no quiere trabajar en una

minifalda.

Sr. de Plata: ¡No es importante que la ropa (**10.**) _____ cómoda!

Es importante que (11.) _____ atractiva.

Tú: Con permiso, señor. (12.) ¿_____ Ud. seguro? ¿Es

posible que Ud. (13.) _____ equivocado (*mistaken*)

sobre los gustos de la mujer moderna?

C. Situaciones. Usa la forma correcta de **ser** o **estar** para describir las personas en las siguientes situaciones.

1. Cenicienta _____ en el baile. _____ con su príncipe. Su

vestido _____ largo. Ella _____ contentísima.

2. Yo _____ en la sala de clases; tomo un examen. _____

nervioso(a); mi ropa _____ muy informal; _____ muy

cansado(a) porque estudié toda la noche.

3. María _____ en su oficina; su ropa _____ muy

conservadora; trabaja mucho porque _____ muy emprendedora;

_____ preocupada porque un cliente de su negocio

_____ enojado a causa de un error.

4. La madre de Elena _____ sola en la casa; _____

estresada porque no sabe dónde _____ su hija. Elena

_____ una joven desconsiderada, que muchas veces preocupa a

su mamá.

D. Una cita importante. Susana tiene una cita con Roberto. Es la
primera vez que salen juntos y quiere verse bien. Su amiga Lola quiere
ayudarla a decidir qué debe ponerse. Completa las frases con la forma correcta
de **este**, **ese** o **aquel**.

Susana: Quiero impresionar a Roberto en nuestra primera cita.

Lola: Pues, _____ vestido victoriano está muy pasado de moda, y _____ zapatos blancos parecen ser para una niña.

Susana: Pero _____ vestido negro es demasiado sofisticado. No quiero que Roberto piense que soy una de esas mujeres. Pero tampoco me gusta _____ blusa con la falda. Y _____ botas son demasiado llamativas.

Lola: ¿Qué vas a ponerte?

Susana: Mis jeans y un suéter. Por lo menos así me siento como mí misma.

L E C T U R A
VOCES DEL MUNDO HISPANO

LA GUAYABERA: CÓMODA, FRESCA Y ELEGANTE

Lee el artículo y completa las actividades que siguen.

DISEÑANDO PARA EL SIGLO XXI

GEORGINA O'HARA, historiadora de la moda en materia de atuendo, sustenta apasionadamente la creencia de que la gente debe tomar la moda con mucha más seriedad de lo que lo hace. Para ella, el estudio de la moda puede ser "una lección simultánea de historia, geografía, economía y matemáticas", y cree, además, que la moda es una ventana cultural y un reflejo de la época.

América Latina es una región de cumbres nevadas y selvas tropicales lujuriosas, cuna de pintores como Fernando Botero y Rufino Tamayo, escritores como Isabel Allende y Octavio Paz y científicos como Franklin Chang Díaz y César Milstein, que también ha aportado al mundo su cuota de modistas de primera línea. Entre los más destacados de éstos, figuran el dominicano Oscar de la Renta, la venezolana Carolina Herrera, y los cubanos Luis Estévez, Adolfo y Fernando Pena, este último nacido en España. Todos ellos han alcanzado un sitial de privilegio en el plano de la moda internacional y son el producto de una región que ha reforzado la trama de su espíritu creativo. Recientemente tuvo lugar la presentación de las colecciones más recientes en el marco del Sexta Gala de la Moda Hispana, que este año fue anunciado en la prensa como "el desfile de modas más esperado de la temporada" y "un himno a la riqueza y diversidad culturales que posee América Latina". El desfile de este año constituyó un despliegue de contrastes: elegancia y extravagancia, sobriedad y efervescencia, luces y sombras— un estudio en claroscuro. Los asistentes se solazaron en el caleidoscopio de colores y texturas, formas y sonidos de América Latina.

"Estamos dotados de una cultura exótica y fascinante", dijo Penny Harrison, directora del festival. "No somos un pueblo, sino varios. Para nosotros lo que cuenta es el entusiasmo, el romance, la pasión y el orgullo, y en el campo de la moda, como en ningún otro, se reflejan claramente estos valores. Oscar de la Renta, Adolfo y Carolina Herrera, para nombrar algunos, brindan a la moda no solamente sus firmas, sino la riqueza y la gloria de su legado cultural".

A. ¿Entendiste? Contesta las preguntas.

1. ¿Cómo se explica la gran popularidad de la guayabera?

_____

_____

_____

_____

> **Palabras útiles**
>
> la chaquetilla — una chaqueta pequeña; en este contexto es una forma de camisa
>
> la leyenda — *legend*
>
> el terrateniente — *landlord*
>
> oriundo — *nativo*

2. ¿Qué tela se usa hoy para hacer las guayaberas?

_____

_____

_____

3. El significado más probable de **se radicó** en el tercer párrafo es...

  a. descubrió   b. nació

  c. se fue a vivir   d. disfrutó

4. El significado más probable de **Encargó** en el tercer párrafo es...

  a. pidió cierto trabajo   b. insistió

  c. envió a otro país   d. compró

5. Según el artículo, ¿quién es responsable por el invento de la guayabera? ¿Cuál fue su motivo?

_____

_____

B. La prenda ideal. La guayabera es una prenda cómoda, útil y perfecto para el clima tropical. Vas a diseñar la prenda de ropa ideal para tu vida y tus necesidades. Usa las expresiones: Me gusta que la prenda...; **Quiero que...; Es mejor que...**, etc. **Usa el presente del subjectivo cuando sea necesario.**

_____

_____

_____

_____

_____

_____

_____

PARA ESCRIBIR

La prenda más cómoda o especial

La guayabera es una prenda muy cómoda. Describe tu conjunto más cómodo. ¿Qué te pones cuando quieres estar cómodo(a)? ¿Tienes una prenda de ropa que tenga un valor sentimental o supersticioso? ¿Cuál es? Explica el valor personal de esta prenda.

_____

_____

_____

_____

_____

_____

_____

_____

_____

_____

La moda no incomoda

V O C A B U L A R I O
I M Á G E N E S   Y   P A L A B R A S

A. Verse bien. Completa la narración con las palabras apropiadas.

Raquel es poeta y filósofa. Algunos la critican por su apariencia. Raquel no

sabe quiénes son ni Oscar de la Renta ni otros diseñadores conocidos, y

por eso nunca compra ropa de (**1.**) _____. Muchas veces

la ropa que lleva es larga o grande porque no es la

(**2.**) _____ apropiada para Raquel, y no le

(**3.**) _____ bien pero a ella no le importa. Siempre lleva

ropa (**4.**) _____ porque no le gusta ropa ajustada; no le

parece cómoda. Su ropa siempre está (**5.**) _____ porque

no tiene tiempo para plancharla.

Algunas de sus prendas favoritas son tan viejas que no sólo están

pasadas de moda, sino que están (**6.**) _____ por estar tan

usadas. Algunos pantalones, originalmente de colores vivos, están

(**7.**) _____ después de tanto lavar. A veces después de

comer, ella lleva la ropa (**8.**) _____, pero no parece

notarlo. Raquel lleva una blusa verde que no hace

(**9.**) _____ con los pantalones rojos, y casi todos sus

jeans están (**10.**) _____ por las rodillas.

Con respecto a los zapatos, Raquel nunca los usa con

(**11.**) _____ altos porque no son cómodos, y cuando sus

zapatos están gastados no los tira a la (**12.**) _____ porque los prefiere

así. ¿No se mira en el (**13.**) _____? Raras veces se mira, porque nunca se

(**14.**) _____ los labios, y a veces se olvida de (**15.**) _____

el pelo. Su novio Jorge, también muy idealista, ve la verdadera belleza de Raquel. Jorge

tiene la misma actitud que Raquel: no (**16.**) _____ la ropa con cuidado.

Además, tiene una (**17.**) _____, no porque le guste, sino porque no

quiere afeitarse. A los dos les importa lo interior en (**18.**) _____ de lo

exterior.

B. ¿Qué hay que hacer? Describe lo que es
necesario que hagan estas personas.

Por ejemplo: Es necesario que la señora repare el tacón.

1. _____

_____

_____

_____

2. _____

_____

_____

_____

3. _____

_____

_____

_____

4. _____
_____
_____
_____

5. _____
_____
_____
_____

5. _____
_____
_____
_____

C. La ropa apropiada. Dales consejos a las siguientes personas respecto a la ropa. Usa una variedad de verbos.

Por ejemplo: ¡Voy a Puerto Rico!

Te recomiendo que lleves un traje de baño y ropa delgada.

Ramón tiene una entrevista de trabajo.

Le recomiendo que se afeite y que lleve una corbata.

1. Ana y Carmen van a una discoteca en Nueva York.

_____

_____

2. Rafael va a pasar el invierno en Alaska.

_____

_____

3. María tiene una entrevista con una agencia de modelos.

_____

_____

4. Tomás va a conocer a los padres de su novia por primera vez.

_____

_____

5. Dolores va a un baile en tu universidad.

_____

_____

6. Tu padre tiene una entrevista con el IRS para discutir sus impuestos (*taxes*).

_____

_____

GRAMÁTICA 1

A. El compañero de cuarto perfecto. Completa las frases con la forma correcta del presente del indicativo, presente del subjuntivo o el infinitivo de los verbos.

Acabas de empezar tus estudios en la universidad y tú _____

(**1.** querer) llevarte bien con tu compañero de cuarto. Para

_____ (**2.** ser) el compañero de cuarto perfecto, es necesario

que tú _____ (**3.** hacer) ciertas cosas. Si tu compañero de

cuarto te _____ (**4.** prestar) su camiseta favorita para que

_____ (**5.** tener) el conjunto perfecto para llevar a una fiesta, es

mejor que tú no la _____ (**6.** dejar) en el suelo después. Para

que tú no _____ (**7.** parecer) un desconsiderado, es importante

que siempre le _____ (**8.** devolver) sus cosas en buenas

condiciones. Cuando tu compañero quiere _____ (**9.** dormir),

es mejor que tú no _____ (**10.** tocar) muy alto tus casetes. Con

respecto a la decoración del cuarto, si a él le gustan los colores vivos y a ti

te gusta el beige, es necesario que Uds. _____ (**11.** llegar) a un

acuerdo para que se _____ (**12.** llevar) bien.

B. ¿Para qué lo haces? Conecta las dos frases con **para que** y escribe conclusiones lógicas.

Por ejemplo: como con cuidado/mi ropa
   Como con cuidado para que mi ropa no se manche.

1. trato de comer menos/mi ropa

_____

_____

2. saco la ropa de la secadora inmediatamente/las camisas

_____

_____

3. el fugitivo lleva gafas y una barba falsa/nadie

_____

_____

4. el hombre que pide dinero en la calle siempre lleva ropa sucia, rota y gastada/la gente

_____

_____

5. el vampiro no tiene espejos en su casa/sus visitantes

_____

_____

6. el lobo (*wolf*) se disfraza de una vieja/Caperucita Roja (*Little Red Riding Hood*)

_____

_____

C. Las quejas. Usa **para que** para darles consejos a las siguientes
personas según el modelo.

Por ejemplo: Mis padres me tratan como un niño.
   **Para que tus padres te traten como un adulto es necesario que
   seas más responsable.**

1. Mi ropa no me queda bien.

   _____

   _____

2. Mis compañeros de clase piensan que soy egoísta.

   _____

   _____

3. Mis profesores dicen que soy perezoso(a).

   _____

   _____

4. Mis amigos creen que no soy sensible, que no escucho sus problemas.

   _____

   _____

5. No puedo encontrar trabajo.

   _____

   _____

6. No puedo organizarme.

   _____

   _____

GRAMÁTICA 2

A. Para comparar. Escribe dos frases según el modelo.

Por ejemplo: Papá Noel tiene la barba más larga del mundo.

       a. Busco un hombre que tenga una barba más larga que Papá Noel.

       b. No hay nadie que tenga una barba más linda que él.

1. Oscar de la Renta diseña la ropa más elegante del mundo.

   a. _____

   b. _____

2. Don Payasito (*Mr. Clown*) se pone la ropa más cómica del mundo.

   a. _____

   b. _____

3. Gabriel García Márquez escribe las novelas más memorables del siglo.

   a. _____

   b. _____

4. Frida Kahlo pinta los cuadros más fabulosos del arte mexicano.

   a. _____

   b. _____

5. Mi amigo Raúl tiene más gorros de béisbol que nadie.

   a. _____

   b. _____

6. Mario lleva los pantalones más largos y sueltos de toda la clase.

   a. _____

   b. _____

B. ¿Qué buscan? En la tablilla de la residencia estudiantil varias personas han puesto anuncios con respecto a sus necesidades. Escribe frases según el modelo.

Por ejemplo: La Sra. Pérez busca una persona que sepa reparar cosas en su casa, que pueda empezar inmediatamente y que tenga sus propias herramientas.

Busco una persona para reparar varias cosas en mi casa. Tiene que empezar inmediatamente y tiene que tener sus propias herramientas. Llame a la Sra. María Pérez, 555-3256.

2. Quiero comprar un carro usado con menos de 10.000 millas, por menos de $2.000. Llame a Ariel Gutiérrez, ext. 8384.

1. Busco alguien para cuidar niños, de por lo menos 18 años con experiencia con niños pequeños. Llame al Profesor Juan Arévalo.

3. Busco una compañera de cuarto para un apartamento cerca de la universidad. Tiene que ser madura y responsable y tiene que pagar $200 al mes. Llame a Carla Díaz, 555-2938.

4. BUSCO UNA PERSONA PARA CUIDAR MI PERRO POR DOS SEMANAS. TIENE QUE SER RESPONSABLE Y QUERER A LOS ANIMALES. LLAME A ISABEL SÁNCHEZ, 555-6112.

5. Quiero emplear un estudiante para ayudar con un proyecto de investigación escolar. Tiene que ser muy trabajador y saber inglés y francés. Llame a la profesora Eva Santos, 555-6978.

1. _____

_____

2. _____

_____

3. _____

_____

4. _____

_____

5. _____

_____

C. Aspectos personales. Conecta las frases con una de estas expresiones: **no hay nadie**; **no hay nada**; **busco... que**; **quiero... que.** Sigue el modelo.

Por ejemplo: cuando estoy triste/entender

Cuando estoy triste no hay nadie que me entienda mejor que mi mamá.

(Cuando estoy triste busco un amigo que me entienda.)

1. cuando tengo un problema/ayudar

_____

_____

2. cuando tengo hambre/gustar

_____

_____

3. cuando voy de compras/ser o gustar

_____

_____

4. cuando no me llevo bien con mi pareja/poder aconsejar

_____

_____

5. cuando estoy nervioso(a)/calmarme

_____

_____

LECTURA
VOCES DEL MUNDO HISPANO

Lee el artículo y completa las actividades que siguen.

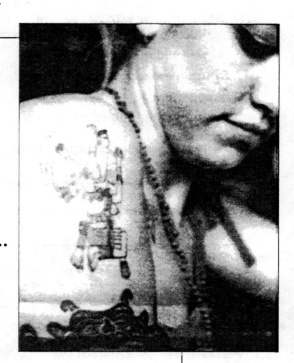

TATUAJES, UNA MODA QUE INCOMODA

A veces por rebeldía o fanatismo, los jóvenes se tatúan el cuerpo y después viene el arrepentimiento o empiezan las dificultades a la hora de encontrar trabajo. Es una técnica que fue tomada de los indios de Tahití, en la Polinesia.

POR SILVIA OTROVSKY

"Me gusta usar el cuerpo como si fuera un cuadro una escultura. Lo voy componiendo, combino los trazos, los colores. Si veo que estoy muy cargado en un lado pongo algo más liviano del otro para equilibrarlo. Yo creo que el tatuaje es el paquete, lo que se ve." Así explica Katun su entusiasmo por esta técnica que sigue haciendo furor entre los jóvenes.

El problema se presenta, a veces, a la hora de buscar trabajo. Ante la enorme cantidad de postulantes para cada puesto vacante, las empresas endurecen sus condiciones de empleo y, en muchos casos, una de ellas es que candidatos no tengan tatuajes. ¿Puede interpretarse esta exigencia como una discriminación? Quizás. Pero la empresa privada tiene el derecho de elegir la imagen que quiere transmitir. En todo caso, la prohibición de los tatuajes es tan cuestionable como pedir jóvenes de pelo corto, traje y corbata o chicas "de buena presencia" sin que se sepa muy bien a qué se refieren.

Por otro lado, también son muchas las reparticiones públicas —entre ellas a la policía y el ejército— que piden que sus empleados no tengan marcas.

A. ¿Entendiste? Contesta las preguntas.

1. ¿Dónde se originó la costumbre de tatuarse?

_____

_____

2. Describe la filosofía de Katun con respecto a su
cuerpo.

_____

_____

3. Según el contexto del segundo párrafo, el
significado más probable de **postulante** es...
   a. posibilidad
   b. una persona que busca empleo
   c. experiencia
   d. una persona que ha perdido su empleo

Palabras útiles	
cargado	overloaded
liviano	light
puesto	empleo
endurecen	hacen más estrictos
el derecho	right
quizás	tal vez, posiblemente

4. ¿Por qué tienen las empresas condiciones de empleo tan estrictas?

_____

5. ¿Por qué puede ser un problema tener un tatuaje?

_____

6. ¿Qué cuestión legal o ética se presenta en el artículo?

_____

B. ¿Para qué se tatúan Muchos jóvenes se tatúan, se afeitan la cabeza
o llevan la ropa de cierto estilo para crear una imagen o para provocar una
reacción en otras personas. Selecciona varios estilos o costumbres populares
de hoy y comenta los motivos posibles.

Por ejemplo: Muchos jóvenes se tatúan para que sus padres se enojan.

Muchos jovenes se tatúan porque creen que los tatuajes son
atractivos.

_____

_____

_____

_____

_____

_____

PARA ESCRIBIR

Los tatuajes

Tienes un/a amigo(a) que piensa tatuarse. Escríbele una carta en la que le das consejos. ¿Qué le aconsejas? Habla de las ventajas y desventajas de los tatuajes.¿Es justo que los adultos les digan a los jóvenes lo que pueden hacer con respecto a sus propios cuerpos? ¿el pelo? ¿la perforación del cuerpo?

_____

_____

_____

_____

_____

_____

_____

_____

_____

_____

El físico es muy importante

VOCABULARIO
IMÁGENES Y PALABRAS

A. La tía Cecilia. Escoge las palabras indicadas para completar la narración.

La tía Cecilia es una vieja amable pero está obsesionada por (**1.** la salud, las manos, el cuello) _____ a pesar de que es bastante sana. Por ejemplo, si alguien estornuda° cerca de ella, Cecilia se preocupa por coger° (**2.** una cintura. una enfermedad, un riñon) _____. Cuando le duele la (**3.** cabeza, muñeca, espalda) _____, está segura de que tiene cáncer del cerebro°. Ella (**4.** cuida, evita, combate) _____ el alcohol, que es malo para el (**5.** hígado, pelo, corazón) _____ y dejó de (**6.** beber, fumar, mover) _____ hace muchos años cuando se supo que era malo para los (**7.** pulmones, tobillos, codos) _____. Toma mucha agua diariamente porque sabe que es bueno para la función de los (**8.** oídos, dedos, riñones) _____. Y aunque Cecilia es vieja, hace (**9.** ejercicios, huesos, pulmones) _____ para mantener los (**10.** músculos, ojos,

Palabras útiles	
estornudar	*to sneeze*
coger	*to catch*
el cerebro	*brain*
el latido	*beat*

pulgares) _____ fuertes. Ella se (**11.** frota, pone, cuida)

_____ bien y trata de (**12.** tapar, evitar, doler)

_____ las enfermedades. Por lo general (**13.** combate, relaja, lleva)

_____ una vida (**14.** fría, sana, abrigada)

_____. El problema es que piensa demasiado en su estado físico.

A veces de noche cuando sufre del insomnio, le parece que puede sentir el movimiento

de la (**15.** cara, sangre, cintura) _____ dentro de sus venas y

empieza a contar los latidosº del (**16.** corazón, tobillo, pulmón)

_____. Cree que puede sentir los (**17.** huesos, hombros, brazos)

_____ del esqueleto poniéndose más pequeños como resultado de

la edad. Si come un plato que no acostumbra comer, siempre sufre un malestar del

(**18.** tobillo, corazón, estómago) _____. Cuando mueve el brazo, le

duele el (**19.** codo, tobillo, oído) _____ y cuando mueve la cabeza

tiene dolor de (**20.** oído, cuello, hígado) _____. ¡Pobrecita! Su

peor enfermedad es el ataque de nervios que le da como resultado de todo el (**21.**

diente, estrés, pecho) _____ producido por todos estos

pensamientos.

B. Un monstruo de película. Alfonso Reyes, el genio de las

películas de terror, ha inventado un nuevo monstruo.
Completa la descripción del monstruo, según la imagen.

El monstruo tiene tres (**1.**) _____

en vez de dos; uno está en el centro de la

(**2.**) _____ . Encima de cada uno

hay una (**3.**) _____ muy peludaº.

Sólo tiene una (**4.**) _____ y está

encima de la (**5.**) _____ . Dentro

de su (**6.**) _____ grande siempre hay

un cigarillo que él (**7.**) _____, no

porque le guste sino porque quiere

(**8.**) _____ a la gente. En el

centro de la cara tiene una

(**9.**) _____ muy pequeña. En

cada mano tiene cuatro (**10.**)

Palabras útiles

peluda	_hairy_
la araña venenosa	_poisonous spider_
agudos	_sharp_
la muchedumbre	_crowd_

_____ y dos (**11.**) _____. Lleva

una pulsera de arañas venenosasº alrededor de cada (**12.**)

_____ para que puedan morderles a sus enemigos.

Tiene los (**13.**) _____ muy agudosº para molestar a la

gente cuando se encuentra entre una muchedumbreº. Sus (**14.**)

_____ son más gruesos que las piernas. En el (**15.**)

_____ tiene un tatuaje de un (**16.**)

_____ con la palabra "Mamá".

C. Aspectos personales. Usa los siguientes verbos para indicar lo que te
pasa o lo que haces en estas situaciones.

molestar   doler   estirar   importar   mejorar   gustar

Por ejemplo: Estás estresado(a).
        **Cuando estoy estresada me duele la cabeza. (Cuando estoy
        estresada me gusta hacer ejercicios.)**

1. Como demasiado.

_____

_____

2. Paso el día frente al televisor.

_____

_____

3. Llevo mi mochila muy pesada todo el día.

_____

_____

4. Hago ejercicios demasiado fuertes.

_____

_____

5. Me siento enfermo(a).

_____

_____

6. Me duelen los músculos.

_____

_____

7. Estoy nerviosísimo(a).

_____

_____

G R A M Á T I C A 1

A. Consejos póstumos (*posthumous*). Tienes la oportunidad de darles consejos a varios personajes famosos. ¿Reconoces a algunos de ellos? Completa los consejos con órdenes informales.

1. Mi amigo MacBeth, _____ (seguir) tu conciencia,

no _____ (escuchar) a tu mujer.

2. Querido Otelo, _____ (creer) lo que te dice tu

mujer, no _____ (creer) las mentiras de Iago.

3. Julieta, no _____ (tomar) el veneno (*poison*),

_____ (vivir) muchos años más.

4. Sansón, _____ (llevar) el pelo largo, no

_____ (permitir) que Delila te lo corte.

5. _____ (Construir) un arca, Noé, no

_____ (perder) ni un minuto. ¡Ya empieza a llover!

6. _____ (Decir) la verdad, Pinocho, para que no te

crezca la nariz. No _____ (decir) mentiras.

B. ¿Qué debo hacer? Usa los verbos indicados para darles consejos a tus amigos(as), según el modelo.

Por ejemplo: Me duele el cuello./mirar
Si te duele el cuello, mira una película; no mires el partido de tenis.

1. Me duele la cabeza./tomar

_____

_____

2. Me duele el estómago./comer

_____

_____

3. Me duele la espalda./ir

_____

_____

4. Quiero encontrar a mi pareja perfecta./buscar

_____

_____

5. Quiero llevarme bien con mi compañero(a) de cuarto./poner

_____

_____

6. Las películas de terror me causan pesadillas (*nightmares*)./ver

_____

_____

7. El café me produce insomnio./tomar

_____

_____

G R A M Á T I C A 2

Haz lo contrario. Dile a tu amigo que haga lo contrario de lo que hace.

Por ejemplo: Me levanto tarde y no desayuno.

No te levantes tarde. Desayuna.

1. No me afeito. Así molesto a mis padres.

_____

_____

2. Siempre me quejo. No me río de mis problemas.

_____

_____

3. Me quedo solo cuando estoy triste. No me junto con mis amigos.

_____

_____

4. Me despierto tarde y me olvido de darle de comer a los caballos del rancho.

_____

_____

5. Me acuesto tarde y por eso no me levanto temprano.

_____

_____

6. Me preocupo por cosas sin importancia y luego no me siento bien.

_____

_____

7. Me muero de estrés; no me relajo.

_____

_____

L E C T U R A
VOCES DEL MUNDO HISPANO

LA ARMONÍA

Lee el artículo y completa las actividades que siguen.

Distintos movimientos de la técnica Tai-Chi-Chuan. Esta suave arte marcial china combina técnicas de defensa con aplicaciones terapéuticas de la medicina tradicional china y ejercicios de meditación y relajación respiratoria.

armonía

Los pequeños estrés cotidianos, esos pinchazos que nos asaltan de improviso a cualquier hora del día, se acumulan sin que nos demos cuenta y acaban por causarnos todo tipo de enfermedades.

Suele decirse que si uno se conoce a sí mismo y se apoya en sus puntos fuertes puede llegar a convivir con el estrés y aceptarlo como una cuota que se debe pagar a esta sociedad del siglo XXI. Cuentos. Todos el mundo sabe que el estrés puede destrozarte el corazón, debilitar el cerebro, disminuir las defensas e incluso mermar la potencia sexual.

Dos sentencias del Tribunal Constitucional italiano admitieron la existencia de enfermedades no reconocidas y que están relacionadas con el modo de vida contemporáneo. Es decir, con el estrés. Igualmente, el Parlamento británico ha reconocido legalmente la enfermedad.

Pero lo que realmente está conquistando a las víctimas urbanas en que nos hemos convertido es el Tai-Chi-Chuan, un estilo interiorizado del Kung-Fu, la técnica china de combate que hace años popularizó el actor Bruce Lee. Su práctica causa furor en Nueva York, donde la síntesis de la relajación y seguridad del Tai-Chi es la receta perfecta contra el estrés de esta ciudad

A. ¿Entendiste? Contesta las preguntas.

1. Según el artículo, ¿por qué es peligroso el estrés?

_____

_____

2. ¿Qué evidencia ofrece el autor del artículo para justificar la idea de que el estrés sea un problema serio para la salud?

_____

_____

3. ¿Qué métodos se emplean en varias culturas para combatir el estrés?

_____

_____

4. ¿Qué método recomienda el autor?

_____

_____

5. En el segundo párrafo, el significado más probable de **mermar** es...

    a. reducirse   c. hacer más grande

    b. eliminar   d. mejorar

Palabras útiles	
el monje	*monk*
desarrollar	*develop*
hallado	encontrado
cotidiano	de cada día
se apoya	*leans on*
el cuento	historia
el despacho	oficina
huir	escaparse
as cifras	cantidades

B. El estrés de la vida diaria. El Tai-Chi-Chuan es una manera de luchar contra el estrés. Escríbele una carta a un/a amigo(a) que sufre del estrés. Usa las órdenes informales para darle consejos sobre cómo combatir el estrés de la vida diaria.

_____

_____

_____

_____

_____

_____

_____

_____

_____

_____

_____

Visión y voz 2E Workbook © 1998 John Wiley & Sons

PARA ESCRIBIR

¿Cómo manejar el estrés?

Leíste sobre otras maneras de reaccionar al estrés. Escribe un párrafo sobre el estrés en tu vida diaria. ¿Qué situaciones o preocupaciones te hacen sentir estresado(a)? ¿Cómo se manifiesta el estrés? ¿Te duele la cabeza? ¿la espalda? ¿el estómago? ¿Qué haces para relajarte y escaparte del estrés?

_____

_____

_____

_____

_____

_____

_____

_____

_____

_____

_____

_____

_____

_____

_____

_____

_____

El mejor remedio

VOCABULARIO

IMÁGENES Y PALABRAS

A. No hice la tarea porque... Completa la conversación entre una maestra y un alumno con las palabras apropiadas.

Alumno: Señora, quise hacer las tareas anoche aunque (**1.** sufría, me protegía, me mejoraba) _____ de la gripe, con una

(**2.** fractura, fiebre, glándula) _____ alta y un dolor de

(**3.** abeja, garganta, curita) _____ tan terrible que casi no podía comer ni hablar. También tuve unos (**4.** cosméticos, jarabes, escalofríos) _____ tan severos que me puse tantos suéteres que no podía mover el brazo para escribir. Los otros (**5.** síntomas, estornudos, hipos) _____ de la gripe eran las glándulas

(**6.** tapadas, alérgicas, inflamadas) _____, la nariz

(**7.** tapada, hinchada, grave) _____ y la (**8.** picadura, tos, venda) _____ que tuve era tan severa que el jarabe más fuerte no ofreció ningún alivio. Cuando llegó el médico, le dije "Tengo que (**9.** protegerme, mejorarme, caerme) _____ pronto porque quiero terminar mis tareas para mañana. Por favor, doctor, recéteme una (**10.** cortadura, roncha, droga) _____ muy fuerte o póngame una (**11.** lastimadura, inyección, hierba) _____ para que no tenga que perderme un día de clases." El médico me (**12.** ardió, picó, recetó) _____

penicilina, que es el (**13.** medicamento, yeso, jarabe) _____

más eficaz, y un (**14.** humo, antibiótico, resfrío) _____

también. Desafortunadamente tuve una reacción alérgica a la penicilina, y

por eso tuve la cara (**15.** hinchada, tapada, alérgica)

_____ toda la noche. Además, tuve una (**16.** roncha,

vacuna, fractura) _____ por toda la piel que me (**17.**

ardía, picaba, corría) _____ como mil (**18.** picaduras,

abejas, fiebres) _____ de mosquito. Total que Ud. puede

ver que estaba (**19.** grave, tapado, increíble) _____ y por

eso no pude hacer la tarea.

Maestra: Pues, es una lástima que no puedas participar en el partido de
baloncesto esta tarde.

Alumno: No, señora, voy a jugar. ¡Es (**20.** lástima, increíble, cierto)

_____ que me haya (**21.** curado, sufrido, cortado)

_____ tan rápido! Hoy estoy completamente bien.

B. La educación física. Completa la narración con las palabras
apropiadas. Es posible que se usen algunas palabras más de una vez.

Alicia es la peor estudiante de educación física de toda la escuela. Ella

odia la disciplina y no le gusta hacer ejercicio. Siempre llega al gimnasio

con una excusa. Un día dijo que tenía (**1.**) _____, que

iba a vomitar. La profesora le permitió ir al baño. Otro día Alicia llegó con

un (**2.**) _____ en el brazo y dijo que tenía una (**3.**)

_____ porque se (**4.**) _____

mientras patinaba. Una vez Alicia le mostró a la profesora una

(**5.**) _____ que tenía en la rodilla y le dijo que (**6.**)

_____ un accidente de bicicleta y se

(7.) _____ en la rodilla. Hay que tener

(8.) _____ con las **(9.)** _____ tan

severas, según Alicia. En otra ocasión, Alicia llegó andando con muletas

(**crutches**) y le dijo a la profesora que no podía participar porque se

(10.) _____ el tobillo. Es una

(11.) _____ que estas excusas de Alicia sólo sean

eficaces temporalmente. Su amiga Rosario es más lista. Ella le dijo a la

profesora que es **(12.)** _____ a los zapatos de tenis

que todos llevan en el gimnasio. Al principio la profesora no se lo creyó.

"He oído hablar de alergias al polvo o al **(13.)** _____ de

las flores o a la picadura de una **(14.)** _____ . Pero ¿a

los zapatos de tenis? Pero los **(15.)** _____ de Rosario

(ah... chis, ah... chis) al acercarse a los zapatos de tenis por fin

convencieron a la profesora. ¡Rosario no tuvo que asistir a la clase de

educación física el resto del año! ¡**(16.)** _____ que

pueda pensar yo en una excusa tan lista!, pensó Alicia.

C. Tus propias excusas. Completa las siguientes frases con tus propias excusas.

1. No pude hacer la tarea anoche porque...

_____

2. No puedo estudiar para el examen de mañana porque...

_____

3. Escribí la composición pero no la tengo porque...

_____

4. No pude leer el capítulo porque...

_____

5. No puedo participar en la clase de educación física porque...

_____

6. No pude investigar el asunto en la biblioteca porque...

_____

G R A M Á T I C A 1

A. Para llegar a la perfección. Usa las órdenes formales de los verbos indicados para darles consejos a las siguientes personas. Para el número 6, escoge tus propios verbos.

Por ejemplo: El Sr. Saenz quiere ser el político ideal. (decir, mentir, entender, pensar)
Dígale la verdad a la gente, no le mienta. Entienda las necesidades de la gente. Piense en el bienestar del país, no sólo en sí mismo.

1. El Sr. López quiere ser el padre perfecto. (ser, proteger, querer, tener)

_____

_____

2. La Sra. Pérez quiere ser la suegra (_mother-in-law_) ideal. (criticar, visitar, ofrecer, hacer)

_____

_____

3. El Sr. Martínez quiere ser el malvado (_villain_) de telenovelas ejemplar. (decir, fingir, parecer, engañar)

_____

_____

4. Victoria Hernández quiere ser la mejor médica del hospital. (saber, explicar, ser, conocer)

_____

_____

5. El Sr. Jiménez quiere escibir una gran novela. (irse, escribir, olvidarse, incluir)

_____

_____

6. El Sr. Gutiérrez quiere ser el marido perfecto. (¿?)

_____

_____

B. ¡Cuídense! Eres un/a enfermero(a) que trabaja en este hospital. Diles a estos pacientes que (no) hagan cosas peligrosas. Usa las órdenes formales de los verbos indicados. Escribe una orden positiva y negativa en cada caso.

Por ejemplo: Sr. Vargas / cuidarse, fumar
Cuídese bien, Sr. Vargas. No fume.

1. Sr. Calderón / tener cuidado, caerse

_____

_____

2. Tomás y Anita / tomar el jarabe, seguir con tos

_____

_____

3. Sra. Ramírez / mirar lo que hace, cortarse

_____

_____

4. niños / llevarse bien, lastimarse

_____

_____

5. niñas / protegerse, quebrarse un hueso

_____

_____

G R A M Á T I C A 2

A. Como agua para chocolate. Completa este relato sobre la novela *Como agua para chocolate* con la forma correcta de los verbos. Usa el presente del indicativo, el presente del subjuntivo o el infinitivo según el contexto.

Tita _____ (**1.** ser) la hija menor de Mamá Elena. Según

Mamá Elena, es imposible que Tita _____ (**2.** casarse).

Tiene que _____ (**3.** quedarse) soltera para

_____ (**4.** cuidar) a su madre. ¿Existe una mujer que

_____ (**5.** ser) más dominante que Mamá Elena? Es una

lástima que a Mamá Elena no le _____ (**6.** importar) la

felicidad de su hija. Es una pena que Tita se _____

(**7.** haber) enamorado de Pedro. Es cierto que Pedro _____

(**8.** querer) a Tita, pero va a casarse con la hermana de su amada. Va a

casarse con una mujer que no quiere para que _____

(**9.** poder) vivir cerca de Tita. Tita y Pedro no pueden casarse a menos

que Mamá Elena se _____ (**10.** morir), y es cierto que ella

_____ (**11.** estar) en buena salud. Es necesario que Pedro

y Tita no le _____ (**12.** decir) a nadie que están

enamorados. Esperan que Mamá Elena no _____ (**13.**

saber) nada de su amor. Ojalá que ellos _____ (**14.**

encontrar) la felicidad, pero nadie cree que _____ (**15.** ser)

posible _____ (**16.** guardar) un secreto tan grande. Me

alegro de que nosotros no _____ (**17.** tener) costumbres

tan opresivas en nuestra familia.

B. Reacciones. Expresa tus opiniones o reacciones usando las expresiones
que siguen. Usa el presente del indicativo o el presente del subjuntivo según el
contexto.

Es necesario que	Es una lástima que	Es imposible que
Es verdad que	Me alegro de que	Es cierto que
Dudo que	Ojalá que	Es una pena que

Por ejemplo: Muchos jóvenes empiezan a fumar.

Es una lástima que muchos jóvenes empiecen a fumar.

1. Pronto descubrirán la cura para el SIDA.

_____

_____

_____

2. No han descubierto la cura para muchas formas del cáncer.

_____

_____

3. Es posible ser alérgico al trabajo.

_____

_____

4. Las hierbas pueden combatir muchas enfermedades.

_____

_____

5. Una roncha es un síntoma de la gripe.

_____

_____

6. El alma (*soul*) se va del cuerpo durante un estornudo.

_____

_____

7. El humo sólo le hace daño a la persona que fuma.

_____

_____

8. Los niños tienen cuidado de no caerse.

_____

_____

9. En Estados Unidos hay un buen seguro (*insurance*) nacional de salud.

_____

_____

C. ¿Ayúdeme, por favor! Tú escribes una columna de consejos que aparece en muchos periódicos. Lee esta carta y completa las frases que siguen para aconsejar a la mujer que la escribió.

Tengo tantos problemas que no sé por dónde empezar. Ayer mi hijo, a quien amo más que a nadie, volvió de la universidad. Vino con él su novia, Marisol, una joven totalmente calva (¡imagínese, se afeitó la cabeza!), con tatuajes por todo el cuerpo. Me parece un poco extraña, pero confieso que es una chica amable. Marisol trajo su "mascota", Lili, una tarántula grande y fea. A veces Lili se escapa de su jaula y anda por la casa. Uno la encuentra donde menos se espera y nos causa un susto, como puede Ud. imaginar.

Mi marido Raúl es un hombre muy conservador, a quien le gusta controlar todo. Dice que si Marisol y Lili se quedan, él se va. Mi hijo dice que Marisol es el amor de su vida y si la rechazamos, se va a ir de la casa para nunca volver.

Cuando pienso en este problema, me da un dolor de cabeza muy fuerte. Tengo los ojos inflamados de tanto llorar. No me siento bien. Ayúdeme, por favor.

    Una madre desesperada

Querida señora...

1. Es una lástima que

    _____

2. Es posible que su marido

    _____

3. Es mejor que

    _____

4. Le recomiendo que

    _____

5. Es imposible que

    _____

6. Es necesario que

    _____

7. No va a vivir tranquila a menos que

_____

8. Puede ser feliz con tal de que

_____

9. Espero que

_____

L E C T U R A
V O C E S   D E L   M U N D O   H I S P A N O

LAURA ESQUIVEL

Lee el artículo y completa las actividades que siguen.

Laura Esquivel y una historia de novela

La escritora **Laura Esquivel** tuvo una racha de mala suerte. Se divorció de su esposo, el cineasta Alfonso Arau (*Como agua para chocolate*) y para rematar terminó demandándolo por las regalías de dicha película. Después de todo, Esquivel es la autora del libro del mismo nombre y del guión en que se basó la exitosa cinta. Con su obra más reciente *La ley del amor*, parece que Esquivel quiere aclarar todos los malentendidos. Aunque no se ha reconciliado con su ex, en su novela Esquivel cuenta la historia de amor de una pareja que debe descubrir en su pasado las causas de su amor perdido. Es una aventura cósmica y espiritual en la cual los enamorados viajan desde la caída del Imperio Azteca hasta un México futurista del siglo 23.

Más aun, *La ley del amor* es la primera novela que integra música (desde Puccini a danzones cubanos) e imágenes (las ilustraciones del gallego Miguelanxo Prado) a la narrativa, convirtiéndose así en una verdadera obra multimedia.

A. ¿Entendiste? Contesta las preguntas.

1. En tus propias palabras, ¿qué problemas tiene Laura Esquivel?

   _____

   _____

2. ¿Cómo se llama la nueva novela de esta autora?

   _____

   _____

3. ¿Qué quieren entender los protagonistas de esta novela? ¿Qué explicación buscan?

   _____

   _____

4. ¿Qué aspectos de esta novela te parecen raros?

   _____

   _____

Palabras útiles	
la racha	rash of events
el cineasta	actor de cine
demandándolo	suing him
las regalías	royalties
el guión	script
exitosa	successful

B. Una carta a la autora. En tu libro de texto leíste una selacción de *Como agua para chocolate* de Laura Esquivel. Ahora acabas de leer sobre su nueva novela y de sus problema personales. Escríbele una carta a la autora en la que reaccionas a sus éxitos (**Me alegro de que...**) y a sus problemas (**Siento que...**). También hazle preguntas sobre las dos novelas mencionadas.

Estimada Srta. Esquivel:

_____

_____

_____

_____

_____

_____

_____

Visión y voz 2E Workbook © 1998 John Wiley & Sons

Para escribir

Una entrevista

Vas a entrevistar al autor de un libro sobre la medicina alternativa. El libro trata de remedios caseros, mágicos, folclóricos y supersticiosos. Algunos pueden ser extraños o aun cómicos. Usa el vocabulario del Capítulo 14 para escribir las preguntas y las respuestas de la entrevista. ¡Usa tu imaginación!

_____

_____

_____

_____

_____

_____

_____

_____

_____

_____

_____

Ciudades de ahora y de siempre

IMÁGENES Y PALABRAS

A. El Sr. "Quejoso". Usa las palabras apropiadas del vocabulario para completar la conversación entre Ramón "Quejoso" y su mujer, Matilde.

Ramón: Estoy harto, Matilde. Tengo ganas de escaparme de esta maldita

ciudad. Quiero que nos mudemos al campo donde no hay

(1.) _____ del aire y uno puede andar por

la **(2.)** _____ sin tropezar con los

(3.) _____ que duermen en la calle. El

(4.) _____ de las bocinas me tiene loco, los

autobuses y camiones echan tanto **(5.)** _____

que no se puede respirar, y los **(6.)** _____

son tan altos que no se puede ver el cielo.

Matilde: Pero, mi amor, cuando vivíamos en el campo te morías de

aburrimiento y te quejabas de la falta de

(7.) _____ público y de que no había

(8.) _____ de los negocios importantes que

se encuentran aquí en la ciudad.

Ramón: No importa. No puedo aguantar tanta delincuencia. Las

(9.) _____ están llenas de criminales y

todavía se encuentran **(10.)** _____ de drogas

en cada **(11.)** _____. Y las calles están tan

(12.) _____ con tráfico que parecen

estacionamientos. Deben hacer las calles más

(13.) _____. Voy a escribirle una carta a la

(14.) _____ para quejarme.

Matilde: Pero, mi vida, en el campo decías que la tranquilidad incesante te
volvía loco.

Ramón: Pues, me muero por tener un solo momento de tranquilidad. Sabes

que esta mañana iba a la oficina de mi contador para discutir una

nueva **(15.)** _____ de computadoras en la

que quiero **(16.)** _____ dinero. No pude

conseguir un taxi porque los **(17.)** _____

no trabajaban a causa de una **(18.)** _____.

Bajé a la **(19.)** _____ de

_____ pero tampoco funcionaban. Hubo

un **(20.)** _____ entre dos trenes. Llegué a

la **(21.)** _____ de autobuses, pero el

autobús estaba tan **(22.)** _____, había

tanta gente, que por fin decidí caminar las veinte

(23.) _____ a la oficina. Allí supe que no

vale la pena empezar un negocio en esta ciudad porque los

(24.) _____ que hay que pagar son tan

altos. Es la culpa del **(25.)** _____ que

elegimos el año pasado. Prometió disminuir los impuestos pero, al

contrario, los ha **(26.)** _____.

B. La ciudad ideal. Eres el (la) planeador/a de una ciudad del futuro.
Indica los beneficios que habrá en tu ciudad para los siguientes grupos.

Por ejemplo: los minusválidos

**Para los minusválidos habrá aceras y edificios con rampas
para que puedan moverse sin problema.**

1. los peatones

_____

_____

_____

2. las madres que trabajan

_____

_____

_____

3. los desempleados

_____

_____

_____

4. los desamparados

_____

_____

_____

5. los ancianos

_____

_____

_____

6. los que no tienen auto

_____

_____

_____

C. Crucigrama.

Horizontales

1. No se debe cruzar la calle cuando el _____ está en rojo.

6. Es una _____ que haya tantos desamparados en la ciudad.

7. Algunos pobres duermen en la _____ enfrente de los rascacielos.

8. El _____ es un metal muy duro que se usa en la construcción de edificios.

12. Es necesario tener más _____ infantiles para cuidar a los niños de las madres que trabajan.

14. Hay una huelga porque hace mucho tiempo que la empresa no _____ los sueldos de los empleados.

16. Los autos nuevos no van a _____ tanto humo.

17. Yo siempre les _____ dinero a los desamparados en la calle.

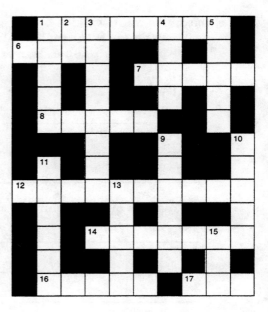

Verticales

1. A veces quiero escaparme de la calles de la ciudad y andar por una _____ en el campo.

2. Muchas máquinas se encuentran _____ una fábrica.

3. El alcalde promete _____ la calidad de los servicios de la ciudad.

4. Van a aumentar los impuestos del diez al _____ o doce por ciento.

5. En la ciudad siempre hay muchas _____ en construcción.

9. Construyen una nueva _____ para los criminales.

10. Habrá muchos desamparados _____ que construyan más residencias.

11. Es necesario cruzar el _____ para llegar al otro lado del río.

13. El gobierno promete disminuir la _____ pública.

15. Mi _____ es muy viejo y vive en un hogar para los ancianos.

GRAMÁTICA 1

A. **"Superhombre" en Nueva York.** Completa la narración con la forma correcta de los verbos. Usa el presente del indicativo, el presente del subjuntivo o el futuro.

El año que viene Superhombre _____ (**1.** mudarse) de su

hogar en Metrópolis y _____ (**2.** vivir) en Nueva York. Cuando

_____ (**3.** llegar) este hombre de acero, todos los habitantes

de la ciudad _____ (**4.** celebrar) porque no

_____ (5. tener) que preocuparse por la delincuencia.

Superhombre _____ (**6.** ser) su protector y todos

_____ (**7.** poder) dormir más tranquilos. Actualmente hay

mucha delincuencia, y los criminales _____ (**8.** estar) muy

activos hasta que _____ (**9.** saber) de la llegada del héroe. La

delincuencia no _____ (**10.** disminuir) hasta que

Superhombre _____ (**11.** estar) allí, luchando por lo bueno

B. Aspectos personales. Expresa tus opiniones según el modelo.

Por ejemplo: yo / estar / contento(a) / cuando
> **Estaré contento(a) cuando reciba una A en la clase de español.**

1. yo / ser / feliz / cuando

_____

_____

2. mis padres / no estar / contentos / hasta que

_____

_____

3. no haber paz en el mundo/ hasta que

_____

_____

_____

4. yo / no casarse / hasta que

_____

_____

_____

5. los problemas urbanos / mejorarse / cuando

_____

_____

_____

6. yo / apoyar un candidato político / cuando

_____

_____

_____

7. yo / tener hijos / cuando

_____

_____

_____

8. cuando una mujer / ser presidente / el país

_____

_____

_____

9. mis padres me / apoyar / hasta que

_____

_____

_____

GRAMÁTICA 2

A. ¿Qué está pasando? Usa el tiempo progresivo de los verbos que siguen para describir lo que está pasando en la imagen.

tocar	dormir	apoyar	dirigir
construir	andar	echar humo	aumentar

1. _____

   _____

2. _____

   _____

3. _____

_____

4. _____

_____

5. _____

_____

6. _____

_____

7. _____

_____

8. _____

_____

B. El alcalde se defiende. Durante una conferencia de prensa el alcalde trata de calmar a sus críticos. Usa el progresivo para expresar las respuestas del alcalde a varios ciudadanos insatisfechos.

Por ejemplo: **Ciudadano:** ¡Ud. prometió que iba a disminuir los impuestos!
Alcalde: Pero estoy disminuyéndolos.

1. **Ciudadano:** Dijo que la municipalidad iba a construir otra carretera.

   Alcalde: _____

2. **Ciudadano:** Nos prometió que la policía iba a disminuir la delincuencia.

   Alcalde: _____

3. **Ciudadano:** Dijo que iba a encontrar los fondos para construir más refugios para los desamparados.

   Alcalde: _____

4. **Ciudadano:** Según Ud., sus representantes iban a visitar los barrios pobres para investigar los problemas.

   Alcalde: _____

5. **Ciudadano:** Prometió que los ingenieros iban a mejorar el transporte público.

   Alcalde: _____

C. ¡Imagínate! Imagínate en las siguientes circunstancias y describe todo lo que está pasando y lo que estás haciendo.

Por ejemplo: una noche romántica
Estoy pasándola con mi pareja. Estamos mirando el fuego de la chimenea y pensando en nuestro amor. En la radio un grupo está tocando "nuestra" canción.

1. tu lugar favorito

_____

_____

_____

2. vacaciones ideales

_____

_____

_____

3. una ciudad muy emocionante

_____

_____

_____

4. una noche romántica

_____

_____

_____

5. una fiesta estupenda

_____

_____

_____

6. un día de descanso

_____

_____

_____

L E C T U R A

Lee el artículo y completa las actividades que siguen.

UN ALCALDE DIFERENTE

En muchas partes del mundo, las personas que se bajan los pantalones en público se arriesgan a que las arresten. En Bogotá, Colombia, el rector de la Universidad Nacional mostró su trasero a un grupo de estudiantes revoltosos y lo eligieron alcalde.

Su comportamiento se consideró indigno de un académico, y se vio obligado a renunciar a su cargo de rector. Pero su trasero fue filmado y apareció en las noticias de la televisión nacional, y al día siguiente, Antanás Mockus se transformó en un personaje célebre.

Tres meses después, en octubre de 1994, seis millones de bogotanos decidieron que su modo singular de controlar grupos merecía un foro más amplio. Desilusionados con la política tradicional de los partidos políticos, eligieron a este filósofo y matemático para gobernar una de las cuidades más violentas de América Latina. El nuevo alcalde de Bogotá no tenía experiencia política y ni se preocupó en montar una campaña.

«No estoy de acuerdo con las promesas falsas y los ataques que caracterizan a las campañas electorales», dice Mockus «lo que deseaba era subrayar mi rechazo a tales prácticas».

En realidad, sus credenciales como político novato no necesitaban reafirmación. Mockus rompe el molde en todos los aspectos. A diferencia de sus colegas y predecesores, el alcalde se viste descuidadamente, y tiene un corte de pelo poco común y una barba. Su apariencia ha sido comparada con la de un monje loco, o con la de uno de los diminutos compañeros de Blanca Nieves.

Desde que es alcalde, las políticas de Mockus han sido tan extrañas como los acontecimientos que lo llevaron al poder. Recorre el centro de la ciudad vestido de «supercívico», para alentar a los compradores y a los vagabundos a que se conviertan en superciudadanos. La prensa local está organizando concursos para encontrar el superciudadano del año, y las empresas locales les conceden a sus empleados tiempo libre para participar.

Mientras tanto, frente a una ambulancia improvisada en el centro de Bogotá, cientos de jóvenes colombianos hacen cola para recibir su «vacuna contra la violencia». Dentro de la ambulancia, Alvaro, de catorce años, pinta la cara de un enemigo suyo en un globo y luego lo rompe, fija un deseo en el árbol de los deseos y recibe su vacuna simbólica, una gota de agua en la lengua.

Otras actividades y programas innovadores de Mockus incluyen:

- la oferta de pagar 100.000 pesos (100 dólares) por cada arma entregada a las autoridades durante ciertos períodos de tiempo

- fiestas al aire libre para los desamparados

- cerrar todos los bares a la una de la mañana durante las fiestas de Navidad para reducir las altas cantidades de alcohol que normalmente se toman. (Durante la Navidad de 1996 el número de personas muertas por la violencia se redujo a la mitad como resultado de esta innovación.)

¿Entendiste? Contesta las preguntas.

1. ¿Qué hacía Mockus antes de ser alcalde de Bogotá?

_____

2. ¿Cuáles son sus intereses académicos?

_____

3. Escribe por lo menos tres razones por qué Mockus es "un alcalde diferente".

_____

_____

4. En tus propias palabras, ¿qué tres métodos emplea Mockus para combatir la violencia?

_____

_____

Palabras útiles	
se arriesgan	se ponen en peligro
el rector	el que dirige la universidad
el trasero	*rear end*
el cargo	empleo
subrayar	dar énfasis
el monje	miembro de una orden religiosa
el concurso	competencia
el globo	*balloon*

5. ¿Cómo trata de inspirarles a los ciudadanos un sentido cívico o un sentido de comunidad?

_____

_____

6. Según el contexto del segundo párrafo, el significado más probable de **renunciar** es...
a. abandonar, dejar de hacer algo
b. criticar
c. seguir, continuir
d. hablar contra

7. Según el contexto del sexto párrafo, el significado más probable de **alentar** es...
a. disminuir
b. prohibir
c. estimular
d. permitir

8. Imagínate que Mockus se presenta el año próximo en las elecciones de tu ciudad. ¿Votarás por él? ¿Por qué o por qué no?

_____

_____

_____

_____

PARA ESCRIBIR

Acciones poco convencionales

¿Qué piensas de las acciones no convencionales del alcalde Mockus? ¿Crees que a veces sus acciones son demasiado absurdas o groseras? ¿Puedes pensar en otras soluciones imaginativas a los problemas urbanos?

_____

_____

_____

_____

_____

_____

_____

¿Qué nos reserva el futuro?

IMÁGENES Y PALABRAS

A. La gente indígena. Completa la narración con las palabras apropiadas.

La gente indígena de las Américas ha mostrado gran respeto por nuestro

planeta, la (**1.**) _____. Esas tribus tenían una unión o

(**2.**) _____ con la naturaleza. Siempre han protegido los

(**3.**) _____ naturales en vez de usarlos hasta el punto de

(**4.**) _____ los. No han agregado a la contaminación del

(**5.**) _____   _____, y no hay especies

(**6.**) _____ a causa de las tribus indígenas. Los animales en

(**7.**) _____ de _____ son el resultado de las

acciones de la civilización moderna. Somos nosotros los que hemos

contaminado los ríos con los (**8.**) _____ que vienen de las

fábricas en el proceso de (**9.**) _____ las cosas que nuestra

sociedad demanda. Nosotros estamos (**10.**) _____ a muchos

animales con los (**11.**) _____ que usamos para matar

insectos. Nosotros (**12.**) _____ nuestra propia salud con las

sustancias a químicas y los productos (**13.**) _____. Y

seguimos reduciendo la cantidad de (**14.**) _____ fósil que

nos queda, y destruyendo la (**15.**) _____ de

_____ que debe protegernos de los rayos dañinos del sol. Si

estudiáramos las (**16.**) _____ de _____ de las tribus

indígenas, podríamos aprender mucho sobre la importancia de cuidar nuestro

(**17.**) _____ .

B. Mitos, leyendas y relatos bíblicos. Nombra el animal asociado con cada historia.

1. Según la Biblia, Jonás pasó un rato en la barriga (el estómago) de este

animal. _____

2. Este animal de la selva se asocia con un cereal de maíz muy popular.

_____

3. Este animal, normalmente lento, es famoso por haber ganado una

competencia contra un conejo. _____

4. Este animal se llama el rey de la selva. _____

5. Según un mito moderno, este animal que normalmente vive en las

ciénagas (*swamps*) está nadando por las alcantarillas (*sewers*) de Nueva

York. _____

6. Este pájaro se usa como el símbolo de los E.E.U.U. _____

7. Hay varios mitos asociados con la capacidad de este mamífero acuático

para comunicarse a través de una lengua. _____

8. El oso "Smokey" representa la campaña para prevenir los

_____ _____ .

C. Aspectos personales. Completa las frases con varias posibilidades.

Por ejemplo: El amor por la Tierra es evidente cuando

a. la gente recoge la basura.

b. reciclamos lo más posible.

1. El amor por la Tierra es evidente cuando

a. _____

b. _____

2. Algunos ejemplos del odio que existen el mundo son

a. _____

b. _____

3. No debemos

a. _____

b. _____

4. La política de conservación será un fracaso a menos que

a. _____

b. _____

5. No habrá suficiente agua potable a menos que

a. _____

b. _____

6. Necesitamos darnos cuenta de (que)

a. _____

b. _____

7. Unos ejemplos del egoísmo humano son

a. _____

b. _____

8. Debemos elegir líderes que

a. _____

b. _____

9. Dos maneras de desarrollar más conciencia sobre los problemas del medio ambiente son

a. _____

b. _____

10. Dos cosas que hago para contribuir al bienestar del planeta son

a. _____

b. _____

G R A M Á T I C A 1

A. El Sr. "Consumelotodo". Completa la descripción con la forma correcta de los verbos. Usa el pretérito del indicativo, el imperfecto del subjuntivo o el infinitivo.

El Sr. Consumelotodo era un vecino mío. Se comportaba (*behaved*) como si

él solo _____ (**1.** querer) _____ (**2.** agotar) todos

los recursos naturales del mundo. Este hombre creía que

_____ (**3.** ser) necesario dejar encendido (*running*) el motor de

su auto por lo menos media hora cada vez que iba a conducirlo. Según él era

importante que el motor _____ (**4.** calentarse) muy bien para

que el auto _____ (**5.** seguir) funcionando a la perfección. No

le importaba que sus vecinos _____ (**6.** respirar) todos los

gases de escape. Una vez él _____ (**7.** encender) el motor,

_____ (**8.** entrar) en su casa para desayunar y

_____ (**9.** olvidarse) del auto. El motor _____

(**10.** andar) una hora y media. Yo siempre esperaba que ese hombre

_____ (**11.** ganarse) la lotería y _____

(**12.** mudarse) a una casa grande y lujosa muy lejos de mí.

Otra mala costumbre del Sr. Consumelotodo se notaba en los veranos. Cuando

no llovía mucho y había escasez de agua, él siempre _____

(**13.** regar) el césped unas horas cada día como si _____ (**14.**

tener) un lago personal para _____ (**15.** utilizar). ¡Ojalá que

_____ (**16.** tener) un vecino más considerado! Era una lástima

que él no _____ (**17.** darse) cuenta de la necesidad de

_____ (**18.** cuidar) el medio ambiente.

B. ¡Ojalá! Para cada una de las siguientes situaciones, expresa un deseo
usando el imperfecto del subjuntivo con **ojalá**.

Por ejemplo: Después de un picnic había basura y desperdicios por toda la
playa.

> **¡Ojalá que la gente recogiera su basura en vez de dejarla en la
> playa!**

1. Las grandes empresas siguen tirando sus desperdicios en los ríos.

_____

2. Algunos políticos prometen cuidar el medio ambiente y no lo hacen.

_____

3. Algunas empresas usan animales de una manera muy cruel para probar
sus productos.

_____

4. Estamos en peligro a causa de los daños a la capa de ozono.

_____

5. En muchas ciudades hay basura en la calles.

_____

6. Se producen virus nuevos que amenazan la salud de todo el mundo.

_____

7. Se usan pesticidas que contaminan la vegetación, el agua y los animales.

_____

8. Siempre hay una guerra en alguna parte del mundo.

_____

C. Aspectos personales. Completa las frases.

Por ejemplo: Mi hermano mayor me trata como si...

Mi hermano mayor me trata como si no supiera nada y necesitara sus consejos para todo.¡Ojalá que me respetara más!

1. Mis padres me tratan como si...

_____

2. Algunos profesores nos dan una gran cantidad de trabajo como si...

_____

3. Algunos políticos nos hablan como si...

_____

4. Algunos jefes de las grandes empresas ignoran el bienestar general como si...

_____

5. Algunas personas tratan a los animales como si...

_____

6. Algunas personas fuman en público como si...

_____

7. Algunos jóvenes no parecen darse cuenta de los riesgos de sus acciones. Se comportan como si...

_____

8. A veces cuando pienso en la pobreza y el odio en el mundo, me parece como si...

_____

GRAMÁTICA 2

A. Si fuera diferente. Usa el imperfecto del subjuntivo y el condicional para reaccionar a las siguientes frases, según el modelo.

Por ejemplo: No tengo un millón de dólares.
Si yo tuviera un millón de dólares, combatiría la pobreza en mi ciudad.

1. No puedo saber el futuro.

_____

2. Tengo que terminar mis estudios.

_____

3. Tengo tanto que hacer.

_____

4. El mundo no es perfecto.

_____

5. Los animales no pueden hablar.

_____

6. No sabemos lo que está pensando otra persona.

_____

7. No hemos desarrollado lo suficiente la energía solar.

_____

8. No nos damos cuenta de que existe una grave escasez de alimentos en varias partes del mundo.

_____

9. No reciclamos lo suficiente.

_____

10. No hay solidaridad humana en el mundo.

_____

B. Causas y resultados. Escribe frases según el modelo. Emplea el condicional en la primera parte de la frase y el imperfecto del subjuntivo en la segunda.

Por ejemplo: Mis padres / estar orgullosos
Mis padres estarían orgullosos si yo sacara una buena nota en la clase de español.

1. yo / tener mucho miedo

_____

2. mis amigos / ser feliz

_____

3. yo / aprender más

_____

4. la vida / ser menos peligrosa

_____

5. no haber / más guerras

_____

6. nadie / conducir borracho (*drunk*)

_____

7. el medio ambiente / mejorarse

_____

C. ¿Qué harías? Escoge cinco de las siguientes personas y en cada caso indica qué harías (o no harías) si fueras él o ella.

Por ejemplo: Cenicienta
Si yo fuera Cenicienta, no toleraría los abusos de mis hermanastras.

1. Romeo o Julieta

_____

2. una persona inmortal

_____

3. el profesor / la profesora

_____

4. el/la jefe(a) de una gran caridad (*charity*) con mucho dinero a donar

_____

5. Blancanieves

_____

6. el líder de un país con una gran selva tropical

_____

7. el/la jefe(a) de una gran empresa

_____

L E C T U R A

V O C E S   D E L   M U N D O   H I S P A N O

GUARDIANA DEL LEGADO SILVESTRE

Lee el artículo y completa las actividades que siguen.

Hace unos años, una tarde de verano apareció en la puerta principal del Zoológico de Belice un viejo de cabellos blancos y rostro arrrugado. Había pasado la hora de cerrar y Sharon Matola, la fundadora y directora estadounidense del único zoológico de Belice, estaba cansada. De cualquier manera, saludó al hombre y lo hizo pasar. Lo acompañó personalmente (como hacía con todos los visitantes durante los primeros días del zoolólogico) llevándolo a ver los tapires, las boas y *currasows*, contándole un poco sobre cada uno. Cuando llegó a los jaguares y comenzó a explicarle por qué estaban en peligro de extinción en muchas partes de América Central, el hombre comenzó a llorar. "Discúlpeme, señorita", le dijo el enjuto visitante, "he pasado mi vida entera aquí en Belice y ésta es la primera vez que veo los animales de mi propio país". Para aquel hombre y, para muchos de los 200.000 habitantes de Belice, el zoológico ofrece un primer mensaje que han oído sobre la necesidad de conservarla.

En sólo una década, el Zoológico de Belice se ha transformado en el centro de la conservación en un país que es vital para la preservación de la vida silvestre de Centroamérica. "Quiero involucrar a la población local con su medio ambiente", dice Matola refiriéndose a su zoológico, situado entre la ciudad de Belice y Belmopán, la capital del país. "A menos que la gente sepa que vale la pena preservar la vida silvestre, destruirán el hábitat de los animales". Aunque sólo tiene una extensión de 209.800 kilómetros cuadrados, Belice ha adquirido una importancia que contradice su tamaño. Mientras que en el resto del istmo se han quemado o cortado la mayoría de los árboles, los bosques tropicales de Belice han permanecido mayormente intactos, y albergan animales raros o extinguidos en otros países.

En realidad, Belice ha destinado casi un tercio de su territorio a parques y reservas de la vida silvestre, salvaguardando así más de su acervo nacional que cualquier otro país centro o sudamericano. Uno de ellos, la Cockscomb Basin Forest Preserve, de 43.700 hectáreas, es el único refugio reservado para jaguares, el felino más grande del Nuevo Mundo. Belice (que se llamaba Honduras Británica hasta 1981) también posee los arrecifes de coral más extensos de las Amércias. "Belice es un ejemplo de biodiversidad", dice William Konstant, asesor de zoológicos y director del programa de especies de Conservation International, un grupo con sede en los Estados Unidos. "Las perspectivas de la preservación de hábitat son mejores en Belice que en cualquier otro lugar de América Central".

Que un zoológico desempeñe un papel tan importante en la preservación de la vida silvestre podrá sorprender a algunos, pero no a los que conocen a Sharon Matola. Alta y atractiva, Matola exuda energía, entusiasmo e indignación. No sólo es la fundadora y la directora del Zoológico de Belice, sino que durante muchos años también su principal custodia, directora de educación, publicista y recaudadora de fondos. También se ha convertido en uno de los voceros más francos y efectivos de la preservación de los animales y el hábitat en Belice. "Sharon ha integrado a un zoológico en un esfuerzo nacional e internacional por salvar los bosques tropicales de América Central", dice Konstant, que como ex director del Wildlife Preservation Trust International ayudó a financiar los programas de Matola. "El Zoológico de Belice está haciendo exactamente lo que debe hacer un buen zoológico".

¿Por qué le han de importar los animales de Belice a una mujer nacida en Baltimore, que trabajó en un circo, fue domadora de leones y asistente de filmaciones? "Tenemos una gran variedad de vida silvestre", dice Matola, que ahora es ciudadana de Belice. "Quiero ayudar a alertar a la población acerca de la importancia biológica de su país. Quiero ayudar a crear un orgullo nacional por la vida silvestre y el medio ambiente de Belice". Y agrega que "he logrado mucho en diez años. Me he involucrado en algo mucho más grande que yo misma. Dedico toda mi energía y mi tiempo al zoológico y a la conservación. Quiero compartir mi sentimiento de que es importante conservar la vida silvestre de Belice. Cuando se ve la magia en los ojos de los niños, se sabe que lo que se está haciendo es correcto".

A. ¿Entendiste? Contesta las preguntas.

1. ¿Cómo reaccionó el viejo al ver los animales? ¿Por qué tuvo una reacción tan fuerte?

_____

_____

2. En el artículo se hacen varias comparaciones entre la política de conservación de Belice y las de los otros países de Centroamérica o Sudamérica. ¿Qué diferencias se presentan?

_____

_____

Palabras útiles	
enjuto	delgado
el tercio	*third*
salvaguardando	protegiendo

3. ¿Qué sabemos de la personalidad de Sharon Matola? ¿Cómo se caracteriza ella? ¿Cuáles son sus pasiones y metas?

_____

_____

4. ¿Cuál es el mérito del esfuerzo de Sharon?

_____

_____

5. Según el contexto del artículo, el significado más probable de **silvestre** es...

    a. relacionado a la plata   **c.** relacionado a la selva, el bosque
        o la naturaleza

    b. civilizado   **d.** contaminado

6. El verbo **involucrar** aparece en el segundo párrafo y otra vez en el quinto. Según el contexto, el significado más probable es...

    a. to get involved   **c.** to transform
    b. to salvage   **d.** to improve

7. Según el contexto al fin del segundo párrafo, el significado más probable de **albergan** es...

    a. dan comida   **c.** facilitan el estudio de
    b. protegen, dan refugio   **d.** ponen en peligro

8. ¿Conoces a una persona que se dedique a una causa tanto como Sharon Matola? ¿Qué ha hecho esta persona?

_____

_____

B. Más guardianes.

Sharon Matola es protectora de la selva tropical y de los animales en peligro. La madre Teresa fue protectora de los pobres y enfermos. Contesta las preguntas.

1. ¿Puedes nombrar a otras personas dedicades a mejorar el mundo? ¿Quiénes son?

_____

_____

_____

2. ¿Como sería el mundo si todos tuviéramos la pasión de resolver o mejorar algún problema de nuestra sociedad? Escribe una lista de seis maneras en que el mundo sería diferente si hubiera más personas dedicadas.

a. _____

b. _____

c. _____

d. _____

e. _____

f. _____

PARA ESCRIBIR

Las pasiones

Leíste sobre la gran pasión de Sharon Matola. Si en este momento tuvieras los recursos para seguir cualquier pasión o meta, ¿cuál sería? ¿proteger algún aspecto del medio ambiente? ¿una obra por el bienestar o la solidaridad humana? ¿una meta artística, económica o política? Escribe un párrafo al respecto.

_____

_____

_____

_____

_____

_____

_____

_____

SELF-TESTS

The self-tests in this secton of the Workbook are not meant to be exhaustive, nor do they presume to fit the variety of course goals of the users of *Visión y voz*. As diagnostic tools, these items are sufficiently open to promote the creativity and flexibilty necessary at this point, before you are presented with your instructor's own Unit test.

Suggestions for use: You may complete sections of these self-tests gradually in preparation for your Unit test. If done as homework, try not to use books or notes so that you can better diagnose your needs. If done in class, compare your responses in groups of three or four to see how you can improve your own performance and expand your response options.

¡Buena suerte!

Autoevaluación
Unidad 1

En la Unidad 1, aprendiste a hacer preguntas y a hablar de ti y de otros con respecto a...

la nacionalidad	**ser** + *nationality*	**¿De dónde** eres / es / son?
la personalidad	**ser** + *adjective*	**¿Cómo** eres / es / son?
lo físico	**ser** + *physical features*	**¿Cómo** eres / es / son?
la edad	**tener** + *años*	**¿Cuántos** años tiene / tienes / tienen?
las fechas	**números** de 1 a 100 y miles	**¿Cuándo?** **¿Cuánto?**
las profesiones	**ser** + *profession*	**¿Qué** eres / es/ /son?
		¿Quién es?
las aspiraciones	**quiero ser** + *profession*	**¿Qué** quieres ser?
		¿Por qué?
planes y actividades	**querer** + *infinitive*	**¿Qué** quieres hacer?
	ir a + *infinitive*	**¿Cuándo** vas a...?
		¿Adónde quieres ir?
los intereses	**tener interés en**...	**¿Quiénes** tienen... ?
los gustos	**gustar** + *infinitive*	**¿Qué** te / le / les gusta?
las obligaciones	**tener que** + *infinitive*	**¿Qué** tienes que hacer?
las hablilidades	**poder** + *infinitive*	**¿Qué** puedes hacer?

También aprendiste a...

conectar tus ideas   **y; también; no... tampoco; además; pero; porque; por ejemplo**

Ahora sabes más de...

quiénes son los hispanos	**grupos y nacionalidades**
cómo se llaman los hispanos	**nombre completo; nombre y apellidos**
cómo hablar por teléfono	**números** y frases idiomáticas
cómo solicitar empleo en el mundo hispano	el **currículum**
el enfoque personal en la entrevista de trabajo	**¿Cómo** eres / es?
	¿Quiénes son sus padres?
	¿Qué es su padre / madre / esposo(a)?

P R U E B A

The following will help you organize and integrate what you have learned in Unit 1. It samples your learning and use of strategies, but it doesn't necessarily represent the emphasis chosen by your particular program or instructor.

I CULTURA

Choose two of the following and, in English, prepare a sensitive response for someone who does not have a sense for cultural differences. Be sure to provide the appropriate information as well as to communicate why cultural sensitivity is necessary in contacts with other people.

1. "Carmen Eliana Naretto Barca. Why write such a confusing, long name? Shorten it and simply put first, middle and last names as we do."

2. "Classify this García-Soto man as Latino race and be done with it."

3. "These people have no right to ask personal questions in a job interview. After all, I am only going to work there for six months."

II VOCABULARIO Y LECTURA

A. Solicitud de beca. Complete the following scholarship application form with your personal data and Hispanic usage for names, dates, addresses, etc.

SOLICITUD DE BECA

DATOS PERSONALES

Nombre: _____
       Nombre de pila   *apellido paterno*   *apellido materno*

Fecha de nacimiento: _____   Sexo: _____   Estado civil: S   C   D

Ciudad y estado de nacimiento: _____   Nacionalidad: _____

Domicilio:_____
      calle nº piso código postal   *ciudad*   *estado*   *país*

Teléf. en la universidad: _____   Teléf. en casa: _____

DATOS FAMILIARES

Padre: _____
      nombre y apellidos   *ocupación*   *edad*

Madre: _____
      nombre y apellidos   *ocupación*   *edad*

ESTUDIOS

    Universidad: _____   Facultad: _____

    Carrera: _____   Título y fecha: _____

ACTIVIDADES Y / O INTERESES EXTRALABORALES

Clubs / instituciones públicas a las que pertenece:

_____

Deportes y otros intereses: _____

Periódicos / revistas que lee, programas de TV que ve: _____

Lugar y fecha: _____

Firma: _____

B. Asociaciones. Think of a friend or family member and make at least five good statements for each category below, using the verbs **ir a**, **poder**, **querer**, **tener**, **ser**, and **gustar**.

    Intereses en octubre, noviembre, diciembre: _____

    _____

    Gustos en junio, julio, agosto: _____

    _____

    Hablidades en el trabajo / la universidad: _____

    _____

    Sus metas para el año 2005: _____

    _____

C. Fechas y precios importantes. Complete with the corresponding dates or prices.

    1. Tengo mi fiesta de cumpleaños _____

    _____.

    2. Las clases del segundo semestre (trimestre) empiezan _____

    _____.

    3. En mi universidad, el año de estudios vale _____

    _____.

4. Un coche no demasiado caro vale _____

_____.

5. Ir a México por julio y agosto vale _____

_____.

D. Dos amigos. Complete the following conversation between two friends.

Luis	Lucía
(Marca el 235 26 34.)	¿ _____ ?
Buenas tardes. ¿ _____ ?	Con ella. ¿ _____ ?
Hola, Lucía. _____	_____

E. Lectura. Use the strategies and vocabulary from this unit to read the
following fragment and then complete the statements that follow to
summarize the article in your own words.

LOS CHICOS MARAVILLA

Con todos los avances recientes en la electrónica y la computación,
tenemos ahora una nueva generación de chicos maravilla que pueden
invadir su universidad, su casa, sus instituciones o sus trabajos sin
grandes problemas. Son los chicos maravilla de la Internet, que pueden
introducir sus ojos en muchos programas o documentos importantes,
secretos o públicos, interesantes o frustrantes, que encuentran en el vasto
mundo de la computación mundial.

Varios de estos chicos tienen problemas con la justicia porque invaden
sitios del gobierno que son supersecretos para la seguridad nacional o
porque roban secretos financieros de los bancos y otras empresas. Algunos
están ahora en prisiones federales o en sitios especiales para los
adolescentes. No es bueno usar las habilidades y talentos para penetrar
sistemas que son protegidos, pero no hay límites para la curiosidad de
estos muchachos.

1. Estos chicos modernos son una maravilla porque

_____

2. Algunos chicos están ahora en prisión porque

_____

3. Podemos usar nuestras hablidades e intereses

_____

III GRAMÁTICA

A. Precisión. Use forms of **ser**, **tener**, or **tener que** to complete the following.

1. En mi oficina de gobierno, el jefe no _____ amable.

Siempre _____ algo que hacer cuando yo quiero

hablar con él. A veces, _____ dificil saber el

nombre del jefe porque nunca está allí.

2. Tú _____ manener el laboratorio impecable porque

el profesor de fisica _____ muy ordenado y no le

gusta _____ sus documentos y libros por todas

partes.

3. Si quieres ganar más de cincuenta mil dólares _____

buscar empleo en una empresa de las que _____

sistemas de computación que _____ más

interactivos, porque ellos _____ modificarlos todo el

tiempo y entonces hay mucha necesidad de programadores.

B. ¿Qué puedo decir? Provide an answer or rejoinder for each of the following.

1. ¿Qué quieres hacer el sábado?

_____

_____

2. Estrella no puede trabajar hoy.

_____

_____

3. ¿Quieres salir con nostotros?

_____

_____

4. ¿Vamos a ir a hacer ejercicio?

_____

_____

5. Hoy no quiero hacer nada.

_____

_____

C. Para invitar tienes que insistir. Invite a friend to do the following. He or she resists so you have to insist twice, each time phrasing your question a bit differently. Use forms of **querer**, **ir a**, **poder**, **tener que**.

1. ¿sacar un título de especialista en Homepages?

2. ¿buscar un empleo en el extranjero?

3. ¿ser dueño(a) de una empresa pequeña?

D. Por una razón muy sencilla. Complete the followiing statements about you and others (fill in the name of a friend or family member). Use forms of **querer**, **tener**, **(que)**, **ser**.

1. Mi amiga _____ es emprendedora porque

_____ .

2. Mi amigo _____ es demasiado perezoso porque

_____ .

3. _____ es muy trabajador porque

_____ .

4. Yo soy algo desordenado(a) porque

_____ .

5. Las otras amigas son muy amistosas porque

_____ .

E. Buen editor. Choose the correct word to complete the following so that
1) the paragraph makes sense, and **2)** nouns, verbs, adjectives, and articles
agree. For some agreements you need to think of the noun's gender, but for the
verbs you need only think of singular or plural.

Mi primo Marcos es muy (**1.**) (deportista / hogareño / especialista) y todos
los sábados (**2.**) (corres / corren / corre) por (**3.**) (muy / mucho / mucha)
tiempo para prepararse para el maratón. Él (**4.**) (es / está / tiene) sólo
dieciséis años ahora y, como es adolescente, es (**5.**) (nada / algo / mucho)
impulsivo y desordenado, pero a mí (**6.**) (le / nuestro / me) gusta su
dinamismo y entusiasmo. También tiene interés en la música
(**7.**) (colombiana / columbina / colombino) y le (**8.**) (gustan / juegan /
gusta) tocar la guitarra y el piano. Yo (**9.**) (tiene que / soy / quiero) ayudar
a Marcos porque él va (**10.**) (ir / a / en) ser muy famoso en el futuro.

‖ EXPRESIÓN ORAL

Prepare five possible questions and answers for one of the following
situations. Then use these questions to converse with your partner.

1. A phone call to someone to ask for a third party.

2. A job or a roomate search interview.

3. A first encounter with a Spanish-speaking exchange student.

‖ EXPRESIÓN ESCRITA

Choose one of the following and develop in Spanish.

1. Write a full description of a person you know well or write your own self-
portrait. Jot down a few questions that you can use as a guide in
providing physical and psychological traits, interests, abilities, and plans
for the future.

2. Prepare your **currículum** in Spanish. Include as much detail as
possible. Pay attention to format and correct spelling.

Autoevaluación
Unidad 2

En la Unidad 2, aprendiste cómo hacer preguntas y cómo hablar de ti y de otros sobre...

actividades rutinarias	*verbs in present tense*	**¿Con quién** estudias los martes?
días de la semana	**lunes, martes, miércoles...**	**¿Cuándo** sales con ellos?
estaciones del año	**primavera, verano, otoño...**	**¿Qué** estación te gusta más?
hablar de tus gustos	**gustar** + *nouns*	**¿Qué** deportes te gustan más?
la rutina diaria	*reflexive verbs in the present*	**¿Dónde** te juntas con él?
lo que tienes ganas de hacer	*present tense*	**¿Por qué** no nos vamos lejos?
los estados de ánimo	**sentirse, estar**	**¿Cómo** se sienten ahora?
tus quejas	**estoy harto de; me muero de**	**¿Por qué** no comemos mejor?
la hora	**es la/ son las + número**	**¿Qué** hora es?
la hora de un evento	**... a la(s) + número + de la mañana/ tarde/ noche**	**¿A qué** hora es la fiesta?
		¿Cuándo es la prueba?
la frecuencia de las actividades/ eventos	**casi nunca/ siempre, a menudo...**	**¿Por qué** no bailas a menudo?
cómo haces las cosas	**bien/ no muy bien, más o menos**	**¿Con quién** trabajas bien?

Ahora sabes más de...

cómo pasan sus ratos libres los hispanos	**actividades**	¿Vamos a **dar un paseo**?
cómo pasan las vacaciones los hispanos	**calendario y actividades**	**¿Dónde** esquías en agosto?

P R U E B A

The following will help you organize and integrate what you have learned in Unit 2. It samples your learning and use of strategies, but it doesn't necessarily represent the emphases chosen by your particular program or instructor.

I CULTURA

Choose *two* of the following and, in English, prepare a sensitive response for someone who does not have a sense for cultural differences. Be sure to provide the appropriate information as well as to communicate why cultural sensitivity is necessary in contacts with other people.

1. "I don't understand; does everyone go on vacation the same day? How does business function with everyone on vacation?"

2. "I think Spaniards and other Europeans have too many holidays. It seems they're always trying to get out of work."

3. "Hispanics take summer vacations too seriously. They should focus more on their work and take vacations only when they can afford the leisure time."

II VOCABULARIO Y LECTURA

A. En la agencia de viajes. A travel agency that specializes in planning dream vacations has asked you to provide information about yourself in order to assess your interests, needs, and lifestyle. Complete the following form with your personal data and Hispanic usage for names, dates, addresses, time, etc.

I. DATOS PERSONALES

Nombre: _____
            Nombre de pila   *apellido paterno*   *apellido materno*

Edad: _____   Sexo: _____

Estado civil: S C D   Ocupación: _____

Domicilio:_____
         calle nº piso código postal   *ciudad*   *estado*   *pais*

Teléf. en la universidad: _____   Teléf. en casa: _____

Días y horas que podermos llamar por teléfono: _____

_____

Visión y voz 2E Workbook © 1998 John Wiley & Sons

II. Gustos, actividades y/o intereses de recreación

Clubs / grupos a los que pertenece: _____

_____

Lugares / países que ya conoce: _____

_____

Lugares / países que quiere visitar otra vez: _____

_____

Deportes y otros intereses: Programas de TV, periódicos, o revistas de viajes

que ve o lee: _____

_____

III. Viajes que desea hacer (Dar respuestas específicas, por favor)

Areas, ciudades, lugares que le interesan: _____

_____

¿Por qué? _____

_____

¿Desea vacaciones-vacaciones o vacaciones con actividades?

_____

_____

¿Qué actividades le gustan más? _____

_____

¿Qué tipo de viaje desea hacer? _____

_____

(Es muy importante indicar si desea acampar, montar en bicicleta, quedarse en hoteles, tomar el tren,etc.)

¿Cuándo desea viajar? (Esto afecta el precio) _____

_____

Clima que prefiere: _____

¿En qué mes? _____

_____

Duración del viaje: _____

¿Con quién viaja? _____

Lugar y fecha: _____

_____
firma

B. El tiempo. Indicate the season and the weather you associate with the following activities.

1. acostarse en la playa

_____

2. esquiar en la montaña

_____

3. dar un paseo

_____

4. acampar

_____

5. bucear

_____

6. ver las flores

_____

7. admirar los colores de los árboles

_____

8. salir por la noche con poca ropa

_____

C. Asociaciones. Tell at least *three* things you do in each of these situations. Do not repeat any activities.

1. Es medianoche y llueve.

_____

_____

2. Es un día festivo y no hay clase.

_____

_____

3. Estoy en la playa con amigos.

_____

_____

4. No tengo dinero y me muero de aburrido(a).

_____

_____

5. En junio empiezan las vacaciones de verano.

_____

_____

6. Es domingo por la noche.

_____

_____

7. Busco la aventura.

_____

_____

8. Me siento mal.

_____

_____

9. Es sábado por la mañana.

_____

_____

D. Mi tiempo libre. Complete the following with two sentences, according to your own ideas and plans. Use the new words and expressions you learned and be original.

1. Para el próximo puente

_____

_____

2. En los días de lluvia me

_____

_____

3. La mejor diversión es

_____

_____

4. No tengo ganas de arreglarme

_____

_____

5. Me muero de aburrido(a) si no

_____

_____

6. Estoy preocupado(a) y me quejo de

_____

_____

E. Lectura. Use the strategies and vocabulary from this unit to read the following fragment and then complete the statements that follow.

Directo al cielo

Movidos por el espíritu aventurero, un grupo de alumnos del Colegio San Ignacio de Santiago piensa ascender la montaña y llegar hasta el punto más alto de Chile en febrero. Piensan escalar el volcán Ojos del Salado y tocar el cielo a 6.983 metros de altura (unos 21.000 pies). Esta es la segunda vez que van a **subir**, porque en 1995 no terminaron (*finished*) su aventura por el frío y el viento. Por un lado, quieren encontrar a Dios en la naturaleza y, por otro, quieren aprender a conocerse, a comprenderse, a ayudarse y vivir juntos esta aventura extraordinaria.

A los profesores del San Ignacio les gusta **promover** los trabajos de verano, las misiones religiosas y los paseos ecológicos. Les gustan los alumnos que prefieren las aventuras únicas y que quieren aprender algo nuevo. La idea es no **gastar** mucho dinero y no divertirse sólo en fiestas todo el verano. "Un retiro espiritual es mucho mejor", dice un profesor.

En el Ojos del Salado, hace muchísimo frío en el verano también y los vientos son de ¡40 a 150 kilómetros por hora! Así es que por veinte días, los chicos tienen que mantenerse bien y sentirse llenos de energía. Es una **locura** estimulante, porque la meta es **apartarse** de la mediocridad, el consumismo y la pasividad.

De: "Con los ojos al cielo". Gabriela Correa. *El Mercurio, Revista del Domingo.* 17 de septiembre de 1995, págs. 14-15.

1. Dos cosas muy buenas de esta aventura son

_____

_____

2. Dos cosas malas o difíciles de este viaje son

_____

_____

3. Si haces una cosa extraordinaria puedes

_____

_____

4. La meta de esta actividad es

_____

_____

5. Puedo comprender algunas palabras nuevas de esta lectura, sin usar mi

diccionario: subir = _____

promover = _____

gastar = _____

locura = _____

apartarse = _____

III GRAMÁTICA

A. Precisión Read the following paragraph. Then, use forms of **irse, juntarse, morirse, divertirse, sentirse, vestirse, dormirse, decirse, aburrirse, escribirse** to complete it.

Si salimos en la expedición al volcán, voy a **1)** _____

muchísimo porque a mí me gusta la aventura y lo extraordinario; no me

gusta **2)** _____ sin pensar en algo nuevo y estimulante.

Claro, creo que ya **3)** _____ de terror cuando pienso en el

frío y la altura del volcán, pero soy joven y si **4)** _____

preocupado y tenso ahora, no va a durar mucho. El lunes,

5) _____ en el tren expreso hasta Antofagasta para

6) _____ con mis compañeros que ya están allá. Para

darnos energía, siempre **7)** _____ notas o cartas y

8) _____ que no somos los primeros, que muchos otros

jóvenes hacen cosas extraordinarias en el mundo. Muchos chicos no tienen

dinero para **9)** _____ ni para comer a veces, pero nosotros

estamos en un buen colegio y tenemos tanta ayuda. En estos días, no

tengo tiempo para **10)** _____ con todas las cosas que tengo

que preparar.

B. ¿Qué puedo decir? Provide an answer or rejoinder for each of the following.

1. ¿A qué hora te levantas cuando hay clases?

    _____

2. ¿Qué tipo de vacaciones te gustan más?

    _____

3. ¿Cuándo es tu graduación de la universidad?

    _____

Visión y voz 2E Workbook © 1998 John Wiley & Sons

4. Cuando te quejas de las clases, ¿de qué te quejas?

_____

5. ¿Por qué se escriben tan poco los amigos ahora?

_____

C. Ay, no puedo. Your new friends invite you to several activities but, each time, you are too busy to go out. Using **pensar**, **no poder**, **querer**, **llover**, **morirse de**, etc., and days of the week, provide two convincing excuses in each case. Connect the two sentences with **porque**, **además**, or **también**.

1. ¿Por qué no vamos a dar un paseo esta tarde?

_____

_____

2. Este jueves hay una fiesta en la Casa Hispana, ¿vamos?

_____

_____

3. Mira, no nos podemos perder el concierto de "Sublime". Nos vemos el martes a las cinco.

_____

_____

D. Misión imposible. Most people have their personal choice of activities, depending on time of day. Complete the following with a description of two things that you or your friends decidedly cannot or will not do at the times indicated. Use reflexive pronouns if necessary.

1. A las cinco de la mañana, nadie _____

_____ .

2. ¡Qué mala idea! A la hora de mi programa preferido no _____

_____ .

3. Al mediodía, no tengo ganas de _____

_____ .

4. A la hora de mi siesta, no me _____

_____ .

5. A las ocho de la mañana, no _____

_____ .

E. Buen editor. Choose the correct word to complete the following so that **1**) the paragraph makes sense; **2**) subjects, pronouns, and verbal forms agree; and **3**) forms of **gustar** are accompanied by phrases with **a mí/ a todos/ a ellos** as well as articles for the things one likes.

No sé (**1.** cuándo/ qué hora/ a qué hora) es la primera reunión del grupo ecológico el jueves. Los grupos siempre (**2.** se juntan/ se junta/ se va) en el salón Barcelona, pero (**3.** se olvidan/ nos olvidamos/ olvidar) de dar la hora de la reunión. (**4.** A mi amiga/ A todos/ A mí) nos gusta el grupo porque siempre podemos (**5.** levantamos /arregla/ aprender) algo nuevo sobre la naturaleza. Hay muchas actividades; si (**6.** hace/ gusta/ ve) sol y es tiempo de turismo, Ud. puede (**7.** hablarse/ pasarlo/ llamarse) muy bien trabajando con los niños que visitan el jardín botánico. Sin embargo, si (**8.** a todos/ a los niños/ a ti) te gusta la naturaleza, si quieres (**9.** hablar/ hablas/ habla) bien el español y si estás harto de (**10.** se queda/ quedarte/ irse) en casa, es mejor (**11.** salir/ irse/ vivir) a Puerto Rico y visitar el parque El Yunque, que es una maravilla ecológica. Pero debes recordar que antes de (**12.** hacer/ viajar/ haciendo) un viaje, siempre tenemos que (**13.** informarse/ informarnos/ informamos) sobre la cultura y las costumbres que vamos a (**14.** buscar/encontrar/verse).

▌ EXPRESIÓN ORAL

Prepare five possible questions and answers for one of the following situations. Then use these questions to converse with your partner. Use the vocabulary and verb forms learned in this unit. Do not forget to use pronouns with reflexive verbs. Also, use phrases with **a mí/ a nosotros** and articles with the verb **gustar**.

1. Your friend would like to go on a long vacation but you cannot afford the time or the money. Propose an alternative plan and give details. Be persuasive and original.

2. You and your friend have to try to persuade a group from another university to come to yours for an international student meeting. Describe activities on your campus and your area or city as attractively as possible to persuade the group to come.

3. Your university is planning to change from quarters to semesters and you agree with the change. Help show those who don't like the plan that longer periods of classes leave more time for traveling to other places and gaining experience with other groups or cultures. Also show that opposite seasons in other countries would allow you to ski in August or do water sports in January.

EXPRESIÓN ESCRITA

Una pintura de palabras. Write a full, interesting description of a particularly enjoyable day during a recent outing or vacation. Be sure to indicate who is with you and at what time and what part of day you do each activity. Remember to use reflexive pronouns when necessary.

Por ejemplo: Es sábado, el primer día de las vacaciones de primavera.
Estoy en el campo, muy lejos de la ciudad...

Autoevaluación
Unidad 3

En la Unidad 3, aprendiste cómo hablar de ti y...

de tu familia	**padre, madre, hijos, hermanos**	**¿A quién** te pareces más?
	tíos, primos, abuelos, padrinos	**¿Qué** tipo de madre es tu mamá?
de eventos del pasado	el tiempo pretérito	**¿Cuándo naciste?**
	verbos **irregulares** del pretérito	**¿Qué puesto conseguiste?**
de actividades rutinarias del pasado	**fui, hice, llegué, busqué, organicé,**	**¿Qué** hiciste ayer?
decir cuándo ocurrió algo	**(ante)ayer, anoche, la semana pasada**	**¿Cuándo** te mudaste a Seattle?
decir cuánto tiempo hace que ocurrió algo	**hace** + expresión de tiempo	**¿Cuánto** hace que se conocen?
describir algo si no sabes el nombre...	**es de..., sirve para..., viene en**	**¿Para qué sirve esto**?
		¿De qué es tu camiseta?
describir qué haces para otros	**me, te, le(s), nos, os** + verbo	**¿Qué te** llevo mañana?
comparar cosas, gente, ideas y acciones	**más/ menos** + adjetivo + que **mejor/ peor que; mayor/menor que**	**¿Qué** tipo de regalo es mejor? **¿Quién** es tu mejor amigo?

Ahora sabes más de...

cómo se forma el nombre completo	**el nombre y los apellidos**	**¿Cómo** se llama Ud.?
quiénes forman la familia de un hispano	**padres, padrinos, hermanos...**	**¿Qué** le diste a tu **ahijado**?
cómo funciona la red familiar	**abuelos, nietos, suegros...**	**¿Quién te consiguió** trabajo?
las tradiciones y las fiestas familiares	**el santo**	**¡Feliz Santo!**
cómo se celebran algunos eventos	**despedida, boda civil/ religiosa, muerte**	**¡Vivan los novios! Sentido pésame.**
qué se dice en cada ocasión	**que seas/sean muy...**	**¿Qué te regalaron?**
cómo se encuentra un piso en un edificio	**primer/segundo/tercer** piso	**¿En qué piso** viven los Gómez?

P R U E B A

The following will help you organize and integrate what you have learned in Unit 3. It samples your learning and use of strategies, but it doesn't necessarily represent the emphases chosen by your particular program or instructor.

I CULTURA

Choose two of the following and, in English, prepare a sensitive response for someone who does not have a sense for cultural differences. Be sure to provide the appropriate information as well as to communicate why cultural sensitivity is necessary in contacts with other people.

1. "This is outrageous! It is our anniversary, our day to remember our wedding, our day to be alone, and you are telling me that your parents, brothers, and a whole bunch of people are coming to have dinner with us here?"

2. "I just don't understand this lady. How come if she is married she doesn't use her husband's last name? Maybe they are not married after all."

3. "Can somebody please explain to me why I can't find my friend's apartment in this building? I am on the third floor and everybody keeps pointing up when I ask for apartamento 305."

II VOCABULARIO Y LECTURA

A. Datos personales. Complete the following form with your personal data (Hispanic usage for names, dates, addresses, please) and your preferences.

I. DATOS PERSONALES

Nombre: _____
　　　　　Nombre de pila　　　　　*apellido paterno*　　　　　*apellido materno*

Domicilio: _____
　　　　　calle nº piso código postal　　　　*ciudad*　　　　*estado*　　　*pais*

Teléf. en la universidad: _____

Teléf. en casa (indique qué meses): _____

Dónde nació: _____

Dónde vivió en los últimos 10 años: _____

Cumpleaños: _____

Visión y voz 2E Workbook © 1998 John Wiley & Sons

Estado civil: S C D Regalos preferidos: _____

Hermanos y edades: _____

A quién se parece más: a _____

II. DATOS FAMILIARES

Días y horas en que podemos encontrarlo con su familia: _____

Actividades familiares preferidas: _____

Fechas importantes: _____

Ocupación del padre: _____ Intereses: _____

    Regalos preferidos: _____

Lugar de nacimiento: _____ Cumpleaños: _____

Ocupación de la madre: _____ Intereses: _____

    Regalos preferidos: _____

Lugar de nacimiento: _____ Cumpleaños: _____

Ocupación de un hermano: _____ Intereses: _____

    Regalos preferidos: _____

Ocupación de un hermano: _____ Intereses: _____

    Regalos preferidos: _____

Ocupación de un hermano: _____ Intereses: _____

    Regalos preferidos: _____

Ocupación de un amigo: _____ Intereses: _____

    Regalos preferidos: _____

Lugar y fecha: _____   _____

                                  firma

B. ¿Con quién y cuándo? Tell with whom and when you do the following.

Por ejemplo: construir algo: Construimos una habitación con mi abuelo
                                  durante mis vacaciones. (Sólo puedo construir
                                  algo con mi abuelo en el verano).

1. compartir buenas ideas

_____

2. influir a los nietos

_____

3. conseguir un buen sueldo

_____

4. llevarse bien

_____

5. morirse de la risa

_____

6. buscar regalos

_____

7. sacar fotografias

_____

8. compartir secretos

_____

9. pagar el alquiler

_____

10. dar consejos

_____

11. pedir un favor

_____

12. pelearse

_____

13. trabajar

_____

14. leer

_____

15. casarse

_____

C. Asociaciones. Provide at least three objects that can be found in the following events or places.

1. un cumpleaños

_____

2. una billetera

_____

3. un libro

_____

4. la cocina

_____

5. un bautizo

_____

6. una despedida

_____

7. una habitación de estudiantes

_____

8. una tienda de cuero

_____

9. bodas de oro

_____

D. ¿Cuál es la ventaja? Complete the following with two sentences, according to your own ideas and plans. Use the new words and comparative structures you learned and be original.

1. La gente se muda de un apartamento a una casa porque

_____

_____

2. A veces es mejor comer en un restaurante que cocinar en la casa porque

_____

_____

3. Algunos solteros prefieren no casarse porque

_____

_____

4. Mucha gente quiere casarse porque

_____

_____

5. Es más fácil crecer en el campo porque

_____

_____

E. Lectura. Use the strategies, grammar and vocabulary from this unit to read the following fragment and then complete the statements that follow.

MAYOR NO ES SIEMPRE MEJOR

Me llamo Mario. Como fui el hermano mayor y tuve que preocuparme de los menores, resulté más tranquilo y conservador que todos los otros. Además, mis padres siempre me exigieron más a mí y, por eso, nunca tuve mucho tiempo para mis intereses. Siempre me saqué las mejores notas de todos los primos y nunca empecé nada sin terminarlo, porque mis mayores no me permitieron excusas de ninguna clase.

Por el contrario, todos mis hermanos y primos menores vivieron sus años de infancia y adolescencia con más alegría, menos obligaciones, más diversiones y aventuras y ¡las peores notas en el colegio! ¡Qué envidia más grande! Una excepción fue mi prima Ángeles, que siempre fue más independiente y despreocupada aunque fue hija única de mi tía Isabel Antonia. Ángeles siempre consiguió todo lo que se propuso: una buena carrera, un buen marido y mejores hijos y amigos. Sin duda, ella fue la más equilibrada y feliz de todas.

1. Mario creció rodeado de _____

_____

2. Como hermano mayor, Mario tuvo que _____

_____

3. Los otros hermanos y sus primos _____

_____

4. Ángeles fue hija única pero _____

_____

5. Ahora Ángeles _____

_____

III GRAMÁTICA

A. Precisión. Primero, lee este párrafo. Después, usa formas de pretérito de los siguientes verbos para completarlo: **decir , despedirse, divorciarse, dormir, empezar, irse, morirse, sacar, sentirse, ser**.

Fue muy duro aceptar la idea del divorcio de papá y mamá. Mi papá

_____ **(1)** de la casa y me dijo que esa primera noche él no

_____ **(2)** nada. Unos días después _____

(3) todas sus cosas del escritorio y _____ **(4)** de nostros. ¡

_____ **(5)** muy triste verlo partir! Unos meses después mis

padres _____ **(6)** y entonces yo _____ **(7)** a

trabajar, para tener más dinero. Me **(8)** _____ muy mal

varios años y casi _____ **(9)** de pena la primera Navidad que

pasamos solos, aunque él me _____ **(10)** varias veces que

me quiere igual, que no importa el divorcio.

Visión y voz 2E Workbook © 1998 John Wiley & Sons

B. ¿Qué puedo decir? Provide an answer or rejoinder for each of the following.

1. ¿Quién influyó más en ti cuando chico(a)? ¿Cómo?

_____

2. ¿Cuándo te mudaste para acá?

_____

3. ¿Quién te dio el mejor regalo para tu cumpleaños? ¿Qué fue?

_____

4. ¿Qué te dijeron en tu casa cuando pediste más dinero?

_____

5. Ayer se murió un amigo de la familia.

_____

C. ¿Qué dijeron? Complete the following conversation between two cousins with past forms of verbs of saying (**decir, insistir, repetir, responder**) and the necessary indirect object pronouns.

Ana Luisa: Mi mamá _____   _____
dos veces: "No debes gastar tanto en regalos este año".

Carmencita: Y a Luis _____   _____:
"Si quieres, puedes usar mi tarjeta de crédito".

Ana Luisa: Claro, por eso nosotras _____

_____ a ella: "Luis puede usar tu tarjeta,
pero nosotras no. Eso no es justo".

Carmencita: De nada sirvió, porque ella _____

_____: "Chicas, no deben gastar tanto
este año".

D. Fue imposible. Complete the following with a description of two things that you or other people **did not** or **could not do** when indicated. Use indirect object pronouns if necessary.

1. Como llovió el día de la boda, nadie _____

_____.

2. ¡Qué barbaridad! En la fiesta, mi sobrino preferido no _____

_____ .

3. El vendedor peleó conmigo. No _____

_____ .

4. Como mis padres se enojaron, yo no _____

_____ .

5. Mi amigo no me dijo su cumpleaños, por eso no _____

_____ .

E. Buen editor. Choose the correct word to complete the following so that
1) the paragraph makes sense; **2)** subjects, pronouns, and verb forms agree;
and **3)** indirect pronouns are accompanied by phrases like **a mí/ a todos/ a
ellos**.

Mario lee **1.** (tanto/ cuánto/ tan) bien porque su tía Isabel **2.** (se/ le/ de)
enseñó a leer cuando **3.** (cumplió/ cumpleaños/ tuviste) cuatro años.
4. (A todos/ A dos/ A los) siempre nos obligaron a leer mucho en casa,
porque mi tía **5.** (pudo/ influyó/ supo) con sus ideas en la familia: ¡la
televisión es **6.** (el peor/ la peor/ el mejor) cosa para los niños porque mata
la imaginación! Es claro que la pobre tía se equivocó, porque los sicólogos
ya **7.** (demostraron/ dices/ comparten) que la tele, los juguetes y las
computadoras son muy **8.** (buenas/ bien/ caro) para la capacidad
intelectual de la gente en los últimos 30 años porque **9.** (me/ se/ nos)
hacen practicar estrategias visuales y espaciales que son **10.** (mucho/
tantas/ muy) importantes para aprender más información en el mundo
moderno.

II EXPRESIÓN ORAL

With a partner, prepare possible questions and answers for three situations you
may be in. Your instructor will rate your performance and that of your partner
in one of the situations. Use the vocabulary, comparative structures, and
preterit verbs learned in this unit. Do not forget to use indirect pronouns with
verbs of saying or verbs that imply a receiver. Also, use phrases such as **a
mí . . . / a nosotros(as) . . .** with these verbs.

1. You would like to give an interesting object to a young couple as a
wedding present. Describe the object to the salesperson (your
partner) without giving its name, by comparing it to other objects or
indicating its uses or main characteristics. The salesperson tries to

find it in the "store" and proposes alternative gifts. Be creative and original. Use the following questions to guide your description: **¿para qué sirve?, ¿cómo es?, ¿de qué es?, ¿cuánto cuesta (vale), más o menos?, ¿en qué departamento está?, ¿quién lo usa?**

2. You and your partner have to try to convince another group to vote for a certain candidate for office. Describe the candidate by contrasting him or her to other people you know and emphasizing his or her personal characteristics and abilities. Describe how well the candidate can perform certain functions as compared to other people. Use the following questions to guide your description: **¿cómo es?, ¿qué hace extraordinariamente bien?, ¿qué cosas hace mejor que los otros?, ¿qué cosas le interesan?, ¿por qué la gente debe votar por él (ella)?**

3. You and your partner are a child and a parent. The child is trying to convince the parent to relax the rules around the house. Argue that such rules don't exist or are laxer in other homes and propose a wider variety of family activities to improve quality time. The parent insists that strict discipline is the best way of bringing up children but may be willing to compromise on some things.

EXPRESIÓN ESCRITA

Choose one of the following and develop in Spanish.

1. Explica qué es la dedicación cualitativa en la familia. Dales consejos a los padres profesionales jóvenes sobre cómo aumentar el tiempo cualitativo con actividades originales y creativas. Dales ejemplos de actividades.

2. Describe a dos o tres familiares o amigos, según los roles que tienen en tu círculo familiar. Explica qué obligaciones tiene cada uno de ellos y también indica por qué son tan importantes para tu familia.

3. Escribe una narración de algo importante, divertido o extraordinario que ocurrió en tu familia cuando niño(a). Explica bien por qué este episodio tiene tanta importancia en tu vida ahora.

Autoevaluación
Unidad 4

En la Unidad 4, aprendiste a hablar del pasado y a contar lo que pasó, haciendo preguntas sobre...

casas y cosas y tu niñez	**era, estaba, había, tenía**	**¿Cómo era** tu casa?
personas o cosas ya mencionadas	pronombres **lo, la, los, las**	¿Y **cuándo la** vendieron?
deseos, planes, habilidades y tareas de antes	el tiempo imperfecto	**¿Qué querían** ser/ hacer?
la rutina diaria y las actividades de antes	el tiempo imperfecto	**¿A qué escuela ibas**?
contar una historia con descripción del ambiente	el tiempo imperfecto	¿Y **hacía frío** allí?
y con narración de lo que ocurrió	el tiempo pretérito	¿Y **por qué** se mudaron?
dar fechas y precios	números de 100 (**cien**) a 1.000.000 (**un millón**)	**¿En qué año** naciste? **¿Cuánto costó** la casa?

También aprendiste a...

indicar el cambio entre descripción y narración	**de repente/ pronto**	¿Y cómo supo de ti?
	cuando..., **al** + infinitivo	¿Cuándo llegaron?
a organizar la narración en secuencias de acciones y eventos	**en seguida, luego, después, por fin, por último**	¿Y **qué hiciste** después? ¿Y qué pasó por fin?

Ahora sabes más de...

algunas casas y cosas del mundo hispano

cómo hablan algunos jóvenes hispanos

P R U E B A

Las siguientes actividades te servirán para organizarte e integrar lo que has aprendido en la Unidad 4. Las actividades ponen a prueba tus conocimientos y tu uso de estrategias, pero no representan exactamente el énfasis elegido o la dirección seguida por tu programa o por tu profesor(a).

Suggestions for use: Students may complete sections of this self test gradually in preparation for Unit test. If done as homework, encourage them to try not to use books or notes so that they can better diagnose their needs. In class, have students compare their responses in groups of three to four to see how they can improve their own performance and expand their response options.

I CULTURA

Elige dos de las siguientes preguntas y, en inglés, prepara una explicación para una persona que no sabe nada de las diferencias culturales. Trata de explicar las cosas de manera que no produzcas una reacción negativa en la persona que te escucha. Es importante darle la idea de que debe respetar y tratar de entender a las gentes del mundo.

1. "Why would all Spanish-speaking countries have different currency? I am sure they all use **pesetas**."

2. "Why don't all Spanish-speaking people get together and agree on one set of words? There's absolutely no way I can learn so many different words for the same thing in different Hispanic countries."

3. "I learned a slang word from Costa Rica but when I used it with a friend of mine from Spain, he didn't know what I was talking about."

4. "Of course, our homes are so much more comfortable. Those cities and streets looked so crowded to me. I don't think they like to have a nice lawn in the front yard."

5. "In Spanish-speaking countries they have separate schools for boys and girls because they want to prevent them from developing relationships and getting married too young."

II VOCABULARIO Y LECTURA

A. Encuesta de viviendas estudiantiles. Después de asistir a un programa de español intensivo en una famosa universidad, te piden que llenes el siguiente cuestionario. Contesta las preguntas en español y no te olvides de dar tus datos personales según el estilo hispano para escribir nombres y direcciones. Agrega todos los comentarios que puedas para usar bien el vocabulario que aprendiste en esta unidad. Si estudias en una universidad extranjera, te van a pedir que llenes una encuesta similar.

ENCUESTA DE VIVIENDAS ESTUDIANTILES

Departamento de Bienestar Estudiantil

I. DATOS PERSONALES

Nombre: _____
                Nombre de pila   *apellido paterno*   *apellido materno*

Edad: _____   Sexo: _____

Estado civil: S C D   Ocupación: _____

Si es casado(a), indicar si el (la) esposo(a) vive en el área   ❏ sí   ❏ no

número de hijos(as) _____

Año de estudios: ❏ primer año   ❏ segundo año   ❏ tercer año
                         ❏ cuarto año   ❏ quinto o más

Lugar de trabajo: ❏ en la universidad   ❏ en el área universitaria   ❏ otras áreas

Domicilio: _____
             calle nº piso código postal

_____
            ciudad   *estado*   *país*

Teléf. en la universidad: _____

Teléf. en casa: _____

Días y horas en que podemos llamarlo(la): _____

Tipo de residencia: _____

¿Cuántos trimestres/ semestres lleva en su habitación/ apartamento/ casa? _____

¿Cuántas veces se mudó desde que empezó sus estudios aquí y por qué (más cómodo,

más barato, más cerca,etc.)? _____

II. PREFERENCIAS DE VIVIENDA

Favor de indicar, específicamente...

Vivienda que quería conseguir: _____

Vivienda asignada por la universidad o que consiguió en el área: _____

_____

Número y/o tipo de habitaciones que deseaba: _____

Número y/o tipo de habitaciones que consiguió: _____

Número de personas con quien pensaba vivir y por qué: _____

_____

Número de personas con quien vive: ____ ❑ en el mismo apartamento/casa

____ ❑ en el mismo cuarto

Número de personas que comparten las distintas habitaciones y servicios (por ejemplo, comparto el baño con tres personas y la lavandería, con quince personas):

_____

Tipo de servicios que pidió (conexión de TV de satélite, estacionamiento, correo

electrónico): _____

Tipo de servicios que obtuvo en realidad: _____

_____

_____

III. CAMBIOS QUE DESEA HACER   (DAR REPUESTAS ESPECIFICAS, POR FAVOR)

Areas, lugares específicos que le interesan: _____

_____

Por qué? _____

Servicios que quiere tener: _____

Aspectos que desea mejorar (por ejemplo, seguridad personal, servicios de limpieza, menos

ruido) _____

¿Qué deseaba encontrar en su residencia presente, pero no fue así (un estar más grande,

conexiones para computadoras, una cafetería cerca)?_____

_____

_____

¿Qué actividades de grupo le gustan ahora? _____

_____

¿Qué actividades de grupo le gustaban antes? _____

_____

B. Para ayudar a un novato. Imagínate que tienes que ayudar a un alumno hispano que acaba de llegar y que necesita comprar algunas cosas para su apartamento. Completa lo siguiente con los precios aproximados de los siguientes artículos, nuevos o usados.

1. un futón o una cama, una mesa y dos sillas _____

_____.

2. un escritorio especial para la computadora y la impresora

_____.

3. un coche (carro) viejo pero bien mantenido _____

_____.

4. platos, tostadora, utensilios de cocina nuevos

_____.

5. un viaje rebajado a Disney World _____

_____.

6. una computadora _____

_____.

C. Buenos amigos. Haz una lista de 8–10 quehaceres de la casa. Luego, piensa en tres amigos(as) y sus características personales. Según la personalidad y las preferencias de cada persona, asígnales tres o cuatro tareas a cada uno(a).

1. Como mi amiga _____ es _____, ella

puede _____, _____,

_____ y _____.

2. Como mi amigo _____ es _____, él

puede _____, _____,

_____ y _____.

3. A mi amigo(a) _____ que es _____, le

corresponde _____, _____,

_____ y _____.

D. Lectura. Usa las estrategias y el vocabulario de esta unidad para leer el siguiente fragmento. En seguida, completa las frases para anotar las cosas más importantes sobre cada niño.

CÓMO PREDECIR EL FUTURO DE LOS NIÑOS

Con todos los avances recientes en la neurología y la psicología, los científicos tratan desesperadamente de descubrir los factores que determinan los valores, las capacidades y las habilidades de los niños del mañana. Quizás, si usan más el sentido común, también pueden aprender muchísimas cosas útiles de los valores e intereses de Mafalda y Susanita, Manolito y Felipe, los niños de Buenos Aires creados por el humorista argentino, Quino. En los años 60 y 70, estos chicos eran un reflejo de su sociedad. A Mafalda le preocupaban el destino del planeta Tierra, la liberación de los oprimidos (*oppressed*) y de las mujeres y, más que jugar o ayudar en la casa, le gustaba pensar y tratar de mostrarles a sus padres lo mal que vivían, constreñidos (*constrained*) por los prejuicios y la vanidad. Por el contrario, Susanita creció deseando casarse, tener muchos hijitos y llevar la casa para la familia. Nunca se interesó ni entendió una palabra de lo que le decía Mafalda, que era una intelectual y vivía analizando las cosas.

Manolito y Felipe siguieron caminos muy distintos. Manolito trabajó muy duro, con la energía que sólo tienen los inmigrantes, para aprender a llevar la tienda de alimentos de su papá. En la escuela, era incapaz de aprender nada, sin embargo, y en él podemos ver al astuto comerciante que depende más de sus estrategias que de sus capacidades. Felipe, por último, fue el retrato más sincero de un niño común y corriente, que prefiere la calle, las cometas y el fútbol a la escuela, las manos limpias, los planes para el futuro y los análisis filosóficos.

Quino, el creador de estos chicos inolvidables, dijo que, un tiempo después que terminó la tira cómica, Mafalda probablemente murió muy joven, dando su opinión en alta voz y luchando temerariamente por sus ideales. Por el contrario, Susanita probablemente vive ahora en una casona muy grande rodeada de sus nietos y nietas. ¿Y qué serán Manolito y Felipe?

1. Estos chicos son muy especiales porque _____

_____ .

2. Puedo imaginarme un día típico de Felipe, cuando era chico y se escapaba de clases. Primero, salía _____

_____ .

3. Mafalda ni jugaba a la mamá ni se trepó a ningún árbol porque

_____ .

4. A Susanita la hacía feliz jugar _____

_____ .

5. Creo que, a los 40 años, Manolito ya _____

_____ .

6. El chico que más me gusta es _____ porque _____

_____ .

III GRAMÁTICA

A. Precisión. Usa formas del imperfecto o del pretérito de los siguientes verbos para completar el párrafo.

| haber | saber | ser | estar | ir a | conocer | poder |

Una vez, _____ **(1)** las doce de la noche y yo

_____ **(2)** en mi habitación, haciendo una tarea de ciencias

sociales; mis padres no _____ **(3)** en casa, porque

_____ **(4)** una cena de la compañía de mi papá. De

repente, por pura intuición _____ **(5)** que una persona me

miraba. Sin embargo, yo no _____ **(6)** ver a nadie en mi

habitación. Mis dos hermanos menores dormían en otro dormitorio.

Después de media hora, otra vez supe que alguien me miraba, pero no

_____ **(7)** hacer ruido para no despertar a los niños.

Cuando ya _____ **(8)** acostarme, después de terminar mi

tarea, sentí la mirada otra vez. Entonces, llamé por teléfono a una señora que _____ (9) muy bien, porque _____ (10)

amiga de mi mamá. Ella vino a mi casa rápidamente y, cuando llegó, vio

que mis dos hermanitos estaban en el jardín, trepando a los árboles y

jugando. ¡Ellos _____ (11) los que me miraban por la

ventana y me tuvieron con tanto miedo!

B. La vida era más fácil. Contesta las siguientes preguntas sobre tu niñez.

1. ¿Qué profesor/a recuerdas mejor? ¿Por qué?

_____

2. ¿Qué cosa querías cuando tenías diez años?

_____

3. ¿Qué excursiones te gustaban más?

_____

4. ¿Qué hacías para no hacer nada en casa?

_____

C. A travieso, travieso y medio. A veces tus compañeros(as) no entienden de inmediato. Prepara dos versiones de cada pregunta que sigue para conversar con ellos(as) sobre travesuras infantiles.

Por ejemplo: ¿aspirar juguetes con la aspiradora? → Cuando eras chico, ¿aspirabas las muñequitas de tu hermana con la aspiradora? Yo le aspiraba las muñequitas a mi hermana, ¿y tú?

1. ¿pintar las paredes del salón con tus creyones?

_____

_____

2. ¿dormir con tus hermanos en el mismo cuarto?

_____

_____

3. ¿tener una bicicleta roja?

_____

_____

4. ¿recibir muchos regalos de tus parientes?

_____

_____

5. ¿jugar a la guerra de las galaxias?

_____

_____

6. ¿vender limonada en la calle?

_____

_____

7. ¿tirar piedras al río/ lago?

_____

_____

8. ¿vivir cerca del centro de la ciudad?

_____

_____

D. ¡Qué diferentes éramos! Completa las siguientes frases sobre tus amigos(as) y sobre tu propia persona (*yourself*). Escribe los nombres de tus compañeros(as) —o familiares— en los espacios dados.

1. Mi amiga _____ no pudo ir de vacaciones porque

_____.

2. Mi amigo _____ fue a esquiar, no a la Florida, porque

_____.

3. _____ soy bastante _____ pero,

cuando era chico, _____

Visión y voz 2E Workbook © 1998 John Wiley & Sons

4. Cuando _____ años, siempre _____

la casa, pero ahora _____.

5. Mi amiga _____ no _____ muy

simpática. Una vez, nos _____.

E. Buen editor. Elige la palabra correcta para completar esta historia. Fíjate que **1)** la historia sea lógica, **2)** las formas del pasado correspondan a las partes descriptivas (imperfecto) o narrativas (pretérito) de la historia, según aprendiste en esta unidad, y **3)** los pronombres de objeto directo concuerden (*agree*) en género (*gender*) y número con sus correspondientes sustantivos.

Como nació en una ciudad bastante grande, Miguelito (**1.** aprendía/ aprendió/ aprende) desde que (**2.** fue/ era/ tiene) muy chico a tomar el autobús en la esquina de su casa para ir al pre-kinder. (**3.** De repente/ A menudo/ Frecuente), cuando (**4.** lo/ las/ la) tomaba para ir a su escuela, ni su mamá ni su hermano (**5.** mejor/ mayor/ más) podían acompañarlo a la parada del autobús. Por eso, una vez nadie (**6.** le/ lo/ se) vio cuando tomó el autobús que iba al circo y no el que (**7.** vas/ fue/ iba) a su escuela. Después, por la tarde, Miguelito (**8.** dijo/ dio/ doy) que no tenía ninguna tarea ese día. Su mamá le preguntó, —Pero, ¿cómo que no tienes tarea? ¿Dónde (**9.** estabas/ es/ estuviste) todo el día, Miguelito? Y él respondió, muy tranquilo: —En el circo. Así (**10.** sabía/ era/ supieron) que Miguelito ya podía leer los letreros (anuncios) del autobús.

IV EXPRESIÓN ORAL

Prepara por lo menos cinco preguntas y respuestas sobre una de las siguientes situaciones. En seguida, úsalas para conversar con tu compañero(a).

1. A phone call to someone selling an article you would like to purchase at a reduced price.

2. An apartment-hunting interview with a landlord.

3. An attempt at helping a married, Spanish-speaking student find affordable living quarters.

V EXPRESIÓN ESCRITA

Elige uno de los siguientes temas y escribe sobre él en español.

1. Write a full description of your or another person's hobbies, collections and interests as a child. List all the activities you remember as a guide in describing what was involved in cultivating the interest or keeping a collection of things. Once you have a good description of activities in the past, weave them together with contrasts with the present to make your description more interesting.

2. Prepare a description of your goals by using a description of activities and experiences of the past that serve as background for your present goals and interests. Include as much detail as possible so you can show how these activities and experiences prepared you for what you are or want to be now.

Por ejemplo: Para mí, la cosa más interesante del mundo es la biología y por eso quiero trabajar en un laboratorio de... para aprender más sobre las estructuras de...

Cuando era chico, siempre iba a explorar... y coleccionaba... Me gustaba estudiar las antenas de los insectos y construí un... para ellos. Un tiempo después, mis padres me regalaron un... y entonces pude ver... Como Ud. puede ver, hace muchos años que soy biólogo. Como profesional, espero estudiar... y trabajar en...

Autoevaluación
Unidad 5

En la Unidad 5, aumentaste tu capacidad de contar cosas de antes.
Aprendiste a dar más detalles del pasado, haciendo resúmenes y
expresando dudas o deseos sobre lo que haya pasado. También
aprendiste a usar pronombres para evitar la repetición y a hacer
preguntas sobre las preferencias de la gente con respecto a...

la comida y su preparación	**Está... crudo, cocido, asado, frito**	**¿Cómo está** tu bistec?
	medidas y porciones	**¿Cuántas cucharadas** son?
cómo poner la mesa	utensilios y envases	¿Me trae un tenedor, por favor?
expresar las gracias y pena	**Gracias por haber** . . . + participio pasado	¿Le diste las gracias por haber traído el pastel?
	Siento (no) haber...	¿Sientes no haberle dado las gracias?
gente y cosas ya mencionadas	pronombres directos y indirectos: **me lo(la), te lo(la), se lo(la)**	**¿Se los** han cortado ya?
		¿No **me lo** has servido todavía?
hacer un resumen del pasado	el tiempo presente perfecto	**¿Ya has comido?**
indicar frecuencia de los eventos	**ya, todavía no, alguna vez, muchas veces**	¿No han servido la paella **todavía**?
expresar dudo o deseo acerca delo que haya pasado	el presente perfecto del subjuntivo: **haya** + participio pasado	¿Crees que **las hayan hervido**?
		¿Crees que **te las haya asado**?

También aprendiste...

cómo es y cómo varía la comida del mundo hispano	**pan, tortillas o arepas; vino, cerveza o chicha**
algunos platos, ingredientes y bebidas **ajo,** del mundo hispano	**papas a la huancaína, cebiche, sopa de** **trucha a la navarra, tortilla a la española**

Visión y voz 2E Workbook © 1998 John Wiley & Sons

P R U E B A

Las siguientes actividades te servirán para organizarte e integrar lo que has aprendido en la Unidad 5. Las actividades ponen a prueba tus conocimientos y tu uso de estrategias, pero no representan exactamente el énfasis elegido o la dirección seguida por tu programa o por tu profesor/a.

I CULTURA

Elige dos de los siguientes comentarios y, en inglés, prepara una explicación para una persona que no sabe nada de las diferencias culturales. Trata de explicar las cosas de manera que no produzcas una reacción negativa en la persona que te escucha. Es importante darle la idea de que debe respetar y tratar de entender a las gentes del mundo.

1. "I don't understand why you'd want to go to the market, with all that noise and weird smells, and all those crowds. Don't they have supermarkets?"

2. "There's absolutely no way I can learn so many different words for the same food in different Hispanic countries. I'll just have steak and french fries or a hamburguer."

3. "Sitting and talking after eating is not my idea of a good time. I'm too busy to waste time like that."

4. "They buy herbal remedies in the marketplace? That's not very safe. Don't they have doctors?"

II VOCABULARIO Y LECTURA

A. Encuesta de preferencias alimenticias. Completa la siguiente encuesta sobre preferencias alimenticias. Escribe tus datos personales con nombres, apellidos, direcciones y fechas a la manera hispana. Agrega comentarios cuando puedas y usa muchas palabras y expresiones aprendidas en esta unidad.

ENCUESTA DE VIVIENDAS ESTUDIANTILES

Departamento de Bienestar Estudiantil

I. DATOS PERSONALES

Nombre: _____

          Nombre de pila   *apellido paterno*   *apellido materno*

Edad: _____   Sexo: _____   Estado civil: S   C   D   Ocupación: _____

Año de estudios: ❑ primer año   ❑ tercer año   ❑ quinto o más

                   ❑ segundo año   ❑ cuarto año

Lugar donde come los días que tiene clase:

❑ en la universidad   ❑ en el área universitaria   ❑ otras áreas

Domicilio: _____
calle nº piso código postal   ciudad   estado   país

¿Cuántas veces se ha cambiado de cafetería/ restaurante y por qué
(más rico, más barato, más cerca)?

_____

_____

II. Preferencias alimenticias. Favor de indicar, específicamente...

En un día normal, cantidad de comidas que come en:

_____ el campus   _____ el área   _____ otro lugar

Comida más frecuente durante los días de clase (marque una):

desayuno   almuerzo   merienda o té   cena

Alimentos más frecuentes en una comida típica (dar al menos dos preferencias de cada grupo):

harinas o carbohidratos   _____

verduras   _____

proteínas animales   _____

proteínas vegetales   _____

grasas animales   _____

grasas vegetales   _____

frutas   _____

antojitos   _____

productos lácteos (de la leche)   _____

bebidas carbonatadas   _____

bebidas no-carbonatadas   _____

vino, cerveza o chicha   _____

otras bebidas   _____

Al venir a desayunar, indique qué prefiere que hayamos preparado.

_____

¿Qué elige de desayuno si ofrecemos sándwich de queso caliente, cereal o huevos con jamón?

_____

Al venir a almorzar, indique qué prefiere que hayamos preparado.

_____

¿Qué elige de almuerzo si ofrecemos pizza, sopa de guisantes o pescado frito?

_____

Al venir a cenar, indique qué prefiere que hayamos preparado.

_____

¿Qué elige de cena si ofrecemos cochinillo asado con papas, pescado a la vasca, pollo con vegetales hervidos?

_____

¿Qué elige de merienda/ té si ofrecemos tarta de manzana, pizza, panecillos con mermelada?

III. Relaciones a la hora de comida

En una semana normal, ¿cuántas veces come:

_____ solo(a) _____ acompañado(a) _____ con familiares?

En una comida normal, ¿cuántos minutos está en la mesa, comiendo

_____ solo(a) _____ acompañado(a) _____ con familiares?

En una comida normal, ¿cuántos minutos hace tareas

_____ solo(a) _____ acompañado(a) _____ con familiares?

En una comida normal, ¿cuántos minutos mira la tele

_____ solo(a) _____ acompañado(a) _____ con familiares?

Número de personas con quien vive: _____ en el mismo apartamento/ casa

_____ en el mismo cuarto

IV. Cambios que desea hacer (dar respuestas específicas, por favor)

Cambios que espera que hayan hecho para el próximo año:

_____

Aspectos que desea mejorar (música, selección, menos ruido):

_____

Comida específica (merienda, cena) que desea que haya cambiado para el próximo año:

_____

Alimentos específicos que desea que hayan cambiado para el próximo año:

_____

¿De qué manera (método de preparación, frescura de los ingredientes, porciones más abundantes)?

_____

Platos específicos que desea que hayan cambiado para el próximo año:

_____

¿De qué manera (método de preparación, frescura de los ingredientes, porciones más abundantes)?

_____

¿Cuál es el plato más importante/ rico para Ud. y qué cambios debemos hacer para hacerlo más rico?

_____

B. A precio módico. Completa los siguientes antojitos con el modo de preparación u otro acompañamiento y la bebida o postre de tu preferencia. También da el precio aproximado en tu área.

1. una hamburguesa, papitas _____

_____ .

2. unos pedazos de pollo _____

_____ .

3. un taco de _____

_____ .

4. una papa _____

_____ .

5. sopa de _____

_____ .

6. helado de _____ con _____

_____ .

C. Amigos sabrosos. Completa lo siguiente para identificar un plato muy rico que preparan tres de tus amigos. Indica el modo de preparación y otros detalles importantes.

1. _____ siempre sirve _____,

   _____ y _____.

2. _____ siempre hace _____,

   _____ y _____.

3. _____ siempre nos da _____,

   _____ y _____.

D. Lectura. Usa las estrategias y el vocabulario de esta unidad para leer el siguiente fragmento. En seguida, contesta las preguntas que siguen a la lectura.

CUIDADO CON LAS ADICCIONES ALIMENTICIAS

No comemos con la boca, sino con el cerebro. Absolutamente todo lo que comemos está dictado por la química cerebral, que decide qué tenemos que comer, cuándo, en qué cantidad y a qué velocidad, de acuerdo a un cuidadoso registro llevado por muchos años. Es que la química cerebral de hormonas y otras sustancias neuronales no sólo determina el estado de ánimo de una persona sino que, cuando hay necesidad, también provoca grandes deseos de comer un antojito o tomarse una taza de café para modificar la situación. Además, la mayoría de los productos alimenticios naturales y manufacturados contienen pequeñas cantidades de sustancias que pueden generar sensaciones agradables en el cerebro, muy similares a los efectos de las drogas. El pan, las frutas, el vino, la cerveza, los huevos—todos le mandan un mensaje al cerebro.

Esta mañana, estas peculiares drogas se nos presentaron ya en el desayuno, ocultas en la leche, el café, el té, el azúcar, las tostadas y la mermelada. Más tarde, otras sustancias de la carne y el pescado, la cerveza, los refrescos y el chocolate también le van a decir algo al cerebro. Para cada comida y con cada alimento, el cerebro ha tomado nota y mañana va a recordar las sensaciones agradables de hoy y va a querer repetirlas sin interrupción, mañana y todos los días.

Por ejemplo, si esta mañana Ud. ha consumido azúcar, el cerebro sintetiza serotonina, un neurotransmisor que lo hizo sentirse bien. Si tenía frío y también ha tomado cacao o cocoa, aparecieron otras moléculas, una de las cuales es la molécula del amor, que alegró su espíritu y lo inundó de bienestar, al punto de haberse olvidado de su prueba de cálculo. ¡Y ojalá que no haya tomado cacao con leche y azúcar, porque entonces su pobre cerebro puede volverse loco con estas deliciosas sensaciones de la mañana!

Durante el día, la cafeína, la agradable sensación que deja la grasa en la boca, el placer del azúcar y otras sustancias parecidas van a condicionar nuestro deseo de más sensaciones exquisitas. Gracias a estas series de reacciones químicas, podemos haber formado hábitos alimenticios que no siempre son los mejores. Esperamos que Ud. no haya desarrollado un mal hábito ya.

Información tomada de "¡Atención: alimentos que enganchan!" por Alejandro F. Cora. *Muy interesante*. Año XIII, 8, enero de 1996, págs. 54-56, 58.

1. ¿Por qué se dice que comemos con el cerebro y no con la boca?

_____

2. ¿Por qué, de repente, te pueden dar deseos de comerte un antojito?

_____

3. ¿Por qué no se pueden evitar las "drogas" contenidas en los alimentos?

_____

4. ¿Por qué puedes olvidarte de una prueba importante?

_____

5. ¿Por qué es fácil ponerse adicto a ciertos alimentos o bebidas?

_____

6. ¿A qué alimentos eres adicto(a) tú? ¿Por qué?

_____

III GRAMÁTICA

A. Precisión. Completa lo siguiente con la forma apropiada del tiempo imperfecto, pretérito o presente perfecto, según el contexto. Usa los pronombres cuando necesario.

Una vez, cuando nosotros (**1.** estar) _____ en México, (**2.** ir)

_____ al mercado de Guadalajara para conocerlo. ¡Qué mundo

espectacular de colores, aromas, gente y pregones (**3.** haber) _____

allí! Las vendedoras (**4.** querer) _____ vendernos de todo, desde mangos y naranjas hasta frijoles y garbanzos secos para el invierno.

¡Nunca (**5.** ver) _____ tanta variedad de productos en toda mi vida!

Después de (**6.** haber mirar) _____ por todas partes, (**7.** tener)

_____ hambre y buscamos un pequeño puesto para almorzar.

"Espero que (**8.** haber hecho) _____ sopa de pescado hoy, señora",

le dije a la propietaria del puesto, "porque hace muchos años que no

(**9.** comerla) _____". ¡Qué rica (**10.** estar) _____ la sopa! Mi

hijo (**11.** pedir) _____ chiles rellenos, pero después no

(**12.** quererlos) _____ porque (**13.** estar) _____ picantes.

Entonces, mi marido (**14.** comérselos) _____ y mi hijo (**15.** pedirle)

_____ a la señora unos chiles en nogada. En fin, a las cuatro de la

tarde, regresamos al hotel, cansadísimos pero muy satisfechos, después de

la visita a ese mundo multicolor.

B. Cortesía antes de nada. ¿Qué les puedes contestar a tus amigos(as)
después que te digan lo siguiente?

1. —Dejé el sartén eléctrico conectado

—Espero que no _____.

2. —Me olvidé de comprar pescado para la sopa.

—Espero que _____.

3. —No creo que tenga huevos para la mayonesa.

—No importa, yo he _____.

4. —¡Ay!, creo que he quemado el puré de papas.

—No, no creo que _____.

5. —Mira, te hice mi mejor especialidad peruana.

—Gracias por _____.

6. —No viniste a mi cena mexicana.

—Siento _____.

C. Para averiguarlo todo. Pregúntale a un/a amigo(a) si él o ella ha hecho lo siguiente. Usa el tiempo presente perfecto y la expresión de frecuencia apropiada.

1. ¿descubrir una manera rápida de hacer el almuerzo?

_____

2. ¿traer un dulce o comida hispana a clase?

_____

3. ¿hacer una reservación para un grupo grande?

_____

4. ¿comer muchos platos diferentes este mes?

_____

5. ¿freír papas en tu propia cocina?

_____

6. ¿resolver comer comida más nutritiva?

_____

7. ¿poner un telegrama a un país hispano?

_____

8. ¿romper algo caro de cristal o de porcelana?

_____

D. Buen editor. En cada paréntesis, marca la palabra correcta para que **1**) el fragmento tenga sentido según el contexto general, **2**) las formas de pasado correspondan a descripciones (imperfecto), narraciones (pretérito), resumen (presente perfecto), o deseos o duda acerca de lo que haya pasado (presente perfecto de subjuntivo), y **3**) los pronombres directos e indirectos estén usados en el orden correcto y además concuerden en género y número con los sustantivos que reemplazan.

Cuando el científico francés Louis Pasteur (**1.** fue/ eres/ era) decano de la

Facultad de Ciencias de Lille, un fabricante de alcohol industrial le

(**2.** contó/ contaba/ contaron) que, en algunos de sus barriles, el jugo de

remolacha azucarera (*sugar beet*) no se convertía en alcohol sino en vinagre. Pasteur estudió los microorganismos del líquido, supo inmediatamente lo que pasaba y (**3.** lo/ se/ le) dijo al fabricante: "No creo que Uds. (**4.** han limpiado/ limpió/ hayan limpiado) muy bien todos los barriles, porque tienen microbios que pueden multiplicarse y arruinar todo el jugo. Es necesario (**5.** hierva/ hiervo/ hervirlo) a 60°C para evitar que se convierta en vinagre". Así (**6.** inventaba/ inventó/ haya inventado) Pasteur el proceso de la pasteurización. Ahora la tecnología de los alimentos (**7.** avanzó/ avanzan/ ha avanzado) muchísimo y tenemos al menos tres procesos distintos: hervir la leche a 60°C por 30 minutos para que dure de dos a tres días o (**8.** hervirla/ hervírsela/ haber hervido) a 70°C por 15 segundos para que dure de cuatro a cinco días o (**9.** pasteurizárselo/ pasteurizarla/ pasteurización) a una temperatura muy alta de 150°C por sólo 1 segundo. Este último método se llama uperización o UHT y, con él, la leche dura de cuatro a cinco meses. En Estados Unidos, existe la leche (**10.** uperización/ uperizada/ uperizado) pero no es tan popular como en el mundo hispánico; la gente prefiere (**11.** comprarle/ comprárselo/ comprársela) pasteurizada y homogeneizada porque así dura una semana en la refrigeradora, más o menos.

II EXPRESIÓN ORAL

Prepara siete posibles preguntas y respuestas para una de las siguientes situaciones. Luego, usa las preguntas para conversar con tu compañero(a).

- Una conversación con un vendedor en el mercado de una ciudad hispana.

- Una entrevista de trabajo en un prestigioso restaurante hispana. Quieres ser chef del restaurante.

- Un programa de TV en el campus: entrevista a un/a alumno(a) universitario(a) para descubrir sus preferencias alimenticias.

I EXPRESIÓN ESCRITA

Elige uno de los siguientes temas y desarróllalo en español.

- Escribe una descripción completa de un plato o un menú que te guste muchísimo. Incluye detalles sobre la preparación, la presentación, otras comidas que se pueden servir con él y las bebidas o el pan o acompañamiento que se sirven con tu plato preferido. Incluye la receta y cualquier otra cosa que ayude a prepararlo a la perfección y también menciona las ocasiones en que se sirve tradicionalmente.

- Escríbele una carta a alguien para agradecerle un favor muy especial que te haya hecho o una oportunidad muy buena que te haya dado. Explica bien por qué era tan importante el favor o la oportunidad para ti y cómo esto te hizo cambiar de perspectiva o de opinión. Da muchísimos detalles para indicarle a esta persona lo importante que fue la experiencia para ti.

Autoevaluación
Unidad 6

En la Unidad 6, aumentaste tu capacidad para hablar de tus cosas. Aprendiste a dar detalles sobre la ropa y los complementos, a explicar qué es lo que buscas en la tienda y a expresar tus deseos de que otros hagan algo con un fin específico. También aprendiste a hacer preguntas sobre las preferencias de la gente con respecto a...

la ropa	**Está... gastado, suelto, a la moda**	**¿Está planchada** tu camisa azul?
	Es... de algodón, lino, poliéster	**¿De qué** es la chaqueta?
blusa?	repaso de **ser** y **estar**	¿Por qué **está manchada** la
	ponerse, probarse, llevar+prenda	¿Qué **me puedo poner** hoy?
indicar cosas específicas	adjetivos demostrativos **este(a)**, **ese(a), aquel(la)**	¿De qué talla es **aquella blusa** verde?
quejarte de la ropa	**estar** + adjetivo	¿Qué tiene la prenda? **¿Está rota**?
devolver la ropa	**me queda** + adjetivo	Es su talla; **¿por qué le queda corta**?
pedir que otros hagan algo	**querer** + presente de subjuntivo	¿Qué **quieres que te devuelva**?
indicar el objetivo de tus acciones falda.	**para que** + presente del subjuntivo	**¿Para qué lo llevaste** al taller? **Para que lo transformen** en
describir lo que buscas	**busco** + prenda + presente del subjuntivo	¿Tiene **una bolsa que haga** juego?
y lo que no encuentras	**no hay nada/ nadie que** + subjuntivo	¿Hay **alguien que pueda** teñirlo?

También aprendiste sobre...

la gracia latina y la ropa apropiada en el mundo hispano	**elegante; está de moda/ está pasado de moda**; se necesita señorita **de buena presencia**
qué se hace con la ropa vieja en el mundo hispano	**Ojalá me la puedan teñir, cortar, reparar.**
cómo se compra la ropa en el mundo hispano	Quisiera un traje **que tenga** varios bolsillos.

P R U E B A

Las siguentes actividades te servirán para organizarte e integrar lo que has aprendido en la Unidad 6. Las actividades ponen a prueba tus conocimientos y tu uso de estrategias, pero no representan exactamente el énfasis o la dirección seguida por tu programa o por tu profesor/a.

I CULTURA

Elige dos de los siguientes comentarios y, en inglés, prepara una explicación para una persona que no sabe nada de las diferencias culturales. Trata de explicar las cosas de manera que no produzcas una reacción negativa en la persona que te escucha. Es importante darle la idea de que debe respetar y tratar de entender a las gentes del mundo.

1. "I wonder why Hispanics pay so much attention to clothes. It would have never occurred to me that different kinds of jackets or suits would impact on your perception of a person."

2. "There's absolutely no way I can learn all these different words for the same clothes in different Hispanic countries. After all, the only words I need are *jeans* and **camiseta**."

3 "If something is old or out of fashion it gets thrown away in this house. Why would you want to go through all the trouble and expense of "recycling" it? I don't understand Hispanics who do that."

II VOCABULARIO Y LECTRURA

A. Encuesta de preferencias en el vestir. Completa la siguiente encuesta sobre preferencias de ropa y complementos. Escribe tus datos personales con nombres, apellidos, direcciones y fechas a la manera hispana. Agrega comentarios cuando puedas y usa muchas palabras y expresiones aprendidas en esta unidad.

ESCUELA DE DISEÑO DE MODA
y
Gran Tienda "Sangre Joven"

Completa esta encuesta y participe en la rifa (*raffle*) de cinco abrigos de piel finísimos. Devuelva la encuesta en el Centro de Estudiantes de Diseño, donde le vamos a dar su cupón para la rifa.

I. DATOS PERSONALES

Nombre: _____
　　　　　　　Nombre de pila　　　　　*apellido paterno*　　　　　*apellido materno*

Edad: _____　　Sexo: _____　　Estado civil: S　C　D　Ocupación: _____

Visión y voz 2E Workbook © 1998 John Wiley & Sons

Año de estudios: ❏ primer año ❏ tercer año ❏ quinto o más

❏ segundo año ❏ cuarto año

Domicilio: _____

calle nº piso código postal *ciudad* *estado* *país*

Describa su "uniforme" de estudiante. Incluya los complementos y el calzado y las telas, por favor.

_____

_____

Describa su "uniforme" de hacer ejercicio. Incluya los complementos, los zapatos y las telas, por favor.

_____

Describa su "camisa de Margarita", por favor. ¿Por qué la considera su "camisa de Margarita"?

_____

_____

II. GUSTOS EN EL VESTIR. Favor de indicar, específicamente...

Cuántas veces se cambia de ropa al día: _____ El cambio es

❏ de formal a casual ❏ de casual a formal

¿Por qué se cambia? ❏ para estar más cómodo ❏ para ir a trabajar

❏ para hacer ejercicio o correr

Si anda con su "uniforme" y decide ir al cine, ¿qué se cambia? _____

Si anda con su "uniforme" y va a cenar con su pareja en el campus, ¿qué se cambia?

_____

En un día de semana, si va a almorzar o cenar fuera del campus, ¿qué se pone?

❏ mejor camisa ❏ mejores jeans ❏ mejores zapatos ❏ un complemento

❏ traje ❏ vestido ❏ falda y blusa ❏ joyas

En el fin de semana, si va a almorzar o cenar fuera del campus, ¿qué se pone?

❏ mejor camisa ❏ mejores pantalones ❏ mejores zapatos

❏ un complemento ❏ traje ❏ vestido

❏ falda y blusa ❏ joyas

Describa la ropa que le queda mejor que ninguna.

_____

Describa la tenida de salir que le queda mejor que ninguna.

_____

Visión y voz 2E Workbook © 1998 John Wiley & Sons

Mire su guardarropa e indique qué tela y qué materiales prefiere.

_____

Dé al menos una preferencia de marca o de almacén cuando compra los siguientes artículos:

calzado: _____   zapatillas deportivas: _____

blue jeans: _____   ropa de diario: _____

camisetas: _____   cinturones, bolsas: _____

camisas: _____   blusas: _____

ropa de salir: _____   chaquetas deportivas: _____

III. VALORES.   Indique qué ropa o complementos le prestan sus amigos y cuándo.

1. _____ siempre me presta _____

   para ir a _____ .

2. _____ siempre me presta _____

   para ir a _____ .

Dé el nombre de la prenda y las características (telas, materiales) de los artículos de vestir más caros que posea.

joyas _____

vestido _____

chaquetas _____

zapatos _____

ropa de esquí _____

complementos _____

B. Asociaciones.   Da al menos dos términos asociados con los siguientes o escribe varias frases en que uses las siguientes palabras. Usa otra hoja de papel.

1. inarrugable	**5.** mangas	**9.** cuero	**13.** tiene que probarse
2. cremallera	**6.** satinado	**10.** morado	**14.** se ve bien
3. taller	**7.** mojada	**11.** mucho frío	**15.** siempre llevo...
4. pana	**8.** finísimo	**12.** gorra	**16.** tirar o regalar

C. Guardarropas. Usa otra hoja de papel para describir tres prendas de tres de los siguientes guardarropas.

1. de una señora millonaria

2. de un artista pobre del Canadá

3. de una astronauta

4. del presidente de los EE. UU.

5. de la hijita de una artista de cine

6. de un jugador de fútbol o béisbol que conoces

D. Por favor, basta. Haz una lista de cinco o seis prendas y artículos de vestir que no te gustan o de los cuales tienes suficientes ya. Luego, escribe un párrafo en que explicas qué no quieres comprar ni recibir de regalo.

Por ejemplo: Espero que para mi cumpleaños nadie me dé... porque...
Además,...

E. Lectura. Usa las estrategias y el vocabulario de esta unidad para leer el siguiente fragmento. En seguida, contesta las preguntas que siguen a la lectura.

¿ROPA INTELIGENTE?

¿Ropa inteligente? ¿Por qué no? No es que el algodón, la lana, la seda y otras fibras naturales ya hayan perdido mucho terreno ante las fibras artificiales. Tampoco es que sea mejor el rayón, que es celulosa modificada, que el nilón, que es un producto químico sintético puro. En el futuro, para que una prenda sea cómoda y hermosa, tendrá que ser hecha de telas que literalmente nos hagan sentir cómodos y que se adapten a las condiciones del medio ambiente (*environment*).

Pantalones que repelen insectos, prendas que cambian de color con la temperatura y la luz, camisas que protegen de los rayos ultravioleta, corbatas que detectan energía, sacos a prueba de (...*proof*) agua, fuego y balas, telas que se calientan cuando hace frío, vestidos con memoria que se planchan solos, trajes más resistentes que el acero. La verdad es que en muchos laboratorios del mundo ya ha nacido la ropa del futuro.

Así es que ya lo sabes: si buscas una camiseta que se enfríe con el calor y se caliente con el frío, espera un poco y ya vas a ver en los catálogos algunas «camisetas piltérmicas». Para que puedan mantenerte siempre cómodo, las telas reciben un baño de polietilenglicol, una sustancia que se solidifica a bajas temperaturas y emite calor. Por el contrario, cuando hace mucho calor, el polietilenglicol se evapora.

Otra novedad viene de Australia, donde un científico descubrió una sustancia que protege del sol mejor que lo que pueda protegerte una loción bronceadora. Esta sustancia se pone en las telas para que protejan a los australianos de los fuertes rayos solares del desierto. Pero la fibra que va a cambiar nuestro concepto de tela seguramente será el «relax», una fibra terapéutica que es posible que pueda aliviar desde un dolor de cabeza hasta el dolor muscular. El principio es muy sencillo: en una fibra de poliéster se inserta un filamento sintético de carbono que tenga la propiedad de rechazar la estática que es tan común en las telas sintéticas. Entonces, la tela se carga negativamente y produce una agradable sensación relajante. «Quiero ir a trabajar con mi pijama terapéutico», va a decir la gente en el futuro.

Si no me crees y piensas que son especulaciones futuristas, pregúntale a un astronauta. El ya ha usado prendas piltérmicas y de relax.

Información tomada de: "La ropa inteligente" por Omar R. Goncebat. Conozca más. Edición Chile. Año 5, 9, septiembre de 1994, págs. 52-56

1. ¿De qué trata este artículo, ¿de las telas artificiales o las naturales?

_____

_____

2. ¿Qué ejemplos de prendas de ropa del futuro te parecen más útiles?

_____

_____

3. De las prendas dadas como ejemplo, ¿qué ropa buscas tú?

_____

_____

4. ¿Quiénes han usado ya las telas del futuro? ¿Por qué las necesitan ahora mismo?

_____

_____

5. ¿Qué otro tipo de tela o de prenda no mencionado en el artículo buscas tú?

_____

_____

6. Entonces, según el artículo, ¿qué características tiene una tela o una prenda inteligente?

_____

_____

III GRAMÁTICA

A. Precisión. Usa formas de subjuntivo de los verbos en paréntesis para completar el siguiente párrafo. Acuérdate de usar los pronombres necesarios en el lugar correcto cuando sea necesario.

El caos ha llegado a tal punto en nuestra casa que vamos a tener que tomar

medidas drásticas para aliviar la situación. En primer lugar, es necesario

que nosotros (**1.** sacar) _____ toda la ropa que está

tirada en la lavandería porque está descolorida, vieja o perdida para que

(**2.** organizarse) _____ mejor y (**3.** tener)

_____ más espacio libre. También espero que

Marcelo (**4.** llevar) _____ algunas cajas de ropa de

talla pequeña al Ejército de Salvación. No hay nadie más aquí que

(**5.** saber) _____ dónde está esa institución caritativa.

Es muy posible que (**6.** haber) _____ algún estudiante

bajo y delgado que (**7.** poder) _____ usar la ropa que

ya nos queda chica a nosotros. Además de limpiar la lavandería, hay que

recoger todas las prendas que (**8.** estar) _____ tiradas

en otras habitaciones o que (**9.** deber) _____ llevar a

la tintorería.

B. Cortesía antes de nada. ¿Qué les puedes contestar a tus amigos(as) después que te digan lo siguiente?

1. —Mira mi camisa verde eléctrico; ¿te gusta? —¡Ay! No hay nadie que

_____ .

2. —Me olvidé de planchar este vestido de algodón. —Espero que

_____ .

3. —Parece que no hay tallas más grandes aquí. —Así es; no creo que

_____ .

4. —¡Ay!, creo que he quemado mi corbata de seda.   —No, no creo que

_____ .

5. —No tengo ganas de cortar estos pantalones.   —Córtalos para que

_____ .

6. —¿Por qué no te compras esta pulsera de plástico?   —Es que no

quiero que _____ .

C. Para encontrar lo que quieres. Pregúntale a un vendedor si
tienen los siguientes artículos. Descríbelos usando el subjuntivo.

1. ¿una blusa transparente, satinada y barata?

_____

2. ¿un saco de caballero de terciopelo negro?

_____

3. ¿pantalones con muchos bolsillos y cremalleras?

_____

4. ¿una cartera de caballero de cuero de napa?

_____

5. ¿un impermeable reversible bien terminado?

_____

6. ¿un saco con ojales hechos a mano?

D. Me importa la ropa. Completa estas frases con tus propias ideas.

1. Debes ir a la modista, si quieres que _____

_____ .

2. ¡Qué aroma tan exquisito! No creo que _____ .

_____ .

3. Como es una ceremonia importante, busco un traje que _____

_____ .

4. No creo que mis padres conozcan un diseñador que _____

_____ .

5. Los supervisores van a pedir los uniformes. Espero que no nos

_____ .

E. Buen editor. En cada paréntesis, marca la palabra correcta para que **1)** el fragmento tenga sentido según el contexto general, **2)** las formas de indicativo correspondan a afirmaciones sobre gente, cosas y prendas de ropa, **3)** las formas de presente perfecto de subjuntivo correspondan a negaciones absolutas, referencias al objeto de una acción, expresiones de duda/ deseos de que suceda algo o de lo que tú quieres que haga otra gente, y **4)** los adjetivos demonstrativos sean usados según la distancia relativa.

¡Ay, Dios! No tengo nada que (**1.** ponga/ poner/ ponerme) para que el supervisor que me va a (**2.** entrevistar/ dar/ entreviste) en (**3.** esa/ ese/ aquel) industria textil me (**4.** da/ dé/ doy) el trabajo que necesito tanto. Me han aconsejado que (**5.** lleve/ llevar/ llevo) un traje azul oscuro para (**6.** inspiraba/ inspiró/ inspirar) respeto y que (**7.** debe elegir/ elija/ han elegido) muy bien los complementos para (**8.** esta/ se la está/ esas) reunión para (**9.** verlo/ veo/ verme) bien, elegante y estupenda.   Creo que es mejor que (**10.** me ponga/ ponerme/ de poner) mi traje de crepe de lana negro con una blusa de color gris perla, aretes de perla y mi anillo nuevo.

IV EXPRESIÓN ORAL

Prepara siete posibles preguntas y repuestas para una de las siguientes situaciones. Luego, usa las preguntas para conversar con tu compañero(a).

- Una conversación con un vendedor de una gran tienda. Te interesa saber qué está de moda y qué telas o materiales son las más comunes en este momento.

- Una entrevista de trabajo para un puesto en una gran cadena de distribución de ropa. Te interesa el puesto de sub-gerente de ventas o de *marketing* de la expansión hacia los territorios del *NAFTA*. Es muy importante conocer bien las preferencias de los clientes hispanos.

- Un programa de TV en el que entrevistas a un/a famoso(a) diseñador/a hispano(a) que quiere iniciar una revolución en el mundo de la moda.

EXPRESIÓN ESCRITA

Elige *uno* de las siguientes temas y desarróllalo en español.

- Escribe una descripción completa de un traje o un conjunto para la sección de moda de una revista. Incluye las telas, materiales y complementos y también describe cómo y cuándo se puede llevar esta ropa. Exagera un poquito y di que no hay nada como este conjunto, usando el subjuntivo. Puede ser un conjunto o traje común y corriente o algo extraordinario, nunca visto antes.

- Ecríbele una carta para poder devolver algo que hayas comprado por correo. Incluye una buena explicación o descripción de por qué quieres devolver la prenda. Dale las gracias al encargado por devolverte el dinero.

Autoevaluación
Unidad 7

Metas cumplidas

En la Unidad 7, aumentaste tu capacidad para hablar de la salud y el bienestar. Aprendiste a dar detalles sobre tus dolores y malestares, a explicar qué haces para cuidarte y a expresar tus deseos de que otros hagan algo para llevar una vida más sana. También aprendiste a hacer preguntas sobre la salud de la gente con respecto a...

los dolores y las quejas	**Me duele(n)** + partes del cuerpo	**¿Dónde/Qué te duele?**
	Tengo... + enfermedad, molestia	¿Qué **tienes**? ¿**Tienes** tos/ fiebre?
las alergias	**Soy alérgico(a) a...**	¿A qué eres alérgico?
la salud y el bienestar	**importarle, molestarle, dolerle**	**¿Le molestan** los ojos?
darle consejos a un amigo	órdenes informales y el subjuntivo para expresar órdenes informales negativas	¿No es mejor que **te acuestes y que tomes** mucho líquido?
o a otra persona	el subjuntivo para las órdenes formales	¿Y no le dijo: "**Evite** el frío"?
expresar tus sentimientos y opiniones	**Siento que/ Me alegro que/ Dudo que...** + presente del subjuntivo	¿Y el médico **duda que tenga** cáncer de la piel?

También aprendiste sobre . . .

cómo se comunican los hispanos	los gestos más típicos **"Es muy tacaño."**
cómo es la vida de algunos hispanos ancianos	la tercera edad y la longevidad
qué dicen algunos hispanos de ciertos avances científicos	las medicinas tradicionales y la moderna
qué remedios tradicionales se usan en el mundo hispano	hierbas (**menta, manzanilla**), homeopatía, curas

P R U E B A

Las siguientes actividades te servirán para organizarte e integrar lo que has aprendido en la Unidad 7. Las actividades ponen a prueba tus conocimientos y tu uso de estrategias, pero no representan exactamente el énfasis elegido o la dirección seguida por tu programa o por tu profesor/a.

I CULTURA

Elige dos de los siguientes comentarios y, en inglés, prepara una explicación para una persona que no sabe nada de las diferencias culturales. Trata de explicar las cosas de manera que no produzcas una reacción negativa en la persona que te escucha. Es importane darle la idea de que debe respetar y tratar de entender a las gentes del mundo.

1. "These people are so uneducated and simple. They think some withered, dusty plants can cure diseases that can be really serious if not treated properly".

2. "I think these people drink too much. They are always hanging around bars and no one educates them on the dangers of drunk driving and addiction".

3. "Most Hispanics follow Indian practices when it comes the time to look for treatment".

II VOCABULARIO Y LECTURA

A. Encuesta de necesidades de atención de salud. Completa la siguiente encuesta sobre preferencias alimenticias. Escribe tus datos personales con nombres, apellidos, direcciones y fechas a la manera hispana. Agrega comentarios cuando puedas y usa muchas palabras y expresiones aprendidas en esta unidad.

ESCUELA DE SALUD PÚBLICA

Encuesta sobre las necesidades y prácticas de salud de los universitarios

Por favor, ayude a sus compañeros de Salud Pública que están interesados en mejorar los servicios de atención médica en la universidad. Devuelva la encuesta en el Centro de Estudiantes de Ciencias Médicas, donde le vamos a dar una copia de la Pirámide alimenticia del joven estresado.

I. DATOS PERSONALES

Nombre: _____
          Nombre de pila   *apellido paterno*   *apellido materno*

Edad: _____ Sexo: _____ Estado civil: S C D Ocupación: _____

Año de estudios: ❏ primer año ❏ tercer año ❏ quinto o más

❏ segundo año ❏ cuarto año

Domicilio: _____

calle nº piso código postal   *ciudad*   *estado*   *país*

Desviación de tu reloj interno respecto al reloj oficial: – _____ horas + _____ horas

Efectos de la desviación: ❏ cansancio ❏ insomnio ❏ irritabilidad

❏ sed ❏ hambre ❏ ansiedad

❏ mucha energía cuando otros quieren dormir

❏ exasperación cuando otras personas quieren acostarse

❏ malas notas

II. NECESIDADES DE ATENCIÓN MÉDICA MÁS COMUNES

Generalmente, la gente tiene enfermedades o molestias que tienden a repetirse. Indica qué te duele(n) o molesta(n) más frecuentemente cuando te enfermas.

__ el pecho   __ las piernas y las rodillas   __ la cabeza

__ la cara   __ la garganta   __ el estómago

__ los brazos y los hombros   __ los oídos   __ el abdomen

__ los ojos

Indica cuántas veces al año sufres de lo siguiente:

__ infección intestinal por alimentos contaminados   __ mononucleosis   __ sinusitis

__ bronquitis   __ otras infecciones   __ resfrío común   __ gripe o influenza

__ laringitis   __ congestión

Indica qué tenías cuando fuiste al servicio médico la última vez.

_____

_____

Indica qué tenías cuando estuviste en el hospital la última vez.

_____

_____

Indica qué problema o afección tienes que no puede ser atendido en el servicio de la universidad.

_____

_____

III. INSTALACIONES Y EQUIPOS

Indica tus preferencias en cuanto a instalaciones o equipos que te gustaría tener en la universidad.

Quieres que la universidad tenga en los edificios grandes:

❑ salas de descanso   ❑ salas de ejercicio contra "los dolores de la computadora"

❑ salas de lectura   ❑ salas de recreación

❑ salas con programas interactivos   ❑ sala de terapia y masajes

❑ piscina de ejercicios acuáticos

Indica qué tipo de ejercicio es mejor para ti.

❑ con máquinas   ❑ deportes al aire libre

❑ gimnasia en la piscina   ❑ gimnasia aeróbica

❑ correr o trotar   ❑ otro _____

Indica qué vacunas te gustaría ponerte gratis.

_____

_____

Indica qué remedios te gustaría recibir gratis.

_____

_____

_____

B. ¿Qué pasó?   Lee las siguientes frases con modismos. Luego, escribe **Bien** o **Mal** según cómo resultó cada situación.

1. _____ Estaba contentísimo porque Alina me dijo que me iban a contratar, pero me estaba tomando el pelo.

2. _____ Me compró una torta de naranja porque la vi y se me hizo agua la boca.

3. _____ Ese día me levanté con el pie derecho. No estudié nada pero me saqué una A.

4. _____ No pude regalarle un anillo caro porque valen un ojo de la cara.

5. _____ Es una lástima pero la hermana de mi novia habla hasta por los codos y no pudimos conversar nada.

C. Asociaciones. Da al menos dos términos asociados con los siguientes o escribe varias frases en que uses las siguientes palabras. Usa otra hoja de papel.

1. riñones	**5.** cejas	**9.** cortadura	**13.** ponte más ropa
2. hígado	**6.** muñecas	**10.** yeso	**14.** deja de fumar
3. caries	**7.** orejas	**11** me pica	**15.** no comas tanta grasa
4. fractura	**8.** ataque	**12.** ronchas	**16.** toma manzanilla

D. Botiquín. Da al menos dos remedios para cada una de las siguientes molestias.

1. la garganta inflamada

2. una lastimadura en la rodilla

3. fiebre alta

4. mucha tos y dolor de pecho

5. una infección intestinal

6. alergia a las picaduras de hormiga o abeja

E. Puedo hacer un gesto. Según el contexto, completa las siguientes frases con verbos de acciones como **abrir, cerrar, tapar(se), ponerse, estirarse, arrugarse, mover, apuntar**, etc. Sigue el ejemplo.

Por ejemplo: Espero que no me pregunten nada personal. Si no, es mejor que... cierre bien la boca.

1. Espero que la película no sea de terror. Si no, es mejor que...

_____

2. Espero que la enfermera entienda mi descripción en español. Si no, es mejor que...

_____

3. Espero que mis amigos no estén enfadados conmigo. Si no, es mejor que...

_____

4. Espero que ellos vean que les estoy cerrando un ojo. Si no, es mejor que...

_____

F. Lectura. Usa las estrategias y el vocabulario de esta unidad para leer el siguiente fragmento. En seguida, contesta las preguntas que siguen a la lectura.

Cómo acabar con el dolor:
Confesiones de un joven como tú

Acabar con el dolor. Es lo que quiere toda persona que sufre de dolores artríticos, migrañas o jaquecas o dolores a la columna vertebral. No pueden dormir ni pensar y, a veces, ni caminar ni conducir. Llevan vidas miserables y a menudo tienen también profundas depresiones porque no pueden divertirse ni funcionar normalmente. Yo tengo sólo 22 años y hace seis años que sufro de fuertes dolores de cabeza y de un oído a causa de un accidente deportivo. Nada ni nadie me ha podido curar. Hay médicos que me han dado analgésicos tan fuertes que he dormido dos días seguidos, ¡imagínate! Pero ya me di cuenta que mi dolor no es para píldoras del doctor.

Hay otros remedios que me han hecho sentir mejor. Al menos para dormir más normalmente cuando tengo exámenes finales o alguna obligación importante que cumplir en mi trabajo. Por ejemplo, si tienes un dolor de cabeza que te mata, toma una infusión grande de valeriana, menta, manzanilla y dos cápsulas de "feverfew" (no tengo idea cómo se dice en español; pregúntaselo a un médico hispano). Relájate, tápate los oídos con un algodón, deja de fumar o de beber, no hagas ejercicios violentos y estudia en un lugar tranquilo por unas tres o cuatro horas. Es el mejor remedio. Por lo menos por una noche, porque fíjate que mi dolor siempre vuelve y nunca me deja. Es mi hermano, como dice mi mamá.

Otra cosa es que uno debe aprender a vivir con el dolor. Aislado y encerrado, sin ver a mis amigos, sin caminar por la calle, me siento peor. Hay días en que me duelen el cuello y la garganta también. Mejor, sal y diviértete un poco y olvídate del dolor por unas horas. Sin embargo, ¡cuidado!, no sueñes como soñaba yo al principio, que el dolor se iba a acabar algún día, porque no será así. En vez de eso, ¡alégrate de estar sano (aunque con dolor crónico) y mantente bien. Mira que con la salud no se juega.

1. Este joven da alrededor de diez consejos para vivir con un dolor fuerte. Haz una lista.

_____

_____

_____ .

2. ¿Qué haces tú cuando tienes un dolor muy fuerte?

_____.

3. ¿Qué crees tú? ¿En qué medicina confía más este joven? ¿Por qué?

_____.

4. ¿Por qué nos dice que el dolor es su hermano? ¿Qué molestia o preocupación es hermana tuya?

_____.

5. Dale dos consejos para que se sienta mejor cuando tiene que estudiar. Él se llama Ryan.

_____.

III GRAMÁTICA

A. Precisión. Usa órdenes informales para completar el siguiente párrafo. Recuerda usar los pronombres en el lugar correcto cuando sea necesario.

El contagio de la bronquitis ha llegado a tal punto en este edificio que

vamos a tener que tomar ciertas medidas para aliviar la situación. Ayer le

dije a Allen: «(**1.** Ayudarme) _____ a limpiar los filtros de

la ventilación, porque me parece que hay muchas esporas ahí». Claro, como

no le gusta trabajar, me contestó: «(**2.** Ir) _____ a buscar

al jefe de mantención mejor, no (**3.** hacerlo tú) _____

porque es algo complicado». Art también lo apoyó y me dijo: «(**4.** Mirar)

_____; a nosotros no nos corresponde cambiar los filtros.

(**5.** Llamar) _____ y (**6.** decirle) _____

al propietario que se preocupe de eso.» En ese momento, perdí la paciencia

y les grité: «(**7.** Cerrar) ¡_____ la boca de una buena vez.

(**8.** No exasperarme) _____ más. Si Uds. prefieren toser

todo el día, ¡entonces no hagamos nada! Allen, (**9.** ponerte)

_____ el abrigo y vayamos a la biblioteca a estudiar». Y

Allen me contestó: «Ja, ja; (**10.** no tomarme) _____ el

pelo, por favor. ¿Para qué quiero abrigo si hay 80 grados?» Como estaba

enojado, ni supe qué dije.

B. Chiquita desobediente. Imagínate que hoy tienes un trabajo de
niñera y que la niña que estás cuidando es muy desobediente. ¿Cómo te
contesta cada vez que le das una orden? Sigue el ejemplo.

Por ejemplo: Yo: —¡Tómate la leche ahora mismo! Ella: —¡Tómatela tú!

1. —Mira; ¡tómate el antibiótico ahora mismo!

_____

2. —Cierra la boca para descansar unos minutos.

_____

3. —Quiero que hagas un poco de ejercicio.

_____

4. —¡Ay!, tráeme tu jarabe que me olvidé de dártelo.

_____

5. —Contesta el teléfono. No puedo levantarme.

_____

6. —Anda a hacer tus tareas. No mires más televisión.

_____

C. Para que no te pase eso. Dale dos soluciones a cada una de las
quejas de tus amigos. Usa órdenes informales de los verbos **dejar de, evitar,
tratar de, poner, tener, relajarse, olvidarse de, salir,** etc., para darles tus
consejos.

1. Siempre me duele la cabeza después de programar algo.

_____

_____

2. No hago atletismo porque tengo miedo de lastimarme.

_____

_____

3. Si juego tenis me doblo los tobillos.

_____

_____

4. Estoy gordo porque como muchos helados.

_____

_____

5. La última vez me dio alergia por dormir aquí.

_____

_____

6. No quiero ir al norte porque hay malaria.

_____

_____

D. De veras, lo siento. Escribe frases que expresen tu reacción a lo siguiente. Empieza tus frases con **Siento que...** o **Me alegro que...**, según sea necesario.

1. Me dolió mucho cuando me quemé la mano.

_____

2. Ayer chocamos el auto pero no nos pasó nada.

_____

3. Ya le sacaron el yeso a mi compañero.

_____

4. No tengo qué llevarle a mi amiga que está enferma.

_____

5. Al médico no le importa que no pueda ir a clases.

_____

E. ¡Ay, doctorcito! Completa lo siguiente con lo que le pides al doctor. Usa órdenes formales con verbos como **darme, ponerme, decirme, explicarme, examinarme, recetarme**, etc.

1. Me duele tanto la garganta. Por favor, _____

_____

2. ¡Me muero! ¡Qué dolor de espalda tengo! Por favor,

_____

3. No tengo idea por qué me agarré esta infección. Por favor,

_____

4. No creo que pueda participar en la actividad de mañana. Por favor,

_____

5. Ni me picó una abeja ni estuve al sol pero tengo esta roncha. Por favor,

_____

F. Buen editor. Marca la palabra correcta de manera que **1)** el párrafo tenga sentido; **2)** las órdenes correspondan al tipo de personas con quienes hablamos; y **3)** se use el subjuntivo para los deseos y las órdenes negativas y formales.

Por fin, hasta los fabricantes de cigarrillos dicen que es mejor que la gente (**1.** dejar/ deje/ den) de fumar. Por mucho tiempo, los fabricantes les dicen a sus empleados: «No (**2.** revelan/ reveles/ revelen) lo que hemos descubierto sobre la adicción». Ahora, el anuncio del Cirujano de la Nación les pide a los jóvenes: «¡No (**3.** consuman/ consumir/ consume) tabaco porque es malo para la salud! Y tú, universitario joven, (**4.** se ayuda/ debe ayudar/ ayúdame) a hablarle a los niños de tu comunidad; (**5.** explícales/ me explican/ te explique) que el tabaco produce adicción, para que los chicos no (**6.** adquirir/ adquieran/ le adquieran) el hábito a temprana edad». Además, ya sabemos que cuando el cerebro aprende a (**7.** experimente/ experimentar/ experimentes) placer con ciertas substancias, después no podemos decirle «(**8.** debe sentir/ siéntete/ sentarse) contento con otras cosas también». Así pues, si Ud. es padre de familia o una persona todavía soltera, por favor (**9.** coopera/ cooperen/ coopere) con la campaña contra el tabaquismo infantil. No (**10.** deja/ deje/ dejan) que falsas modas arruinen la vida y la salud de los menores.

‖ EXPRESIÓN ORAL

Prepara siete posibles preguntas y respuestas para una de las siguientes situaciones. Luego, usa las preguntas para conversar con tu compañero(a).

- Una conversación con un profesional de la salud (médico(a), enfermero(a), nutricionista, terapista, experto(a) en salud pública/ de la familia). Te gustaría saber más sobre las bondades de las vitaminas, los minerales, los antioxidantes y otras sustancias buenas para la salud.

- Una encuesta sobre las actitudes de los hispanos hacia la salud. Trata de descubrir cuáles son sus creencias y prácticas más comunes cuando están sanos y cuando están enfermos.

- Un programa de la televisión en el cual entrevistas a distintos jovenes a raíz de una campaña en contra de la drogadicción.

‖ EXPRESIÓN ESCRITA

Elige *uno* de los siguientes temas y desarróllalo en español.

- Escribe una descripción de una serie de ejercicios o de una buena práctica de slaud. Tu descripción va a aparecer en una publicación de la universidad y debe estar dirigida a la gente joven como tú. Piensa en los lectores y dales consejos o datos de cómo adaptar tu sistema para chicos o chicas, estudiantes casados o solteros, más jóvenes o mayores.

- Escríbele una carta a un/a líder estudiantil para que consiga que mejoren la universidad para que todos estudien en un ambiente más sano y más agradable. Dale una descripción completa del programa que te preocupa y luego proponle una o dos soluciones. Dale las gracias por su apoyo a tus ideas, ofrécele tu ayuda y despídete cortésmente de él/ella.

Autoevaluación
Unidad 8

En la Unidad 8, aumentaste tu capacidad para hablar de las ciudades de hoy y de mañana y para contrastar el presente y el futuro. Aprendiste a describir los ambientes urbanos, a pedir y dar instrucciones para ir a distintos lugares, a explicar qué podrías hacer para cuidar la naturaleza y el equilibrio ecológico en el próximo siglo y a proponer soluciones para los problemas del mundo. También aprendiste a hacer preguntas sobre el futuro, el ambiente, las ciudades y su gente en general con respecto a...

lo que hay ahora	**Actualmente hay...,.** + partes de la ciudad	¿**Qué hay** en ese edificio?
lo que está pasando ahora	**Están/ Paso/ Ando/ Sigo** + participio presente	¿Qué **andas buscando**?
dar y pedir instrucciones	**Siga/ Doble/ Manténgase + a la derecha/ izquierda**	¿**A cuántas cuadras está**?
lo que habrá después	**En el próximo siglo habrá...** + nuevas cosas	¿Qué **habrá** ahí después?
lo que pasará después	**En el año 2000/ el próximo año...** + futuro	¿Cómo **viajaremos** después?
lo que puede pasar	**Cuando/ Hasta que...** + subjuntivo	¿Qué harás **cuando termines**?
lo que tú deseas que pasara	**Ojalá** + imperfecto del subjuntivo	Ojalá **no contaminaran** tanto.
lo que podría pasar si algo sucediera	**Si** + imperfecto del subjuntivo	**Si aumentaran**, ¿qué harías?

También aprendiste sobre...

cómo son algunas ciudades hispanas	**"Eres grande como aquel inmenso mar"**.
cómo es la vida de algunos hispanos de las ciudades	Los ciclistas somos parias y eso que no contaminamos.
qué retos ecológicos enfrentan los países hispanos	**¡Ojalá pudiéramos** proteger mejor nuestros bosques!
qué visiones del futuro tienen en el mundo hispano	¿Qué clase de mundo vamos a legarles a nuestros hijos? Si seguimos destruyendo la capa de ozono...

Visión y voz 2E Workbook © 1998 John Wiley & Sons

P R U E B A

Las siguientes actividades te servirán para organizarte e integrar lo que has aprendido en la Unidad 8. Las actividades ponen a prueba tus conocimientos y tu uso de estrategias, pero no representan exactamente el énfasis elegido o la dirección seguida por tu programa o por tu profesor/a.

I CULTURA

Elige dos de los siguientes comentarios y, en inglés, prepara una explicación para una persona que no sabe nada de las diferencias culturales. Trata de explicar las cosas de manera que no produzcas una reacción negativa en la persona que te escucha. Es importante darle la idea de que debe respetar y tratar de entender a las gentes del mundo.

1. "These people cannot govern themselves. If they had strong administrations they would not allow their natural resources to be exhausted this way".

2. "I think these people all live in cities with too many buses, too many people, too little sanitation, and way too much noise. If they built suburbs like us, the cities would be much nicer".

3. "Why would one want to live in a big city like México, D. F., if the smaller towns are so much cleaner and less crowded?"

4. "Thank goodness that one can eat at "Taco Bell" in Mexico now. I used to worry about contaminated food before".

II VOCABULARIO Y LECTURA

A. Encuesta de vida urbana. Completa la siguiente ecuesta sobre la calidad de vida urbana. Escribe tus datos personales con nombres, apellidos, direcciones y fechas a la manera hispana. Agrega comentarios cuando puedas y usa muchas palabras y expresiones aprendidas en esta unidad.

ESCUELA DE PLANIFICACIÓN URBANA
ENCUESTA DE OPINIÓN SOBRE LA CALIDAD DE VIDA EN LA CIUDAD

Por favor, ayude a los alumnos de Asuntos Urbanos que están interesados en mejorar la imagen de la ciudad. Devuelva la encuesta en el Centro de Estudiantes de Asuntos Urbanos, donde le vamos a dar una entrada gratis al concierto de la Orquesta Filarmónica.

I. DATOS PERSONALES

Nombre: _____
           Nombre de pila   *apellido paterno*   *apellido materno*

Edad: _____ Sexo: _____ Estado civil: S C D Ocupación: _____

Año de estudios:
❑ primer año   ❑ tercer año   ❑ quinto o más
❑ segundo año   ❑ cuarto año

Domicilio: _____
        calle nº piso código postal   *ciudad*   *estado*   *país*

Marque cinco de los siguientes términos que describan su apreciación de la ciudad:

❑ cansancio	❑ orgullo	❑ irritabilidad
❑ impuestos	❑ esperanza	❑ miedo
❑ delincuencia	❑ cultura	❑ atascos de tráfico
❑ exasperación	❑ oportunidades	❑ poco estacionamiento
❑ espectáculos buenos	❑ contaminación atmosférica	❑ basura y desperdicios
❑ tantas universidades	❑ enojo	❑ zona verde

II. NECESIDADES MÁS URGENTES EN EL ÁREA DEL CAMPUS

Para mejorar la imagen de la ciudad, podemos empezar por la universidad. Denos su opinión; marque todos los medios que Ud. considere apropiados para mejorar la calidad de vida en el barrio universitario. Agregue otros que le parezcan importantes.
Sería mejor que...

❑ ahorraran agua   ❑ mantuvieran el paisaje natural   ❑ aumentaran las sendas de bicicletas

❑ redujeran los desperdicios de las cocinas   ❑ redujeran el uso de insecticidas

❑ ahorraran luz y gas   ❑ construyeran estacionamientos subterráneos

❑ invirtieran en más árboles, menos pavimento   ❑ hubiera más solidaridad

❑ hubiera menos desigualdad   ❑ tuviéramos autobuses a gas natural

También podrían

_____

_____

III. VOLUNTARIOS

Ninguna acción comunitaria tiene éxito si la gente no coopera. Por favor, indique de qué manera podría colaborar Ud. y qué necesitaría para poder ser voluntario.
Yo podría cooperar...

❑ limpiando   _____

❑ haciendo clases de   _____

❑ invirtiendo en   _____

❏ recogiendo _____

❏ enterrando desperdicios de _____

❏ construyendo _____

Sería necesario que me dieran/ ayudaran con . . .

_____

_____

_____

B. Asociaciones.
Da al menos dos términos asociados con los siguientes o escribe varias frases en que uses las siguientes palabras. Usa otra hoja de papel.

1. escasez	**5.** promover	**9.** aprovechar	**13.** recoger
2. tasa	**6.** la guerra y la paz	**10.** botadero	**14.** no agotar los recursos
3. darse cuenta	**7.** rascacielos	**11.** impuestos	**15.** paisaje
4. pobreza	**8.** puentes	**12.** ballenas	**16.** semáforos

C. Curas dolorosas.
Da al menos dos remedios para cada uno de los siguientes problemas.

1. No se dan cuenta que construir más carreteras invita más vehículos al centro.

_____

_____

2. Ojalá no hubiera tantas centrales eléctricas que usen carbón.

_____

_____

3. Como la economía está mejor, estamos produciendo más CO_2.

_____

_____

4. Hay demasiada deforestación.

_____

_____

5. Está agotada el agua.

_____

_____

6. Hay demasiados rascacielos.

_____

_____

D. Podría hacer algo. Según el contexto, completa las siguientes frases con verbos de acciones como **darse cuenta de, recoger, elegir, aumentar, disminuir, desarrollar, reducir, prevenir, proteger, amenazar,** etc. Sigue el ejemplo.

Por ejemplo: Ojalá que evitaran la destrucción del valle. Si no, sería mejor que... **protegiéramos** a los animales.

1. Ojalá que disminuyeran el anhídrido carbónico (CO_2). Si no, sería

mejor que... _____

2. Ojalá que no amenazaran las sierras de Wyoming. Si no, sería mejor

que... _____

3. Ojalá que redujeran las emisiones de gases peligrosos. Si no, sería

mejor que... _____

4. Ojalá que no corten más árboles ni contaminen los ríos. Si no, sería

mejor que... _____

E. Lectura. Usa las estrategias y el vocabulario de esta unidad para leer el siguiente fragmento. En seguida, contesta las preguntas que siguen a la lectura.

RECUPERAR EL MEDIO AMBIENTE:
UNA TAREA QUE EMPIEZA POR CASA

Los problemas ambientales son tan graves que, no en vano, mueren diariamente 35 mil niños en el mundo como consecuencia de las enfermedades producidas por la degradación ambiental, el hambre y la sobrepoblación. A fines de 1994, por ejemplo, había trece millones de infantes muertos por estas razones. "Sería bueno poder hacer algo" es lo que han pensado muchas empresas y organizaciones, aunque haya soluciones que requieran grandes inversiones. Si cada uno de nosotros ayudara un poco, se podrían alcanzar algunas metas a largo plazo y el Programa Permanente de Protección al Medio Ambiente nos indica cómo podría disminuir los daños el ciudadano común:

- Si todos lleváramos una bolsa de basura cuando salimos de paseo, los ríos, lagos y parques permanecerían más limpios y los fondos que le ahorráramos a la administración de los parques, podrían ser dedicados a otros fines.

- Si los exploradores enterraran sus restos de comida y desperdicios cuando fueran de camping, ayudarían a enriquecer el suelo con materia orgánica. Los microorganismos que viven en el suelo descompondrían los desperdicios y así servirían como fertilizante para el bosque, en vez de llenar los basureros del lugar y atraer animales.

- Si clasificáramos la basura como se hace en Europa y Japón, reduciríamos en alguna medida la escasez de terrenos para botaderos. La única verdadera basura son los desperdicios no reciclables como los desechos hospitalarios, algunos plásticos y, en general, cualquier cosa contaminada, sucia o que contiene sustancias peligrosas, como las baterías y pilas y los cartuchos de las fotocopiadoras. Hay muchísimas otras cosas que pueden reutilizarse (como las latas, plásticos y empaques de vidrio, cartón o papel), que debieran ser separadas en casa, para que disminuyeran los costos de clasificación en el botadero municipal (que nosotros mismos mantenemos por medio de los impuestos).

Otras medidas generales pueden ser caminar o montar en bicicleta en vez de conducir, usar menos artículos de papel o reusarlos más, no imprimir el trabajo que se hace en la computadora hasta que esté totalmente terminado, no plantar árboles que exijan demasiada agua en su casa, no generar mucho ruido que canse a sus vecinos. Por supuesto, otra acción importante es organizarse para que la industria limpie y recicle también.

Tomado de "Recuperar el medio ambiente ¡Una tarea que empieza por casa!"
Carrusel No. 802, 3 de junio de 1994, págs. 8-9. Suplemento de *El tiempo*, Bogotá.

1. ¿Qué consecuencias tiene la degradación ambiental, el hambre y la población? Haz una lista.

   _____

   _____

2. En resumen, ¿qué medidas generales se recomiendan en este artículo?

   _____

   _____

3. ¿Qué crees tú? ¿Es conveniente enterrar los desperdicios de camping o sería mejor hacer otra cosa? ¿Por qué?

   _____

   _____

4. ¿Cuántas veces imprimes tus trabajos incompletos? ¿De qué manera podrías ahorrar papel?

   _____

5. Dale dos consejos a tus vecinos para que tu comunidad alcance algunas metas nuevas.

   Sería mejor que _____

   _____

III GRAMÁTICA

A. Precisión. Cuando sea necesario, usa formas de subjuntivo presente o pasado, el tiempo futuro, condicional, progresivo o infinitivo para completar el siguiente párrafo. Acuérdate de usar los pronombres en el lugar correcto cuando sea necesario.

No todo lo recicable se recicla ni todo lo entregado se recicla

inmediatamente. En general e idealmente, es mejor (**1.** ahorrar)

_____ y no usar que malgastar y entonces tener

muchas cosas que reciclar. Ojalá que nosotros no (**2.** ser)

_____ la sociedad que produce más basura en el

mundo, pero así es. Y como la mayoría no (**3.** darse cuenta de)

_____ los efectos de la contaminación directamente,

pocos (**4.** desarrollar) _____ la conciencia para que

en su casa se (**5.** evitar) _____ abusar el ambiente.

Creo que si la gente (**6.** saber) _____ cuánta

cantidad de agua total gastan en lavarse o en lavar los platos (para después

meterlos en el lavaplatos), (**7.** haber) _____ menos

pérdida de recursos tan preciosos como el agua. Después de estudiar este

capítulo, yo (**8.** andar + pensar) _____ cuánta

energía se perderá en los edificios que quedan con luz toda la noche o cuánta

gente (**9.** desarrollar) _____ cáncer de la piel porque

el agujero en la capa de ozono (**10.** seguir + crecer)

_____ sobre la Antártida, Argentina y Chile. Bueno,

desde hoy enterraré la basura vegetal como lo hacen los exploradores y

(**11.** evitar) _____ usar tantas servilletas y artículos

de papel.

B. Ando pensando en el ambiente. Imagínate que quieres evitar que el propietario de tu casa o apartamento use sustancias que son dañinas para el ambiente. Ofrece hacer las cosas tú mismo(a), sin usar sustancias químicas peligrosas ni destruir el ambiente. Sigue el ejemplo.

Por ejemplo: **Propietario:** —Voy a ponerle herbicida al jardín.
     Yo: —Ojalá que no pusiera herbicida; yo podría limpiar el jardín a mano.

1. —Mire; pondré insecticida en el sótano.

 — _____.

2. —¿Sabe Ud.? Mañana tiraré las ruedas a la basura.

 — _____.

3. —Nadie se dará cuenta si tiro el aceite de motor en la calle.

 — _____.

4. —Todos meten la cabeza en la arena; podemos matar este árbol enfermo.

 — _____.

5. —Es muy caro reciclar; los papeles y el vidrio van a la basura.

— _____ .

6. —El refrigerador viejo tiene gases dañinos; lo tiraremos al patio.

— _____ .

C. Sensible. Da tu reacción a los siguientes desastres ecológicos; usa una frase con **si**, pasado del subjuntivo y condicional, como en el ejemplo.

Ejemplo: Parece que murieron los delfines del show.
¡Ay, no! Si murieran, sería una gran desgracia/ se acabaría el show/...

1. Parece que se extinguieron las tortugas de las Galápagos.

_____

2. Amenazaron con cortar el bosque virgen de Oregón.

_____

3. No quieren proteger los pantanos (_swamps_) de la Florida.

_____

4. Se agotó el agua pura en ese valle de Montana.

_____

5. Quemaron varias ruedas de auto en el estadio.

_____

6. El virus Hanta se extendió a mi estado.

_____

D. Ni idea. Completa lo siguiente con un comentario como en el ejemplo. Usa formas verbales de futuro y los pronombres necesarios como en el ejemplo.

Ejemplo: No sé si **han terminado** esos rascacielos del centro. No tengo idea cuándo **los terminarán**.

1. No creo que hayan abierto esa fábrica todavía.

_____

_____

2. ¡Qué escándalo que no hayan construido un puente!

_____

_____

3. Si ya hubiera pagado estaría tranquilo.

_____

_____

4. No creo que allí haya estación del metro todavía.

_____

_____

5. Ni los ancianos ni los niños tienen la preferencia ahora.

_____

_____

E. Buen editor. Marca la palabra correcta de manera que **1)** el párrafo tenga sentido; **2)** los verbos correspondan al tipo de especulación o afirmación que estamos haciendo; y **3)** se use el subjuntivo para los deseos y las órdenes negativas y formales.

Ahora que he vivido en varios países (**1.** supiera/ sé/ sabiendo) el significado de las palabras *recursos naturales preciosos*. Por mucho tiempo, repetía mecánicamente cosas como "Es necesario reciclar". "Para que no (**2.** aumente/ aumentes/ aumentan) el agujero de ozono, no (**3.** conducir/ conduzca/ conduce) su coche y forme un grupo para viajar juntos a la oficina". "Ojalá que cada ciudadano del mundo (**4.** se hace/ haga/ se hiciera) responsable de consumir sólo lo necesario". Ahora paso (**5.** a recordar/ recordando/ recuerdo) los efectos del abuso del ambiente y de la degradación por la contaminación industrial porque los vi en otros países. Cuando (**6.** vuelva/ vuelvo/ vuelve) a Rusia el próximo año, el lago salado ya (**7.** estaría/ estará/ estar) totalmente seco y en las estepas de África que visité no (**8.** va a estar/ están/ habrá) ni un solo árbol pues todos los usaron los pobres para calentarse, y en Costa Rica se habrán extinguido decenas de especies más. Así pues, ¿qué no (**9.** daría/ daré/ darías) yo por poder extender el mensaje de la fragilidad de nuestra tierra? A veces pienso que mi trabajo sería más fácil si (**10.** hubiera/ habrá/ hay) más jóvenes que pudieran ver el futuro en otras tierras conmigo.

⫿ EXPRESIÓN ORAL

Prepara siete posibles preguntas y respuestas para una de las siguientes situaciones. Luego, usa las preguntas para conversar con tu compañero(a).

- Una conversación con un/a ingeniero(a) que está decidido(a) a reducir el presupuesto para la constucción de un nuevo camino/ puente/ cruce de tráfico. El/La ingeniero(a) piensa reducir los gatos de la obra cambiando el curso de un pequeño río y cortando varios árboles viejos que están a la orilla del agua.

- Una encuesta de actitudes hacia el uso del terreno de tu universidad. Trata de averiguar si hay diferencias entre las respuestas de alumnos de distintas facultades de la universidad.

- Un programa para la televisión de la universidad en el que entrevistas a varios jóvenes sobre sus actitudes hacia una campaña en contra de la construcción de más edificios de estacionamiento en la universidad. Los que se oponen dicen que sería mucho mejor hacer una campaña para que la gente usara otras maneras de movilizarse como montar bicicletas, tomar el autobús/metro, caminar por sendas apropiadas y seguras, etc.

⫿ EXPRESIÓN ESCRITA

Elige uno de los siguientes temas y desarróllalo en español.

- Escríbele una carta abierta a la comunidad (universitaria o de la ciudad), en la cual defiendes tu posición ante algún problema ambiental o de degradación de la naturaleza. Explica claramente por qué has tomado la posición que tienes, da todas tus razones para proponer esto y también describe cómo te podrían ayudar otros estudiantes para llevar a la práctica tus planes, si te dieran la oportunidad.

- Escríbele una carta a un/a líder estudiantil para que lancen una campaña en contra del mal uso de los recursos en la universidad. Incluye una lista de los recursos energéticos, espaciales y temporales que se pierden o se malgastan en la universtidad y explícale claramente cómo se podría hacer más eficiente su uso. Ofrece tu ayuda.

ANSWER KEYS

Workbook Answer Key

LECCIÓN PRELIMINAR

Vocabulario

A. Answers may vary. **1.** En la biblioteca hay muchos libros, muchas computadoras, muchas cintas y sillas. **2.** En la universidad hay muchos alumnos, muchos profesores, muchas salas de clase, muchas residencias estudiantiles, muchos laboratorios. **3.** En mi mochila hay muchos lápices, muchos libros, bolígrafos, cuadernos. **4.** En mi cuaderno hay muchas hojas de papel y muchos apuntes. **5.** En la residencia estudiantil hay muchos alumnos, muchas sillas y muchos televisores. **6.** En el laboratorio de idiomas hay muchas cintas y computadoras.

B. tal, Bien, difícil/mala, va, muy bien, tarea, siento, se llama, Me llamo, profesora, te llamas, Me llamo, alumno, horario, curso, matrícula, gracias.

C. Answers may vary. **1.** a. profesores buenos b. una biblioteca grande c. una cafetería buena d. cursos fáciles. **2.** a. profesores malos b. cursos difíciles/malos c. matrícula d. mucha tarea

D. Answers will vary. **1.** a. leer mucho b. tomar apuntes c. hablar español d. escribir mucho **2.** a. mucho trabajo b. una calculadora. c. exámenes d. mucha tarea

CAPÍTULO 1

Vocabulario

A. **1.** perezosos **2.** reservada **3.** amable, sensible **4.** hogareña **5.** divertidas, serias **6.** deportista **7.** impulsiva **8.** hogareño/tranquilo/perezoso **9.** bien educado

B. Answers may resemble the following. **1.** No quiero ser periodista porque no me gusta viajar. **2.** No quiero ser analista de sistemas porque no me gusta trabajar en la computadora. **3.** No quiero ser abogado(a) porque no me gusta hablar. **4.** No quiero ser arquitecto(a) porque no me gusta dibujar.

C. Paso 1. **1.** c   **2.** El estilo general de enseñanza es rápido, fácil y divertido.   **3.** Los profesores son norteamericanos (Son de los Estados Unidos).   **4.** Los alumnos son dedicados y serios. **5.** Muchos de los alumnos son de América Latina.

Paso 2. **1.** a. guarantee b. opportunities c. obtain d. certified e. state f. evaluation g. advanced   **2.** a. life b. better c. reasons

D. **1.** Necesitan un ingeniero químico y un contador.   **2.** Los requisitos similares son escolaridad y experiencia.   **3.** Los requisitos diferentes son: a. la edad b. buena presentación c. estar casado d. el sexo masculino   **4.** a. hacer cita b. mandar currículum vitae c. presentarse a una entrevista

Gramática 1

A. **1.** es **2.** son **3.** son **4.** son **5.** son **6.** es **7.** es **8.** Es **9.** soy **10.** Es **11.** Eres **12.** es **13.** Es **14.** Es **15.** son **16.** es **17.** son

B. The second answer in each item may vary.   **1.** Eres; Sí, soy impaciente a veces.   **2.** Son; Sí, somos deportistas.   **3.** son; Mis abuelos son de Arizona.   **4.** es; Mi autor favorito es Gabriel García Márquez.   **5.** es; Mi autor favorito es de Colombia.

C. **1.** son; Son rubias.   **2.** soy; Soy norteamericano(a).   **3.** eres; Eres trabajador/a.   **4.** es; Es divertida.   **5.** son; Son gruesas.   **6.** son; Son escritores.   **7.** somos; Somos listos.   **8.** es; Es viejo.

Gramática 2

A. **1.** los lápices rojos   **2.** las alumnas alegres   **3.** los profesores deportistas   **4.** las dentistas organizadas   **5.** las buenas personalidades   **6.** las personas mayores

B. **1.** Andy García y Cristina son hispanos, famosos y populares. **2.** Frida Kahlo y Ana María Matute son serias y trabajadoras. **3.** Ana y Carlos son pesimistas.   **4.** Oprah Winfrey es emprendedora y puntual.   **5.** Los alumnos son desordenados pero responsables.

C. Answers will vary.

D. Answers will vary.   **1.** Soy reservado(a), no me gusta ir a discotecas. **2.** No soy perezoso(a), me gusta trabajar.   **3.** Soy hogareño(a), me gusta mirar la tele.   **4.** Soy trabajador/a, no me gusta descansar.

Gramática 3

A. Answers will vary.

B. Answers may vary.   **1.** A Frida Kahlo le gusta pintar.   **2.** A Andy García le gusta estar con su familia.   **3.** A Gloria Estefan le gusta cantar.

C. **1.** les **2.** nos **3.** te **4.** les **5.** me **6.** le **7.** les **8.** nos

D. **1.** A María le gusta trabajar porque es emprendedora. **2.** A Marcelo y Teresa les gusta ir al gimnasio porque son deportistas. **3.** No nos gusta ir a fiestas porque somos hogareños. **4.** A Diego y Frida les gusta pintar porque son artistas. **5.** Al Sr. Gore le gusta hablar porque es político. **6.** A Ramón le gusta escuchar porque es terapista.

E. Answers may vary. **1.** Luis y Clara son trabajadores. Les gusta trabajar. **2.** Ana y Elena son serias. Les gusta estudiar. **3.** Fernando es hogareño. Le gusta cocinar. **4.** Teresa es tranquila. Le gusta leer.

F. Cómo; Quién; de dónde; Cómo; dónde; Cómo

G. Answers may vary. **1.** a. ¿Quiénes son de México? b. ¿De dónde son Frida y Diego? **2.** a. ¿Quiénes están en Hollywood? b. ¿Dónde están Ancy García y Gloria Estefan? **3.** a. ¿Quién es sensible? b. ¿Cómo es la enfermera? **4.** a. ¿Quiénes son puntuales? b. ¿Cómo son las personas ordenadas? **5.** a. ¿De dónde es Gabriel García Márquez? b. ¿Cómo es Gabriel Garcia Márquez?

Lectura

I. **1.** a. Diego Rivera es el esposo de Frida Khalo. b. Diego Rivera es un artista mexicano muy popular. **2.** Diego Rivera es de México. **3.** Quiere comunicar temas de problemas sociales. **4.** Las personas que pinta son gruesas y bellas. **5.** Su matrimonio no es muy tranquilo. Es difícil e intenso. **6.** El problema es que Diego demuestra interés por otras mujeres. **7.** La evidencia de la pena de Frida está en su arte.

II. 1. Juan Luis Guerra es artista, es cantante. **2.** Es dulce, tranquilo y alto. Tiene los ojos oscuros y el pelo negro. **3.** Nora es la esposa de Juan Luis. **4.** Ella es de estatura pequeña. Tiene los ojos claros y el pelo rubio. **5.** Juan Luis es de la República Dominicana. **6.** Canta en los clubs de Nueva York. **7.** Le gusta más la personalidad. **8.** A Juan Luis y a Nora les gusta ir a la playa, ir de compras por la ciudad, ir a los restaurantes. **9.** A Juan Luis no le gusta ser el centro de atención porque es muy tímido.

Para escribir. Answers will vary.

C A P Í T U L O 2

Vocabulario

A. 1. recordar 2. fechas 3. colegio 4. resolver 5. tomar 6. idiomas
7. empresa 8. países 9. conocer 10. extranjero 11. banco
12. sueldo 13. escuela primaria 14. tocar 15. jugar

B. Answers will vary.

C. 1. tomar decisiones 2. correr 3. pensar 4. equipo 5. resolver 6. tocar

D. 1. Alfonso es el menor. 2. Carlos es el mayor. 3. Alfonso quiere ser
artista. 4. Berto tiene interés en la música. 5. No, a Berto no le
gusta trabajar con la tecnología. 6. Berto puede tocar un
instrumento. 7. Berto tiene veintisiete años. Carlos tiene veintinueve
años. 8. Los programadores de computadoras pueden ganar sueldos
magníficos. 9. Carlos es muy sensible. 10. Berto es muy
materialista. 11. c.

E. 1. el doce de agosto 2. el dos de junio 3. el treinta de septiembre
4. el quince de julio 5. el dos de mayo

F. 1. dieciocho mil noventa 2. treinta y seis mil ciento dieciséis
3. veintiséis mil sesenta y cinco 4. cuarenta y un mil setenta y tres

G. Answers will vary.

Gramática 1

A. 1. tengo 2. tengo 3. puedo 4. Tengo 5. tiene 6. tenemos que
7. tiene que 8. puede 9. tienen 10. puedo 11. tienen que

B. Answers may resemble the following. 1. Sí, tengo problemas como los
de Elena. Soy desordenado(a) también y no puedo organizarme.
2. Tengo que ordenar mi dormitorio mañana. 3. Puedo mantener el
orden si escribo una lista de cosas que tengo que hacer. 4. Puedo
vivir con una persona desordenada porque soy desordenado(a)
también. 5. Sí, podemos estudiar en un lugar desordenado porque
nos gusta el desorden.

C. 1. pueden cocinar bien. 2. puede resolver problemas 3. puede
hablar dos o tres idiomas. 4. pueden pintar bien 5. puede cantar
bien. 6. pueden escribir bien

Gramática 2

A. 1. quiere, va a 2. quieren, van a 3. quieres, vas a 4. quieren, van a
5. quiere, va a

B. Answers will vary but should contain the following.
1. Yo quiero... Por eso voy a... **2.** Mi papá/mamá quiere... Por eso va a... **3.** Mi mejor amigo quiere... Por eso va a... **4.** El Presidente quiere ... Por eso va a...

C. 1. Tienen que llamar a la Oficina de Turismo. El número es cincuenta, treinta, cero cinco. **2.** Tiene que llamar a las Ambulancias. El número es cincuenta y uno, cero nueve, cero nueve. **3.** Puede llamar a la Estación de Autobuses. El número es cincuenta, treinta y cuatro, diez. **4.** Tiene que llamar a la Policía Municipal. El número es cincuenta, cero uno, quince.

D. Answers may vary. **1.** Quiero ver "Tornado". **2.** Voy a ver "El Jorobado de Notre Dame" con mis hermanitos. **3.** No voy a ver "Strip Tease" o "El Protector" con niños pequeños. **4.** El Sr. Toledo va a ver "Corazón de Dragón". **5.** Voy a ver "Día de la Independencia". **6.** a. dibujos animados b. habita en c. malvado d. traidor e. contrario f. atrapar **7.** G, PG, R, X

Lectura

I. 1. Luis, Arturo y Guillermo van a hacer algo nuevo. **2.** Arturo y Tomás tienen que ser diferentes. **3.** Luis va a ganar un sueldo mejor. **4.** Clara va a tener una experiencia romántica. **5.** Ana va a tener dificultades con sus padres o hermanos.

II. Answers will vary.

Para escribir. Answers will vary.

C A P Í T U L O 3

Vocabulario

A. 1. mal tiempo **2.** llueve **3.** sol **4.** playa **5.** lago **6.** pescar **7.** excursiones **8.** cocinar **9.** acampar **10.** dormir **11.** jugar **12.** básquetbol **13.** esquiar **14.** agua **15.** descansar **16.** vacaciones

B. Answers may vary. **1.** esquiar en el agua/en el verano. **2.** patinar en el hielo/en el invierno. **3.** ver los colores de los árboles/en el otoño **4.** esquiar/en el invierno (cuando hace frío). **5.** navegar en bote de vela/hace buen tiempo (viento).

C. Answers may vary. Jorge: dar un paseo, ver la tele, leer el periódico, tomar el sol; Enrique: hacer excursiones, jugar tenis, patinar sobre ruedas, navegar en bote de remos.

D. Answers will vary.

Gramática 1

A. 1. gusta 2. voy 3. es 4. podemos 5. queremos 6. piensa
7. tienen 8. nada 9. esquía 10. lee 11. duerme 12. quiere
13. juega 14. escucha 15. quiero 16. conozco 17. vamos
18. bailan 19. gusta 20. va 21. ve 22. pensamos 23. sé

B. 1. haces 2. corro 3. hace 4. jugamos 5. montamos 6. miramos
7. llueve 8. hace 9. hago 10. descanso 11. veo 12. tiene
13. alquila 14. hacen 15. vivo 16. conozco 17. doy 18. limpia
19. compro 20. cocino 21. salgo/salimos 22. estudian 23. hago
24. Sé 25. son 26. ves 27. trabajo

C. 1. a. Raúl y Juanita juegan tenis. b. Los niños nadan en la piscina.
2. a. La familia Toledo hace excursiones. b. Los García acampan.
3. María y Daniela van de compras. b. Juan y Paulina van al museo
c. Los Gómez dan un paseo por la ciudad. 4. a. Marta juega con sus
perros. b. Pepe toca sus discos compactos. c. Pedro y Pablo ven la
tele. d. Ángela lee un libro. 5. a. Juanita y Raúl toman el sol.
b. Carlos y Juan esquían en el agua. c. Roberto y Raquel navegan en
bote de remos.

D. **Horizontales:** 1. pescan 5. dormimos 6. ve 7. damos 10. nadan
11. toman 13. leo 14. navego 16. tienes 18. veo 19. juegas
Verticales: 1. paso 2. cocinas 3. nado 4. piensan 5. descansan
8. somos 9. dan 12. montamos 13. leen 15. vamos 17. son

Gramática 2

A. Choices may vary. 1. ¿A Smokey le gusta más la playa o las
montañas? A Smokey le gustan las montañas. 2. ¿A los niños les
gusta más el lago o la piscina? Les gusta el lago. 3. ¿A ustedes les
gustan más los domingos o los lunes? Nos gustan los domingos.
4. ¿A tu mejor amigo(a) le gustan más los deportes de verano o los
deportes de invierno? A mi mejor amigo(a) le gustan más los deportes
de verano. 5. ¿Te gusta más el otoño o la primavera? Me gusta más el
otoño. 6. ¿A tus padres les gusta más la música rock o la música
clásica? Les gusta más la música clásica. 7. ¿A ustedes les gustan
más las fiestas o los exámenes? Nos gustan más las fiestas.

B. Answers will vary but should contain the following; pay attention to
singular (gusta) and plural (gustan) of gustar and noun(s). 1. A Jorge
le gusta(n)... 2. A los Vásquez les gusta(n)... 3. A Arturo y Roberto
les gusta(n)... 4. A los jóvenes de hoy les gusta(n)... 5. A Carolina le
gusta(n)... 6. A los "yuppies" les gusta(n)...

C. Answers will vary.

Lectura

A. 1. Los turistas bucean y visitan las ruinas arqueológicas.   **2.** Hay ruinas de tres templos mayas.   **3.** Answers may resemble the following: Sí, tengo interés en la arqueología. Voy a estudiarla.
4. Puedo bucear y nadar en Xcaret.   **5.** a. diminutive b. paradise c. alternative d. visitor e. ruins f. exhibits g. terrain h. focus i. temperate j. extends k. fascinate   **6.** Answers will vary.

B. Answers will vary.

Para escribir.   Answers will vary.

CAPÍTULO 4

Vocabulario

A. Paso 1. 1. despertarse **2.** alegre **3.** lleno **4.** levantarse **5.** asistir **6.** Después **7.** despertarse **8.** acostarse **9.** levantarse **10.** enojado **11.** arreglarse/ducharse **12.** llegar **13.** cansado **14.** harto **15.** temprano **16.** quedarse

Paso 2. Answers will vary.

B. Answers will vary.

C. Answers will vary.

D. Answers will vary.

Gramática 1

A. 1. a. ¿A qué hora te levantas? b. Me levanto a las...   **2.** a. ¿Te levantas lleno(a) de energía o cansado(a)? b. Me levanto...   **3.** a. ¿Te bañas o te duchas? b. Me...   **4.** a. ¿Te vistes bien o de una manera informal para trabajar? b. Me visto...   **5.** a. ¿Te arreglas rápido o con cuidado? b. Me arreglo...   **6.** a. ¿Te preocupas por hacer todo el trabajo? b. Sí, me preocupo...

B. Answers will vary but should contain the following.
1. Me divierto mucho cuando...   **2.** Para relajarme...   **3.** Me quejo de...
4. Mis padres se quejan de...   **5.** Me siento muy contento(a) cuando...
6. Me siento muy triste cuando...   **7.** A veces puedo reírme de mis problemas, pero me siento estresado(a) cuando...   **8.** Me siento estresado(a) cuando estudio porque...   **9.** Me muero de aburrido(a) cuando...   **10.** A veces tengo ganas de quedarme solo(a) porque...

C. Answers may vary.   **1.** Juan y Pablo se quedan solos en la casa.
2. Juan se queja de estar aburrido.   **3.** Juan y Pablo se cansan de ver
la tele.   **4.** Juan y Pablo se quejan de no tener nada que comer.
5. Juan y Pablo se sienten mal.

D. Answers will vary but should contain the following. **1.** Cuando me
muero de aburrido(a)...   **2.** Cuando me siento lleno(a) de energía...
3. Cuando me preocupo por los exámenes ...   **4.** Cuando me canso de
la rutina diaria...   **5.** Cuando me siento deprimido(a)...

E. **1.** me levanto   **2.** me ducho   **3.** me visto   **4.** me miro   **5.** me siento
6. me preparo   **7.** me divierto   **8.** relajarme   **9.** se despierta   **10.** se
acuesta   **11.** se queja   **12.** se duerme   **13.** se ríen   **14.** se enoja
15. nos divertimos   **16.** te preocupas   **17.** dormirte

Gramática 2

A. **1.** Son las tres.   **2.** Son las cuatro y media.   **3.** Son las ocho y veinte.
4. Son las once y cuarto.   **5.** Es la una y ocho.   **6.** Son las dos y
treinta y dos.   **7.** Son las diez menos cuarto.   **8.** Son las once menos
diez.   **9.** Son las seis menos veinticuatro.   **10.** Son las doce y diez.

B. Answers will vary.

C. Answers may vary. **1.** Me visto antes de arreglarme.   **2.** Me ducho
antes de comer el desayuno.   **3.** Me ducho después de arreglarme.
4. Me levanto antes de arreglarme.

Lectura

A. **1.** El primer reloj de pulsera, el reloj de sol y los relojes de bolsillo son
los relojes más ornados.   **2.** No, no sabemos la fecha de la invención
del reloj.   **3.** No, no sabemos quién es el inventor del reloj.

B. **1.** pintura   **2.** perlas   **3.** funcionan   **4.** cuarzo   **5.** requiriendo

C. Answers will vary.

Para escribir.   Answers will vary.

C A P Í T U L O 5

Vocabulario

A. **1.** reunión   **2.** juntarnos   **3.** cumpleaños   **4.** bisabuela   **5.** cumplir
6. parientes   **7.** menor   **8.** nietos   **9.** viuda   **10.** menor
11. comprometidos   **12.** llevamos   **13.** tía   **14.** primos   **15.** parecen
16. solteros   **17.** casarse

B. **1.** nieta   **2.** sobrinos   **3.** tío   **4.** padrastro   **5.** única

C. Answers will vary.

D. **1.** Ramón es mayor que Lucinda./Lucinda es menor que Ramón.
2. Ramón y Lucinda están enamorados.   **3.** Ramón y Lucinda están comprometidos.   **4.** Lucinda es una novia./Lucinda y Ramón se casan.

Gramática 1

A. **1.** me junté   **2.** cumplió   **3.** hicieron   **4.** invitaron   **5.** se olvidó
6. habló   **7.** fue   **8.** comenzó   **9.** terminó   **10.** se peleó   **11.** se divorciaron   **12.** se llevaron   **13.** vimos   **14.** decidimos   **15.** me mudé

B. Answers will vary but should contain the following verb forms.
1. Fui ....   **2.** Nos juntamos...   **3.** Sí, vi a...   **4.** Sí, compartimos...
Hablamos de...   **5.** Hablé con...   **6.** ... hizo la fiesta. Fue...   **7.** Sí, conocí a... Es...

C. **1.** Juan y Amelia se casaron en mil novecientos cincuenta y tres.
2. Su hija, Alicia, nació en mil novecientos cincuenta y cinco.   **3.** Juan y su familia pasaron las vacaciones en Acapulco en mil novecientos sesenta.   **4.** La familia de Juan se mudó en mil novecientos sesenta y tres.   **5.** Alicia llegó a la universidad (empezó sus estudios universitarios, se matriculó en la universidad) en mil novecientos setenta y dos.

D. **1.** Ayer me levanté tarde.   **2.** Ayer no hice mi tarea.   **3.** Ayer no me llevé bien con mi hermano.   **4.** El año pasado no viajé mucho.   **5.** La semana pasada mis amigos no fueron al cine.   **6.** Anoche no me quedé en casa.

Gramática 2

A. **1.** se vistió; Carolyn se vistió con sencillez y sensualidad.   **2.** se casó; Se casó con John Kennedy Jr.   **3.** fue; El padre famoso fue John F. Kennedy.   **4.** se murió; Este hombre famoso se murió en mil novecientos sesenta y tres.   **5.** envidiaron; Envidiaron a Carolyn porque ella se casó con John F. Kennedy Jr.   **6.** Influyó; Sí, su vestido influyó al estilo de otros vestidos.   **7.** se divirtieron; Sí, todos se divirtieron en la fiesta.

B. **1.** fui   **2.** fueron   **3.** se conocieron   **4.** vieron   **5.** se sintieron
6. decidieron   **7.** consiguió   **8.** invitaron   **9.** se rieron   **10.** nos divertimos   **11.** fue   **12.** se durmieron   **13.** me dormí   **14.** encantó

C. **1.** leí   **2.** se vistió   **3.** se vistieron   **4.** gustó, se divirtieron

D. **Note: Horizontales: 1.** dieron   **4.** leí   **5.** diste   **7.** oyó   **8.** quedó
9. busqué   **11.** oí   **12.** hice   **Verticales: 1.** durmió   **2.** fue   **3.** vi
4. leyeron   **5.** dio   **6.** saqué   **10.** sacó

Lectura

A. **1.** César Evora es actor de telenovela. **2.** Vive en Ciudad México. **3.** César vive con su esposa y su hija. **4.** Tiene un hijo que vive con él y dos hijos que están en Cuba. **5.** Rafael es el mayor de los hijos. **6.** Los dos mayores no viven con él porque viven con su mamá en Cuba. **7.** César tiene memorias tristes de su niñez cuando su papá estaba muy lejos. **8.** César ve a sus hijos una vez al año durante las vacaciones escolares. **9.** César es un padre a "larga distancia" como su propio padre.

B. **1.** resido **2.** aspecto **3.** realidad **4.** catarsis **5.** sentimientos **6.** madurez

C. **1.** b. **2.** c. **3.** a.

D. Answers will vary.

Para escribir. Answers will vary.

C A P Í T U L O 6

Vocabulario

A. **1.** viene, traer **2.** vienen, recomiendas, recomiendo, cuesta, gastar **3.** decir, llevas, piden **4.** dijeron, dijo **5.** vendieron, pedí, pidió, pagó

B. **1.** cosas **2.** caras **3.** artículos **4.** caja **5.** regalos **6.** reloj **7.** cumpleaños **8.** rosa **9.** cartas **10.** tarjetas **11.** cajita **12.** guantes **13.** lana **14.** botella **15.** pastel **16.** hogar **17.** cadena **18.** oro **19.** novia **20.** llave

C. **1.** Es un vaso de cristal **2.** Son aretes de plata. **3.** Es un marco de madera. **4.** Es una maleta de cuero. **5.** Es una camiseta de algodón

D. Answers may vary. **1.** Puedo comprar chocolate y pasteles en la dulcería. **2.** Puedo comprar llaves y herramientas en la ferretería. **3.** Puedo comprar libros y tarjetas en la librería. **4.** Puedo comprar aretes y cadenas de oro en la joyería. **5.** Puedo comprar plumas y llaveros en el almacén.

Gramática 1

A. Answers may resemble the following. **1.** a. Le digo "holá" o "dígame". b. Le digo "Buenos días." **2.** a. Le pregunto "¿Cuántas semanas de descanso hay? b. Le pregunto "¿De dónde es usted?" **3.** a. Les envío una carta o una solicitud. b. Le envío un regalo o una tarjeta. **4.** Nos venden herramientas.; Nos venden bombones.; Nos venden aretes.; Nos venden tarjetas.

Visión y voz 2E Tapescript and Answer Keys © 1998 John Wiley & Sons

B. Answers may vary. **1.** Ernesto le dice "Te quiero." **2.** Ernesto les lleva dulces a los padres de Marisol. **3.** Ernesto le escribe cartas de amor y le envía las cartas. **4.** Ernesto les muestra su carro y su casa. **5.** Ernesto le escribe un poema y le lee el poema. **6.** Marisol le dice a Ernesto que le da su corazón.

C. Answers will resemble the following. **1.** Mi abuela me hace regalos de cumpleaños. **2.** La profesora nos enseña el español. **3.** Mi mejor amiga me presta ropa. **4.** Mi profesor de matemáticas me pide cosas imposibles. **5.** Mi profesor de historia nos da muchas tareas.

D. Answers will vary.

Gramática 2

A. Answers may resemble the following. **1.** Saco peores notas en la clase de historia que en la clase de español. **2.** Presto más atención en la clase de español que en la clase de historia. **3.** Les pido más dinero a mis padres en diciembre que en octubre. **4.** Me río más cuando estoy con mis amigos que cuando estoy con mis parientes. **5.** Me demuestro mejor amigo(a) cuando estoy de vacaciones que cuando estoy en clase. **6.** Me visto peor cuando estudio para los exámenes que cuando salgo con mis amigos. **7.** Les envío más correo electrónico a mis amigos que a mis parientes. **8.** Compro mejores regalos en una tienda pequeña que en un almacén.

B. Answers may vary. **1.** Mis parientes son menos guapos que los actores del cine. **2.** Los aretes son más caros que una cadena de oro. **3.** Montar en bici es mejor para la salud que ir en auto. **4.** La rosa es más romántica que el cacto. **5.** Una semana de exámenes es peor que una semana de descanso. **6.** La lana es más suave que el cuero.

C. Answers will vary but should include the following. **1.** La cadena de oro es tan cara que... **2.** Los jóvenes están tan enamorados que... **3.** Mario llega tan tarde a la clase que... **4.** Teresa tiene tantos problemas que... **5.** Mi amigo tiene tantas cintas de música que... **6.** El alumno está tan estresado que... **7.** Tengo tanta tarea que....

Gramática 3

A. **1.** tuvo **2.** leyó **3.** pudo **4.** pareció **5.** pudo/quiso **6.** fue **7.** fue **8.** nació **9.** cambió **10.** llamó **11.** preguntó **12.** dijo **13.** trajo **14.** supe **15.** pude/quise **16.** tuvo **17.** resultó

B. Answers will vary but should include the following verb forms. **1.** estuviste; estuve **2.** supieron; supimos **3.** pudiste; pude **4.** quisiste; quise **5.** dijiste; dije

C. 15 de abril: Tuve; mostró; saqué; me divertí; encontré 16 de abril: presentó; fuimos; vi; pensé; dio; se divirtió; pidió 18 de abril: Me despedí; dio; pasamos; dijo; me morí 19 de abril: me fui; estuve; costó; quiso; fue; quiso 20 de abril: vino; pidió; mostré; se rió; dijo; sacaste; vio; se murió; Estuviste; pensaste; se fue 25 de abril: dijeron; salió

Lectura

A. **1.** Alex cumplió tres años. **2.** Son las abuelas de Alex. **3.** Abrió sus regalos porque los invitados insistieron.

B. **1.** b **2.** c **3.** a

Para escribir. Answers will vary.

C A P Í T U L O 7

Vocabulario

A. **1.** apartamento **2.** ordenar **3.** lavar **4.** platos **5.** puso **6.** platos **7.** secar **8.** poner **9.** estantes **10.** afueras **11.** ladrillos **12.** limpia/ordena **13.** pone **14.** hace **15.** pasa **16.** lavaplatos **17.** lavadora **18.** secadora **19.** quehaceres **20.** patio **21.** jardín **22.** poner

B. **1.** Tiene que lavar los platos. **2.** Tiene que sacudir el retrato. **3.** Tiene que sacar la basura. **4.** Tiene que darle comida al perro. **5.** Tiene que sacar a pasear al perro. **6.** Tiene que barrer el suelo. **7.** Tiene que cortar el césped. **8.** Tiene que lavar (limpiar) la ventana. **9.** Tiene que limpiar la estufa.

C. **1.** El gato grande está encima; el gato pequeño está abajo. **2.** El perro grande está arriba; el perro pequeño está abajo. **3.** El gato está cerca de la comida; el perro está lejos de la comida. **4.** El perro pequeño está adentro; el perro grande está afuera.

Gramática 1

A. Tuve que escuchar a mi madrastra: ... escucharla; ¿Ya pasaste la aspiradora?: ¿... la pasaste?; No pude pasar la aspiradora, Madrastra: No la pude pasar (No pude pasarla); Pues, tienes que reparar la aspiradora: Pues, la tienes que reparar (... tienes que repararla); Invité a don Felipe a almorzar: Lo invité...; Tu hermana quiere conocer a don Felipe: ... quiere conocerlo (... lo quiere conocer); ¿Por qué no riegas la planta?: ¿...la riegas?; ¿por qué no sacudiste los muebles?: ¿...los sacudiste¿; ¿Cuándo vas a terminar tus quehaceres?: ¿... los vas a terminar? (¿... a terminarlos?)

B. **1.** No, Doc no las lavó. **2.** Alegre los terminó. **3.** Enojado tiene que limpiarlo (lo tiene que limpiar). **4.** Sí, Tímido lo limpió. **5.** Dormilón va a lavarlos (los va a lavar). **6.** No, Tímido no la guardó. **7.** Enojado tiene que secarlos (los tiene que secar). **8.** Doc las hizo. **9.** Dormilón y Enojado no los hicieron (no hicieron ninguno).

C. Answers will vary.

Gramática 2

A. **1.** vi **2.** era **3.** Eran **4.** me desperté **5.** entré **6.** Busqué
7. había **8.** estaba **9.** recibí **10.** dijo **11.** iba **12.** tenía **13.** era
14. molestaba **15.** quería **16.** estaba **17.** pude **18.** llegó **19.** vio
20. conocía **21.** dijo **22.** era **23.** gustaba

B. Answers will vary but should contain the following. **1.** En la tele
miraba... **2.** Mi programa favorito era... **3.** Jugaba... los sábados.
4. Pasaba las vacaciones... **5.** Quería... para mis cumpleaños.

C. **1.** Arturo escuchaba música. **2.** Carlos lavaba al perro Máximo en el
baño. **3.** María cocinaba. **4.** Rodolfo comía la comida. **5.** Diego y
Carmen miraban la tele.

Lectura

A. **1.** Lo llamaba "Papi". **2.** Marcos y su abuelo se paseaban juntos.
3. Marcos se acuerda del olor de su colonia y de su áspera barba.
4. El día de los padres fue la ocasión de este tributo.

B. **1.** c **2.** b

C. Answers will vary.

Para escribir.   Answers will vary.

C A P Í T U L O   8

Vocabulario

A. **1.** muñecas **2.** finge **3.** mascotas **4.** lagartijas **5.** ranas
6. vecindario **7.** pájaro **8.** cae **9.** miedo **10.** daño **11.** peligrosas
12. tiran **13.** castigan **14.** hambre **15.** sed **16.** sueño
17. sueñan

B. **1.** Los niños juegan al papá y mamá. **2.** Los niños juegan al
escondite. **3.** Los niños construyen cosas. **4.** El niño colecciona
estampillas. **5.** Los niños hacen ruido. **6.** Los niños ven los dibujos
animados.

C. Answers may vary. **1.** Laura llora porque rompió su muñeca.
2. Guillermo llora porque su padre lo castiga. **3.** Los niños lloran
porque se perdieron. **4.** Enrique llora porque tiene miedo del
monstruo. **5.** Federico y Luisa lloran porque su pez se murió.

Gramática 1

A. **1.** escribió **2.** era **3.** nació **4.** perdió **5.** tenía **6.** podía **7.** llegó **8.** trabajaba **9.** dijo **10.** quería **11.** iba **12.** se fue **13.** supo **14.** era **15.** hacía **16.** cuidaba **17.** dio **18.** duró **19.** era **20.** pudo

B. **1.** Rafael tiene treinta y siete años y es arquitecto. Cuando tenía nueve años soñaba con ser bombero. **2.** Luisa tiene cuarenta y un años y es pilota. Cuando tenía trece años quería ser cantante. **3.** Carlos tiene cincuenta y cinco años y Teresa tiene cincuenta y siete años. Trabajan en un laboratorio. Cuando eran jóvenes soñaban con ser jugadores de béisbol. **4.** Ramón tiene quince años y es cantante. Cuando era más pequeño soñaba con ser príncipe. **5.** Julia tiene veintinueve años y es programadora. Cuando tenía diez años soñaba con ser escritora.

C. Answers may vary. **1.** Juan era desordenado porque siempre dejaba sus cosas en el suelo. **2.** Rosita y Diego eran amables porque siempre ayudaba a los animales. **3.** Teresa era muy inteligente porque siempre sacaba buenas notas. **4.** Gerardo era muy tímido porque siempre estaba solo. **5.** Sarita era muy divertida porque hacía reír a los otros niños. **6.** Pablo era muy travieso porque siempre molestaba a su hermana. **7.** Guadalupe era perezosa porque veía dibujos animados en la tele y no hacía la tarea.

D. Answers will vary.

Gramática 2

A. **1.** gustaba; gustó; traían; trajeron; había; venían; hubo; vino **2.** Eran; dormíamos; estaba; durmió; supe; sabían **3.** se vestía; se vistió; vieron; murieron; empezaron; se rieron; pidieron

B. **1.** fui **2.** estaba **3.** parecía **4.** Me sentía **5.** se preocupaban **6.** enseñaron **7.** empecé **8.** deseaba **9.** Nací **10.** perdía **11.** regaló

Lectura I

A. **1.** No son los abuelos biológicos de los niños. Se llaman "abuelos" porque son viejos y cuidan a los niños como abuelos. **2.** Los abuelos se sienten útiles y reciben cariño de los niños. Los niños tienen el beneficio del cariño y de los valores de los "abuelos". **3.** Marta Pascual empezó el programa. **4.** Quería curar el problema de niños que sufren maltrato o abuso sexual en sus familias.

B. **1.** b **2.** c **3.** d

C. **1.** Los abuelos no se sentían útiles. Necesitaban algo importante que hacer. **2.** Los niños vivían con sus padres y sufrían el maltrato o abuso sexual. **3.** Answer may vary. La vida de los abuelos es más feliz y más útil después de Casa Grande. **4.** Answer may vary. La vida de los niños es más tranquila y menos peligrosa.

Lectura II

A. mainframe, Internet, switches, networking, Web

B. **1.** a **2.** a **3.** b **4.** b. **5.** b **6.** c. **7.** c. **8.** b **9.** b

C. Answers may resemble the following.   **1.** Es la hora en que uno tiene que estar en casa.   **2.** Es un castigo. Tienes que quedarte en casa; no te permiten salir.   **3.** Es una cantidad de dinero que un joven recibe de sus padres cada semana o cada mes.   **4.** Es una joven, o un joven, que canta y baila para dar ánimo o espíritu a los jugadores de un deporte.   **5.** Es un joven que le gusta pasar mucho tiempo en un centro comercial.   **6.** Es la ocasión cuando algunos amigos pasan la noche en casa de un amigo.   **7.** Es un baile muy elegante para estudiantes.   **8.** Es un fin de semana cuando los alumnos recién graduados vuelven a su escuela secundaria para visitar y para ver a sus viejos amigos.

Para escribir.   Answers will vary.

C A P Í T U L O   9

Vocabulario

A. **1.** cocer **2.** agria **3.** quemada **4.** cruda **5.** queso **6.** tomate **7.** piña **8.** picante **9.** fresas **10.** freír

B. **1.** desayuno **2.** huevos **3.** jamón **4.** pan **5.** mantequilla **6.** jugo **7.** sopa **8.** pavo **9.** carne **10.** pescado **11.** pollo **12.** ensaladas **13.** tarta **14.** helado **15.** postre

C. Answers will vary.

Gramática 1

A. **1.** Sus cuadros están pintados con colores vivos.   **2.** Los frijoles siempre están quemados.   **3.** Las tareas siempre están hechas con cuidado.   **4.** Sus novelas están escritas con un sentido de magia. **5.** Las lecciones están enseñadas con imaginación.   **6.** El pollo siempre está cocido con demasiada sal.   **7.** La carne de res está cubierta con cebollas.

B. **1.** a. Los padres le dieron un auto (coche, carro) a su hijo. b. —¡Gracias por haberme dado este auto (coche, carro)!   **2.** El ratón le quita la espina de la pata al león. —Gracias por haberme quitado la espina.   **3.** El hada madrina le dio un vestido muy bello a la Cenicienta. —Gracias por haberme dado este vestido.   **4.** Los padres

le dan una manta a la niña. —Gracias por haberme dado la manta.
5. Le dan el Premio Nóbel a la mujer. —Gracias a mis profesores por
haberme enseñado bien. **6.** El hombre inteligente le dijo el secreto al
joven. —Gracias por haberme dicho el secreto.

Gramática 2

A. **1.** Marta ya ha asado el pollo. **2.** Luisa ya ha escrito la receta pero
todavía no ha limpiado el baño o preparado la tortilla. **3.** Dolores ya
ha cocido los frijoles y ha puesto la mesa pero todavía no ha frito las
papas ni ha comprado la langosta.

B. **Paso 1.** **1.** ha ido **2.** ha tratado **3.** he quedado **4.** he salido **5.** he
estado **6.** hemos hecho **7.** ha sido

Paso 2. **1.** Le han gustado la gente, las tradiciones y la cultura de
México. **2.** No ha podido ver más de la región porque ha estado
grabando una película. **3.** Answer may resemble the following. He
visto varias películas de Antonio Banderas. Por ejemplo... **4.** Answer
may resemble the following. Sí. Antonio Banderas se ha casado con
Melanie Griffith.

C. Questions may vary; responses will vary. **1.** ¿Has visto una película
fantástica alguna vez? **2.** ¿Cuántas veces has oído tu conjunto de
rock favorito? **3.** ¿Ya has encontrado el gran amor de tu vida?
4. ¿Has comido platos de otra cultura alguna vez? **5.** ¿Has comido
pescado crudo alguna vez? **6.** ¿Has pasado una noche sin dormir?
7. ¿Has roto algo de mucho valor? **8.** ¿Te has olvidado del
cumpleaños de una persona querida? **9.** ¿Has hecho algo alguna vez
que después has sentido? **10.** ¿Ya has escrito una carta de "Querido
Juan" o "Querida Juana"?

Lectura

A. **1.** El profesor de cocina de Celia Cruz ha sido su esposo. **2.** A Celia le
gusta cocinar cuando vuelve a casa después de un viaje. **3.** Se cultiva
mucho azafrán en España. **4.** Según Celia las tres ventajas de este
plato son: es fácil de preparar, sabe delicioso y no tiene grasa.
5. Baptize(d) **6.** b. cumin

B. Answers will vary.

Para escribir. Answers will vary.

C A P Í T U L O 1 0

Vocabulario

A. **1.** ajo   **2.** galletas; golosinas   **3.** hierbas; olla; hierven   **4.** avena
5. palomitas; maíz; papitas fritas   **6.** sartén   **7.** rebanadas; tocino
8. miel; vinagre   **9.** chocolate   **10.** mostaza

B. **1.** sacar   **2.** pelar   **3.** ajo   **4.** agregar   **5.** olla   **6.** orégano   **7.** libras
8. picados   **9.** medir   **10.** falta   **11.** mezclar   **12.** aroma   **13.** oler
14. fideos

C. The second response in each item may vary.   **1.** El tocino se pesa por
libras. Yo lo como con huevos fritos.   **2.** Las papitas fritas se venden
por paquetes. Las como cuando veo la tele.   **3.** Las galletas se pesan
por libras. Las como con leche.   **4.** Las palomitas de maíz se venden
en paquetes. Las como en el cine.   **5.** La mermelada se vende en
frasco. La como con pan tostado.   **6.** La mostaza se vende en frasco.
La como con perros calientes.

Gramática 1

A. **1.** Carlos se lo dio.   **2.** La bruja se las ofreció.   **3.** Diablito se los
agregó.   **4.** La mamá se la quitó.   **5.** El médico se los prohibió.   **6.** El
gigante se los dio.   **7.** Los dioses se la dio.

B. Answers may resemble the following.   **1.** Mi madre me la preparó.
2. Mi hermano me lo sirvió.   **3.** Sí, se la he servido.   **4.** El restaurante
Rincón de España nos los prepara.   **5.** Julia Childs me lo enseñó.
6. Mi mamá me la preparaba.   **7.** Sí, voy a preparárselo.

C. **1.** Los dioses griegos se la dieron.   **2.** Los habitantes de una isla
extraña se la sirvieron.   **3.** La vieja malvada se la dio.   **4.** Los antiguos
griegos se lo dieron.

Gramática 2

A. **1.** Espero que Ofelia no haya preparado la cena.   **2.** Espero que no me
haya olvidado de dejarle propina.   **3.** Espero que no la haya dejado en
el restaurante.   **4.** Espero que no haya quemado la sopa.   **5.** Espero
que no haya dejado una cebolla podrida por alguna parte.   **6.** Espero
que no lo haya roto.

B. Answers may vary with regard to belief (indicative) and disbelief
(subjunctive).   **1.** han dicho; No creo que siempre hayan dicho la
verdad.   **2.** ha cocinado; Creo que mamá siempre nos ha cocinado
comidas con mucho cariño.   **3.** ha tenido; No creo que siempre haya
tenido cariño por los "Who".   **4.** ha sido; No creo que siempre haya
sido generoso con los pobres.   **5.** ha querido; Creo que siempre ha

querido al pueblo Argentino.   **6.** ha deseado; Creo que ha deseado una vida más tranquila.   **7.** ha tenido; Creo que siempre ha tenido ganas de pintar.

C. 1. No creo que se hayan olvidado de darle comida al gato. Espero que el pobrecito no se haya muerto.   **2.** No creo que ella haya dejado encendida la estufa. Espero que la casa no se haya quemado.   **3.** Creo que ha regado las flores. Espero que mis rosas no hayan muerto.
4. No creo que hayan olvidado de cerrar la puerta con llave. Espero que no haya entrado un ladrón y nos haya robado.

Lectura

A. 1. c   **2.** a   **3.** d

B. Answers will vary.

Para escribir.   Answers will vary.

C A P Í T U L O 1 1

Vocabulario

A. Answers may vary somewhat.   **1.** gafas (anteojos) de sol, una chaqueta (de cuero), pantalones (de cuero) y botas (zapatos)   **2.** una sudadera y zapatos de correr   **3.** un traje con un pañuelo en el bolsillo, una corbata a rayas   **4.** un vestido estampado, un collar de perlas, una pulsera y un anillo de diamantes   **5.** pantalones de pana (a rayas), una camisa a cuadros, un chaleco y gafas (anteojos)   **6.** un suéter, un abrigo y una bufanda   **7.** un impermeable y un paraguas   **8.** un traje de baño a rayas

B. Answers will vary.

C. Horizontales: 1. probarse   **6.** traje   **7.** pana   **10.** conjunto   **11.** va
12. marrón   **13.** moda   **14.** pasada   **Verticales: 2.** rojo   **3.** ropa interior   **4.** encaje   **5.** gris   **8.** pijama   **9.** moradas

Gramática 1

A. 1. sufre   **2.** admiren   **3.** respeta   **4.** tener   **5.** visita   **6.** dice
7. mire   **8.** se vista   **9.** se haga   **10.** se olvide   **11.** se ponga
12. cambiar   **13.** seguir   **14.** se mira   **15.** ve   **16.** reciben
17. piensa **18.** dice   **19.** quiere

B. 1. A Jacinto le gusta que otras chicas lleven faldas cortas pero no quiere que Marisa las lleven.   **2.** A Jacinto le gusta que otras chicas

compren blusas de encaje pero no quiere que Marisa las compre.
3. A Jacinto le gusta que otras chicas salgan con sus amigos hasta
muy tarde pero no le gusta que Marisa salga con sus amigos.   **4.** A
Jacinto le gusta que otras chicas escojan vestidos muy llamativos pero
no quiere que Marisa los escojan.   **5.** A Jacinto le gusta que otras
chicas tengan tatuajes pero no quiere que Marisa los tenga.   **6.** A
Jacinto le gusta que otras chicas se pongan trajes de baño mínimos
pero no quiere que Marisa se los ponga.

C. Answers will vary.

Gramática 2

A. **1.** Es   **2.** está   **3.** está   **4.** es   **5.** es   **6.** es   **7.** está   **8.** es   **9.** es
10. ser   **11.** sean   **12.** es   **13.** estar   **14.** son   **15.** son   **16.** es
17. sea

B. **1.** es   **2.** es   **3.** Soy   **4.** sea   **5.** ser   **6.** Es   **7.** son   **8.** está   **9.** está
10. sea   **11.** sea   **12.** está   **13.** esté.

C. **1.** está; Está; es; está   **2.** estoy; Estoy; es; estoy   **3.** está; es; es; está;
está   **4.** está; está; está; es

D. este; estos; ese; aquella; aquellas

Lectura

A. **1.** La guayabera es tan popular porque es cómoda cuando hace calor.
2. Hoy se usa algodón para hacer las guayaberas.   **3.** c   **4.** a   **5.** Un
español que vivía en Cuba era responsable por el invento de la
guayabera. Su motivo fue que su ropa era demasiado abrigada para el
clima tropical.

B. Answers will vary.

Para escribir.   Answers will vary.

CAPÍTULO 12

Vocabulario

A. **1.** marca   **2.** talla   **3.** queda   **4.** suelta   **5.** arrugada   **6.** gastadas
7. descoloridos   **8.** manchada   **9.** juego   **10.** rotos   **11.** tacones
12. basura   **13.** espejo   **14.** pinta   **15.** peinarse   **16.** elige
17. barba   **18,** vez

B. Answers may vary somewhat.   **1.** Es necesario que el hombre repare la manga de la camisa.   **2.** Es necesario que la mujer planche la camisa (blusa).   **3.** Es necesario que el hombre corte los pantalones (compre pantalones más cortos).   **4.** Es necesario que la joven le saque la mancha al vestido.   **5.** Es necesario que el chico pegue los botones.   **6.** Es necesario que la mujer repare la cremallera.

C. Answers may resemble the following.   **1.** Les recomiendo que lleven faldas cortas.   **2.** Le recomiendo que compre ropa abrigada.   **3.** Le recomiendo que se ponga ropa de marca.   **4.** Le recomiendo que se ponga un traje.   **5.** Le recomiendo que lleve jeans.   **6.** Le recomiendo que lleve ropa gastada y descolorida.

Gramática 1

A. **1.** quieres   **2.** ser   **3.** hagas   **4.** presta   **5.** tengas   **6.** dejes   **7.** parezcas   **8.** devuelvas   **9.** dormir   **10.** toques   **11.** lleguen   **12.** lleven

B. Answers may vary.   **1.** Trato de comer menos para que la ropa me quede bien.   **2.** Saco la ropa de la secadora inmediatamente para que no esté arrugada.   **3.** El fugitivo lleva gafas y una barba falsa para que nadie sepa su identidad.   **4.** Siempre lleva ropa sucia, rota y gastada para que la gente se sienta compasiva (para que la gente le dé dinero).   **5.** El vampiro no tiene espejos en su casa para que sus visitantes no vean que no tiene reflejo.   **6.** El lobo se disfraza de una vieja para que Caperucita Roja no sepa quién es.

C. Answers may resemble the following.   **1.** Para que tu ropa te quede bien es necesario que comas menos.   **2.** Para que tus compañeros no piensen que eres egoísta es necesario que seas generoso(a).   **3.** Para que tus profesores no digan que eres perezoso(a) es necesario que trabajes y estudies.   **4.** Para que tus amigos crean que eres sensible, es necesario que escuches sus problemas.   **5.** Para que puedas encontrar trabajo es necesario que tus profesores te den buenas recomendaciones.   **6.** Para que puedas organizarte es necesario que tu compañero(a) de cuarto quite todas sus cosas.

Gramática 2

A. **1.** a. Busco un hombre que diseñe ropa más elegante que Oscar de la Renta. b. No hay nadie que diseñe ropa más elegante que Oscar de la Renta.   **2.** a. Busco un hombre que se ponga ropa más cómica que don Payasito. b. No hay nadie que se ponga ropa más cómica que don Payasito.   **3.** a. Busco un autor que escriba novelas más memorables que García Márquez. b. No hay nadie que escriba novelas...   **4.** a. Busco un artista que pinte cuadros más fabulosos que Frida Kahlo. b. No hay nadie que pinte...   **5.** a. Busco una persona que tenga más gorros de béisbol que Raúl. b. No hay nadie que tenga...   **6.** a. Busco un joven que lleve los pantalones más largos y sueltos que Mario. b. No hay nadie que lleve...

B. **1.** El profesor Arévalo busca una persona que pueda cuidar niños, que tenga por lo menos 18 años y que tenga experiencia con niños pequeños.   **2.** Ariel Gutiérrez quiere comprar un carro usado que tenga menos de 10.000 millas y que cueste menos de 2.000 dólares.   **3.** Carla Díaz busca una compañera de cuarto que sea madura y responsable y que pueda pagar 200 dólares al mes.   **4.** Isabel Sánchez busca una persona que pueda cuidar su perro por dos semanas, que sea responsable y que quiera a los animales.   **5.** La profesora Eva Santos quiere emplear un alumno que le ayude con un proyecto de investigación escolar, que sea trabajador y que sepa inglés y francés.

C. Answers will vary.

Lectura

A. **1.** La costumbre de tatuarse se originó con los indios de Tahití, en la Polinesia.   **2.** Según Katun su cuerpo es como una obra de arte.   **3.** b   **4.** Las empresas tienen condiciones de empleo tan estrictas porque hay tantas personas que buscan cada empleo (hay tantos candidatos para cada puesto.)   **5.** Porque algunas empresas prohiben que sus empleados tengan tatuajes.   **6.** En el artículo se cuestiona si una empresa tiene el derecho de determinar la apariencia de sus empleados.

B. Answers will vary.

Para escribir.   Answers will vary.

C A P Í T U L O 1 3

Vocabulario

A. **1.** la salud   **2.** una enfermedad   **3.** cabeza   **4.** evita   **5.** hígado
6. fumar   **7.** pulmones   **8.** riñones   **9.** ejercicios   **10.** músculos
11. cuida   **12.** evitar   **13.** lleva   **14.** sana   **15.** sangre   **16.** corazón
17. huesos   **18.** estómago   **19.** codo   **20.** cuello   **21.** estrés

B. **1.** ojos   **2.** frente   **3.** ceja   **4.** oreja   **5.** cabeza   **6.** boca   **7.** fuma
8. molestar   **9.** nariz   **10.** dedos   **11.** pulgares   **12.** muñeca
13. codos   **14.** tobillos   **15.** pecho (estómago)   **16.** corazón

C. Answers will vary.

Gramática 1

A. **1.** sigue; escuches   **2.** cree; creas   **3.** tomes; vive   **4.** lleva; permitas
5. Construye; pierdas   **6.** Di; digas

B. Answers will vary but should contain the following. **1.** Si te duele la cabeza, toma... no tomes... **2.** Si te duele el estómago, come... no comas... **3.** Si te duele la espalda, ve ... no vayas... **4.** Si quieres encontrar a tu pareja perfecta, busca... no busques... **5.** Si quieres llevarte bien con tus compañeros de cuarto, pon... no pongas... **6.** Si las películas de terror te causan pesadillas, ve... no veas... **7.** Si el café te produce insomnio, toma... no tomes...

Gramática 2

1. Aféitate. No molestes a tus padres. **2.** No te quejes. Ríete de tus problemas. **3.** No te quedes solo. Júntate con tus amigos. **4.** No te despiertes tarde y no te olvides de darles de comer a los caballos del rancho. **5.** No te acuestes tarde, levántate temprano. **6.** No te preocupes por cosas sin importancia. Siéntete bien. **7.** No te mueras de estrés; relájate.

Lectura

A. **1.** El estrés es peligroso porque puede causar enfermedades. **2.** El autor nos dice que dos gobiernos, el italiano y el británico, reconocen legalmente enfermedades causadas por el estrés. **3.** Answers will vary. Varios métodos empleados para combatir el estrés son: hacerse hipnotizar; visitar a psicoanalistas; y practicar las artes marciales. **4.** El autor recomienda el Tai-Chi-Chuan. **5.** a

B. Answers will vary.

Para escribir. Answers will vary.

CAPÍTULO 14

Vocabulario

A. **1.** sufría **2.** fiebre **3.** garganta **4.** escalofríos **5.** síntomas **6.** inflamadas **7.** tapada **8.** tos **9.** mejorarme **10.** droga **11.** inyección **12.** recetó **13.** medicamento **14.** antibiótico **15.** hinchada **16.** roncha **17.** picaba **18.** picaduras **19.** grave **20.** increíble **21.** curado

B. **1.** náuseas **2.** yeso **3.** fractura **4.** cayó **5.** venda **6.** sufrió **7.** cayó **8.** cuidado **9.** lastimaduras **10.** quebró **11.** lástima **12.** alérgica **13.** polen **14.** abeja **15.** estornudos **16.** Ojalá

C. Answers will vary.

Gramática 1

A. Answers may resemble the following.   **1.** Sea cariñoso, proteja a sus hijos, quiéralos y tenga paciencia con ellos.   **2.** No critique a nadie, no visite sin ser invitada, ofrezca consejos sólo cuando se los piden y hágale favores a la familia.   **3.** Siempre diga mentiras, finja ser buen amigo, parezca ser honrado y engañe a todo el mundo.   **4.** Sepa los nuevos conocimientos, explíqueles bien los problemas a los enfermos, sea paciente, conozca bien a sus pacientes.   **5.** Váyase a un lugar tranquilo, escriba sobre un tema que conozcas bien, olvídese de cosas triviales e incluya el amor.   **6.** Answers will vary.

B. **1.** Sr. Calderón, tenga cuidado; no se caiga.   **2.** Tomás y Anita, tomen el jarabe; no sigan con tos.   **3.** Sra. Ramírez, mire lo que hace; no se corte.   **4.** Niños, llévense bien; no se lastimen.   **5.** Niñas, protéjanse; no se quiebren un hueso.

Gramática 2

A. **1.** es **2.** se case **3.** quedarse **4.** cuidar **5.** sea **6.** importe **7.** haya **8.** quiere **9.** pueda **10.** muera **11.** está **12.** digan **13.** sepa **14.** encuentren **15.** sea **16.** guardar **17.** tengamos

B. Answers may vary. **1.** Ojalá que pronto descubran la cura para el SIDA.   **2.** Es una lástima que no hayan descubierto la cura para muchas formas del cáncer.   **3.** Dudo que sea posible ser alérgico...   **4.** Es imposible que las hierbas puedan combatir...   **5.** Dudo que una roncha sea...   **6.** Es imposible que el alma se vaya...   **7.** Dudo que el humo sólo le haga daño a ...   **8.** Me alegro de que los niños tengan cuidado...   **9.** Es necesario que en los Estados Unidos haya...

C. Answers will vary.   **1.** Es una lástima que Ud. tenga tantos problemas. **2.** Es posible que su marido tenga celos de su hijo (sea demasiado estricto.) **3.** Es mejor que su hijo no se vaya. **4.** Le recomiendo que conozca y entienda a Marisol. **5.** Es imposible que este problema dure mucho tiempo. **6.** Es necesario que tenga paciencia. **7.** No va a vivir tranquila a menos que tenga buenas relaciones con su hijo. **8.** Puede ser feliz con tal de que respete a cada persona de su familia. **9.** Espero que todo le vaya bien.

Lectura

A. **1.** Laura Esquivel se divorció y tiene problemas legales con respecto a su película.   **2.** Su nueva novela se llama *La ley del amor*.   **3.** Los protagonistas quieren entender las causas de su amor perdido. Buscan una explicación en sus acciones del pasado.   **4.** Los aspectos raros son que la novela cubra tanto tiempo y que integre música.

B. Answers will vary.

Para escribir.   Answers will vary.

CAPÍTULO 15

Vocabulario

A. **1.** contaminación **2.** calle **3.** desamparados **4.** ruido **5.** humo **6.** rascacielos **7.** transporte **8.** sucursales **9.** cárceles **10.** vendedores **11.** esquina **12.** atascadas **13.** anchas **14.** municipalidad **15.** empresa **16.** invertir **17.** conductores **18.** huelga **19.** estación, metro **20.** choque **21.** parada **22.** lleno **23.** cuadras **24.** impuestos **25.** alcalde **26.** aumentado

B. Answers may resemble the following. **1.** Para los peatones habrá sendas bonitas y zonas verdes. **2.** Para las madres que trabajan habrá guarderías infantiles buenas. **3.** Para los desempleados habrá servicios de educación. **4.** Para los desamparados habrá instalaciones especiales. **5.** Para los ancianos habrá hogares para los ancianos. **6.** Para los que no tienen auto habrá más transporte público y mejores estaciones de metro.

C. **Horizontales: 1.** semáforo **6.** pena **7.** acera **8.** acero **12.** guarderías **14.** aumenta **16.** echar **17.** doy **Verticales: 1.** senda **2.** en **3.** mantener **4.** once **5.** obras **9.** cárcel **10.** hasta **11.** puente **13.** deuda **15.** tío

Gramática 1

A. **1.** se mudará **2.** vivirá **3.** llegue **4.** celebrarán **5.** tendrán **6.** será **7.** podrán **8.** estarán **9.** sepan **10.** disminuirá **11.** esté

B. Answers will vary but should contain the following. **1.** Yo seré feliz cuando... **2.** Mis padres no estarán contentos hasta que... **3.** No habrá paz en el mundo hasta que... **4.** Yo no me casaré hasta que... **5.** Los problemas urbanos se mejorarán cuando... **6.** Yo apoyaré un candidato político cuando... **7.** Yo tendré hijos cuando... **8.** Cuando una mujer sea presidente, el país... **9.** Mis padres me apoyarán hasta que...

Gramática 2

A. **1.** El policía está dirigiendo el tráfico. **2.** El conductor de taxi está tocando la bocina. **3.** El autobús está echando humo. **4.** Los ciudadanos están apoyando a un candidato. **5.** Los hombres están construyendo un edificio. **6.** Los peatones están andando por la calle. **7.** La basura está aumentando. **8.** El desamparado está durmiendo en la acera.

B. **1.** Pero está construyéndola. **2.** Pero está disminuyéndola. **3.** Pero estoy encontrándolos. **4.** Pero están visitándolos. **5.** Pero están mejorándolo.

C. Answers will vary.

Lectura

1. Antes de ser alcalde de Bogotá, Mockus era rector de la Universidad Nacional.   **2.** Sus intereses académicos son la filosofía y las matemáticas.   **3.** Es un alcalde diferente porque: no tenía experiencia política; se viste y se arregla de una manera casual y rara; va por la ciudad vestido de "supercívico".   **4.** Paga dinero por armas; cierra los bares temprano durante las fiestas; y ofrece una vacuna simbólica contra la violencia.   **5.** Trata de inspirarles un sentido cívico por vestirse de "supercívico" y por apoyar concursos para encontrar el superciudadano del año.   **6.** a   **7.** c   **8.** Answers will vary.

Para escribir.   Answers will vary.

C A P Í T U L O   1 6

Vocabulario

A. **1.** Tierra   **2.** solidaridad   **3.** recursos   **4.** agotar   **5.** medio ambiente   **6.** amenazadas   **7.** peligro, extinción   **8.** desperdicios   **9.** fabricar   **10.** matando/envenenando   **11.** pesticidas   **12.** amenazamos   **13.** dañinos   **14.** combustible   **15.** capa, ozono   **16.** políticas, conservación   **17.** planeta

B. **1.** la ballena   **2.** el tigre   **3.** la tortuga   **4.** el león   **5.** el caimán   **6.** el águila   **7.** el delfín   **8.** incendios forestales

C. Answers will vary.

Gramática 1

A. **1.** quisiera   **2.** agotar   **3.** era   **4.** se calentara   **5.** siguiera   **6.** respiraran   **7.** encendió   **8.** entró   **9.** se olvidó   **10.** anduvo   **11.** se ganara   **12.** se mudara   **13.** regaba   **14.** tuviera   **15.** utilizar   **16.** tuviera   **17.** se diera   **18.** cuidar

B. Answers may vary.   **1.** Ojalá que limpiaran sus desperdicios en vez de tirarlos en los ríos.   **2.** Ojalá que cuidaran el medio ambiente en vez de agotarlo.   **3.** Ojalá que trataran a los animales con compasión en vez de dañarlos.   **4.** Ojalá que protegiéramos la capa de ozono en vez de destruirla.   **5.** Ojalá que recogieran la basura en vez de tirarla en las calles.   **6.** Ojalá que previnieran los virus en vez de producirlos.   **7.** Ojalá que se usaran métodos naturales en vez de pesticidas.   **8.** Ojalá que la gente del mundo pudiera vivir en paz.

C Answers will vary.

Gramática 2

A. Answers will vary but should contain the following.
1. Si pudiera saber el futuro... **2.** Si no tuviera que terminar mis estudios... **3.** Si no tuviera tanto que hacer... **4.** Si el mundo fuera perfecto... **5.** Si los animales pudieran hablar... **6.** Si supiéramos lo que está pensando otra persona... **7.** Si hubiéramos desarrollado lo suficiente la energía solar... **8.** Si nos diéramos cuenta de que... **9.** Si recicláramos lo suficiente... **10.** Si hubiera solidaridad...

B. Answers will vary but should contain the following.
1. Yo tendría mucho miedo si... **2.** Mis amigos serían felices si... **3.** Yo aprendería más si... **4.** La vida sería menos peligrosa si... **5.** No habría más guerras si... **6.** Nadie conduciría borracho si... **7.** El medio ambiente se mejoraría si...

C. Answers will vary but should contain the following.
1. Si yo fuera Romeo/Julieta... **2.** Si yo fuera una persona inmortal... **3.** Si yo fuera el profesor/la profesora... **4.** Si yo fuera el jefe/la jefa de... **5.** Si yo fuera Blancanieves... **6.** Si yo fuera el líder de... **7.** Si yo fuera el jefe/la jefa de una gran empresa...

Lectura

A. 1. El viejo lloró. Tuvo una reacción tan fuerte porque fue la primera vez que había visto los animales de su propio país. **2.** En Belice no han quemado los bosques tropicales. Belice ha preservado más de su tierra como parques y reservas. **3.** Sharon Matola tiene gran entusiasmo y energía. Su gran pasión es la naturaleza: los bosques y los animales. Su meta principal es guardar y preservarlos. También quiere crear un orgullo y conciencia entre la gente con respecto a sus recursos naturales. **4.** El mérito de su esfuerzo se encuentra en la reacción de maravilla de los niños. **5.** c **6.** a **7.** b **8.** Answers will vary.

B. Answers will vary.

Para escribir.   Answers will vary.

Self-Tests Answer Key

This answer key to each Unit's **Autoevaluación** may help you check or improve your answers. Each **Autoevaluación** is a diagnostic test that samples your ability to retrieve discrete items from memory and also to compose personal answers using several different aspects of your learning as well as the different strategies practiced. In many cases, a specific appropriate answer cannot be provided, either because you are expected to give a personal answer or because your answer will depend on the emphasis given by your instructor to different sections of the material in each unit. Whenever this is the case, the phrases *Variable answers* or *Personal answers* will be used to indicate that your answer can vary within certain acceptable parameters. Sometimes, a possible appropriate answer will be suggested.

PRUEBA: UNIDAD 1

I. Cultura

Variable answers that contain at least the following.

1. Hispanic people's names encapsulate the family's history in its structure. A Hispanic person has a given or Christian name that may be a granparent's or parent's or *both*, or it may have as a central point the name of a revered patron saint or Jesus, Joseph or Mary's. Following the **nombre**, come both the paternal and the maternal family names or **apellidos**. Thus, names cannot be shortened for ease of reading without dropping some important element of the person's identity.

2 There isn't such a thing as Latino race. Hispanic people may come from different races; what unites them is their cultural traditions and tendencies. **La Raza** is a label used to mean *"the Hispanic people"* but it does not correspond to a race as such.

3. Hispanics focus on the person (rather than education or accomplishments) in a job interview. After feeling comfortable with the candidate as a person, they go on to review background and plans.

II. Vocabulario y lectura

A. Solicitud de beca. *Personal answers*, but answer every question and use Hispanic writing conventions for name, address, dates.

B. Asociaciones. *Personal answers*, but make sure your answers are appropriate to the season and the occupation, characteristics, and interests of the person chosen.

En octubre, ... le gusta/ tiene interés en... salir con amigos/ ir de compras/ viajar a... porque es... tranquilo y amistoso

En junio, ... quiere descansar/ viajar/ comprar/ hacer ejercicio/ trabajar en... porque quiere ser...

Es muy emprendedor/a y puede trabajar en la computadora/ hablar dos idiomas... Tiene interés en...

Para el año 2005 va a... sacar fotografías para revistas/ sacar su título en.../ ser ingeniero en.../ programar computadoras en...

C. Fechas y precios importantes. *Personal answers*, but answer every question and use Hispanic writing conventions for name, address, dates.

D. Dos amigos. Lucía: ¿Aló? **Luis:** Buenas tardes. ¿Puedo hablar con Lucía, por favor? **Lucía:** Con ella. ¿Quién es? **Luis:** Hola, Lucía. Soy Luis, de la clase de administración de empresas. **Lucía:** ¡Hola, Luis! ¿Cómo estás?

E. Lectura. Los chicos maravilla. *Variable answers*; suggestions follow.

1. ... pueden resolver secretos de las computadoras/ introducir sus ojos en documentos importantes.

2. ... roban (super)secretos/ invaden sitios prohibidos/ penetran sistemas protegidos.

3. ... para resolver problemas/ conocer otra gente/ ganar más sueldo/ buscar un puesto.

III. Gramática

A. Precisión. 1. es, tiene es **2.** tienes que, es, tener **3.** tienes que, tienen, son, tienen que

B. ¿Qué puedo decir? *Personal answers*; suggestions follow. **1.** Quiero ir a... y a..., pero también tengo que... **2.** Podemos ir a... o podemos salir con... Además, también podemos.... **3.** No puedo, porque tengo que buscar empleo/ tomar una prueba.../ Claro, podemos ir a...
4. No, porque quiero estudiar/ trabajar/ mirar la televisión... Claro, ¿vamos a salir con...? **5.** Pero podemos ir a nadar/ tocar la guitarra. Podemos escuchar música y después ir de compras/ cocinar algo...

C. Para invitar tienes que insistir. *Personal answers*; suggestions follow. **1.** ¿Quieres sacar un título de...? ¿Por qué no sacamos un...? Creo que podemos sacar un... Para 2005 tenemos que sacar un...
2. ¿Quieres buscar un empleo en...? ¿Por qué no buscamos un empleo en...? Tú y yo podemos buscar empleo en... **3.** ¿Te gusta ser dueño(a) de...? Tú y yo podemos ser... Creo que para 2010 podemos ser...

D. Por una razón muy sencilla. *Personal answers*; suggestions follow.
1. tiene que ganar un sueldo magnífico/ quiere comprar otro coche/ le gusta conocer otra gente/ buscar un puesto interesante **2.** no quiere mandar una solicitud.../ no es emprendedor/ no quiere buscar un

puesto   3. quiere encontrar empleo/ quiere sacar el título pronto/ quiere ganar un sueldo magnífico   4. no pago mis cuentas/ no tengo tiempo/ soy algo impaciente/ soy muy perezoso(a)   5. les gusta salir con.../ quieren conocer otra gente/ tienen interés en...

E. Buen editor.   **1.** deportista   **2.** corre   **3.** mucho   **4.** tiene   **5.** algo   **6.** me   **7.** colombiana   **8.** gusta   **9.** quiero   **10.** a

IV. Expresión oral

Personal answers; suggestions follow. **1.** ¿Aló? ¿Puedo hablar con...? ¿Con quién hablo? Con... ¿Trabaja XX aquí? No, trabaja en... **2.** ¿Qué te interesa hacer los sábados? ¿Eres ordenado(a) o desordenado(a)? ¿Te gusta...? **3.** Soy...; ¿y tú? ¿Cómo te llamas? Me llamo XX y trabajo en... ¿Qué estudias? ¿Qué te gusta hacer los...?

V. Expresión escrita

Variable answers; suggestions follow.   Use the vocabulary, strategies, and structures learned.   **1.** Use model of **Así soy yo** on p. 49 or *begin*: En la residencia, tengo un/a amigo(a). Es muy simpático(a), ... También es algo desordenado(a), ... y ...   **2.** Follow Carmen Elena's **currículum** on p. 77.

P R U E B A :   U N I D A D   2

I.   Cultura

Variable answers that contain at least the following.

1. Not everybody but many... Some business operations will be put on hold for two/ three weeks or managers will rotate to maintain essential activities. Many customers are on vacation also or know the "down" period and will act accordingly. As is to be expected, essential businesses, public services, and institutions do not stop normal operations.

2. In comparison to Americans, Europeans do get more vacation time and this is traditional. Germans and Swedes seem to get the longest vacation period with 5 or 6 weeks a year.

3. Yes, as time for family and relaxation, vacations are taken very seriously by Hispanics and other Europeans. It does not follow, however, that businesses, careers or jobs are neglected.

II. Vocabulario y lectura

A. En la agencia de viajes. *Personal answers*, but answer every question and use Hispanic writing conventions for name, address, dates.

B. El tiempo. **1.** verano, hace calor, hace sol **2.** invierno, hace mucho frío, hay nieve **3.** verano, primavera, otoño, no llueve, hace sol, me siento/ estoy bien/ cansado(a) **4.** verano, primavera, otoño, hace calor, hace fresco **5.** verano, hace sol, hace mucho calor **6.** primavera, verano, hace calor, hace sol **7.** otoño, hace fresco **8.** verano, hace calor

C. Asociaciones. *Variable answers;* suggestions follow. **1.** me acuesto/ duermo/ hago una fiesta/ toco mis discos compactos/ alquilo una película **2.** voy a la playa a tomar el sol/ hago una fiesta/ navego en bote de vela/ monto en bici, patino, me divierto en grande con mis amigos **3.** tomo sol/ esquío en el agua/ doy un paseo/ navego en bote de vela/ buceo/ nado **4.** llamo a mis amigos/ toco mis discos compactos/ miro la televisión/ voy a(l)... a... **5.** voy a casa/ a nadar en la piscina/ a la playa a tomar el sol/ a bucear en el mar/ pescar/ esquiar en el agua/ navegar en canoa/ ir a un parque de atracciones/ montar en bici **6.** aprendo algo nuevo/ limpio mi habitación/ lavo la ropa/ duermo **7.** voy a acampar/ al río a pescar/ a esquiar/ a navegar/ al campo a montar a caballo/ a esquiar **8.** duermo/ descanso/ llamo a mis amigos/ leo/ alquilo una película **9.** duermo/ descanso/ llamo a mis amigos/ voy a la playa a tomar el sol/ doy un paseo/ juego con mi perro/ lavo la ropa

D. Mi tiempo libre. *Variable answers;* suggestions follow. **1.** quiero irme a... porque quiero... **2.** me quedo en casa o duermo, me siento triste/ deprimido(a), me junto con los amigos, no me arreglo, me despierto tarde **3.** pescar/ tomar el sol/ vestirme bien y juntarme con mis amigos/ esquiar en el agua o navegar, montar/ acampar/ ir a un parque/ patinar porque quiero olvidarme de... **4.** porque no tengo ganas de lavar la ropa/ vestirme bien para ir a trabajar otra vez/ no quiero ir a trabajar **5.** hago deportes/ juego baloncesto/ hago una fiesta/ aprendo algo nuevo/ me junto con... **6.** los estudios, los horarios, los problemas, la rutina. Estoy harto(a) de levantarme temprano/ ducharme rápido/ acostarme tarde

E. Lectura. **1.** que los alumnos no gastan mucho dinero/ pueden encontrar a Dios en la naturaleza/ aprenden a conocerse/ comprenderse/ ayudarse. También se apartan de la mediocridad, el consumismo y la pasividad **2.** el frío, el viento, tener que mantenerse bien y sentirse llenos de energía **3.** encontrar a Dios, aprender a conocerte/ comprenderse/ ayudarse, apartarte de la mediocridad/ el consumismo **4.** apartarse de..., divertirse en la montaña, no sólo pasarse en fiestas **5. subir** = *to climb* **promover** = *to promote* **gastar** = *to spend* **locura** = *madness, unusual activity* **apartarse** = *to distance oneself*

III. Gramática

A. Precisión. **1.** divertirme **2.** aburrirme **3.** me muero **4.** estoy/ me siento/ me voy **5.** nos vamos **6.** juntarnos **7.** nos escribimos **8.** nos decimos **9.** divertirse/ vestirse **10.** divertirme/ aburrirme/ dormirme

B. ¿Qué puedo decir? *Variable answers;* suggestions follow. **1.** Me levanto a las... **2.** Me gustan las vacaciones, me gusta irme a..., me gusta quedarme en... **3.** Me gradúo el... de... de... **4.** Generalmente, me quejo de... los estudios/ el/la profesor/a de.../ las tareas/ las lecturas/ la rutina/ los problemas...   **5.** Porque se preocupan por los estudios/ están muy (pre)ocupados/ se llaman por teléfono/ se escriben notas por el correo electrónico...

C. Ay, no puedo. *Variable answers*; suggestions follow.   **1.** Porque llueve/ hace frío/ me muero de cansancio/ no tengo ganas de salir. Además, no tengo dinero/ estoy deprimido(a)/ no tengo energía/ estoy aburrido(a)/ mañana jueves tengo prueba...   **2.** No, porque tengo ganas de ir a una discoteca/ comer/ alquilar una película. Además, quiero juntarme con...   **3.** El martes tengo... y también hay... y ahora hace calor/ frío. Además, tengo que arreglar mi cuarto y lavar la ropa también.

D. Misión imposible. *Variable answers*; suggestions follow.   **1.** se levanta, toma sol, asiste a clases, se arregla bien   **2.** quiero/ puedo trabajar/ arreglar mi cuarto/ hablar por teléfono/ leer/ asistir a clases/ jugar...   **3.** asistir a clases/ acostarme/ ducharme/ bañarme/ salir a bailar   **4.** preocupo por nada/ limpio nada/ llamo a nadie/ hablo por teléfono/ lavo la ropa   **5.** me duermo, me acuesto, me levanto, me siento lleno(a) de energía

E. Buen editor.   **1.** a qué hora   **2.** se juntan   **3.** se olvidan   **4.** A todos   **5.** aprender   **6.** hace   **7.** pasarlo   **8.** a ti   **9.** hablar   **10.** quedarte   **11.** irse   **12.** hacer   **13.** informarnos   **14.** encontrar

IV. Expresión oral

Personal answers; suggestions follow.

1. ¿Quieres irte de vacaciones? ¿Cuándo te diviertes en grande? No puedo irme de vacaciones porque no tengo mucho dinero. Podemos ir a la playa porque es muy barato. Quiero quedarme aquí. Además, me preocupo mucho por los estudios.

2. ¿Qué hacen para divertirse? Nosotros nos juntamos en/ con, vamos a..., navegamos, tenemos un grupo de... ¿Qué deportes hacen? Aquí los estudiantes juegan.../ esquían/ trabajan en... ¿Cuándo tienen vacaciones Uds.? ¿Cuándo es verano en su/ tu país? Aquí tenemos unos puentes muy largos en... y entonces nos gusta... Además, también hacemos fiestas y...

3. ¿Por qué no te gusta el sistema nuevo? ¿Cuándo te gusta asistir a clase y cuándo prefieres irte de vacaciones? En enero, nos podemos ir a la playa a... y después regresar a clases en febrero. En junio trabajamos y en julio podemos...

V. Expresión escrita

Una pintura con palabras. *Variable answers.* Use the vocabulary, strategies, and structures learned. Use reflexive pronouns when necessary. *Begin:* Es..., el primer día de las vacaciones de.... . Estoy en..., muy lejos de la universidad.

P R U E B A : U N I D A D 3

I. Cultura

Variable answers that contain at least the following.

1. In Hispanic culture, important events are always shared with the family. An anniversary is a joyous occasion, and they want to celebrate with the family so everyone can share in their happiness, just like the day when they got married.

2. In Hispanic countries, wives often keep their paternal and maternal last names as a sign of loyalty to their family, since their last name is composed of the **apellidos** of both parents. If a wife chooses to add her husband's last name, his paternal last name will follow the other names preceded by **de**.

3. In many Hispanic countries, what Americans would consider to be the first floor is the ground floor instead. So **apartamento 305** would be on what Americans consider to be the fourth floor, rather than the third.

II. Vocabulario y lectura

A. Datos personales. *Personal answers*, but answer every question and use Hispanic writing conventions for name, address, dates.

B. ¿Con quién y cuándo? *Variable answers*; suggestions follow.
1. Compartimos buenas ideas con... **2.** Los abuelos influyen a los nietos porque... **3.** Consigo un buen sueldo cuando hablo con... **4.** Nos llevamos bien con mis primos... **5.** Nos morimos de la risa cuando mi tía... **6.** Con mi papá buscamos regalos para el Día de la Madre... **7.** Sacamos fotografías con mi.../ cuando voy a casa de... **8.** Compartimos muchos secretos con mis hermanos... **9.** Pago el alquiler con mi amigo(a)... **10.** Con XX y XX nos damos consejos cuando tenemos problemas... **11.** Siempre pido un favor a... **12.** Nos peleamos con mis amigos de la escuela porque... **13.** Con mi hermano(a) trabajamos juntos(as) para la Navidad... **14.** Leemos... con mi amigo... **15.** Nos vamos a casar el mismo día con mi prima...

C. Asociaciones. *Variable answers*; suggestions follow. **1.** unas tarjetas, un pastel, regalos... **2.** una licencia de conducir, tarjetas de crédito, dinero, monedas... **3.** páginas, cuentos, papel, tinta, historias... **4.** vino, vasos, botellas, comida... **5.** padrinos, un bebé, regalos, tarjetas, la familia... **6.** lágrimas, familia, amigos, tren, avión... **7.** ropa, libros, cuadernos, la cama... **8.** guantes, cinturones, botas, zapatos... **9.** la familia, pastel, regalos, tarjetas...

D. ¿Cuál es la ventaja? *Variable answers*; suggestions follow. **1.** nació un bebé y se necesita más espacio. Además, ganan más sueldo y tienen más dinero. **2.** así no tienes que limpiar. Las mujeres no cocinan tampoco y pueden compartir más durante la comida.

3. prefieren cuidarse solos. Les gusta vivir solos y no quieren cambiar sus costumbres. **4.** quieren tener hijos. Les gusta tener hijos y compartir su vida con sus seres queridos. **5.** tienes menos presión social. Además, puedes jugar en el campo sin tener miedo de mala gente, las drogas...

E. Lectura. **1.** ... parientes/ gente de la familia. **2.** ... cuidar a los menores y estudiar mucho para sacar buenas notas. **3.** ... se divertían y sacaron las peores notas del colegio. **4.** ... siempre terminó bien sus cosas. **5.** ... es la más feliz de todas.

III. Gramática

A. Precisión.

1. se fue **2.** durmió/ sintió/ dijo **3.** sacó **4.** se despidió **5.** fue **6.** se divorciaron **7.** empecé/ me fui **8.** sentí **9.** me morí **10.** dijo

B. ¿Qué puedo decir? *Personal answers*; suggestions follow. **1.** Mi... influyó más porque... **2.** Me mudé para acá cuando tenía... años. **3.** ... me dio el mejor regalo para mi cumpleaños. Fue un/a... **4.** ¿Para qué lo quieres?/ No hay más dinero/ Sólo tengo... **5.** Reciba mi más sentido pésame (por esta irreparable pérdida).

C. ¿Qué dijeron?

Ana Luisa: me repitió/ me dijo **Carmencita:** a Luis le dijo **Ana Luisa:** le respondimos/ dijimos a ella **Carmencita:** nos insistió/ nos respondió/ nos insistió

D. Fue imposible. *Variable answers*; suggestions follow. **1.** le llevó flores/ le tiró arroz **2.** le dio un beso a la abuela **3.** me dio una rebaja/ le di las gracias/ me despedí de él/ le pedí un recibo **4.** me despedí de ellos/ les di regalos de Navidad/ les compré nada/ les ayudé **5.** le mandé una tarjeta/ le compré un regalo

E. Buen editor. **1.** tan **2.** le **3.** cumplió **4.** A todos **5.** influyó **6.** la peor **7.** demostraron **8.** buenas **9.** nos **10.** muy

IV. Expresión oral

Personal answers; suggestions follow.

1. Busco una cosa que sirve para la mesa, que tiene..., que es de... ¿Para qué sirve? ¿Cómo es? ¿De qué es? ¿Cuánto cuesta/ vale, más o menos? ¿En qué departamento está?

2. Es una persona que tiene interés en... y le gusta... Siempre le ayuda a sus amigos y, además, también... Deben votar por XX porque es tan... ¿Cómo es? ¿Qué hace extraordinariamente bien? ¿Qué cosas hace mejor que los otros?

3. ¿Por qué no me das permiso para...? ¿Por qué le das... a mi hermano(a) pero no a mí? Sólo por esta vez, ¿por qué no me...? No puedo darte/ permitirte/ llevarte a... porque...

V. Expresión escrita

Variable answers. Use the vocabulary, strategies, and structures learned. Use indirect object pronouns when necessary.

PRUEBA: UNIDAD 4

I. Cultura

Variable answers that contain at least the following.

1. Each Spanish-speaking country has its own culture, local traditions and celebrations, its own vocabulary, depending on different cultural influences. Because of this, each country has its own currency, customs, food, music, etc., making each different from all the others.

2. Each Spanish-speaking country has its own vocabulary due to different language influences like Italian in Argentina, indigenous languages in Bolivia, or English in Puerto Rico. These make each country's vocabulary, pronunciation and intonation different. However, it's not necessary to learn the vocabulary from each country, since there are generally accepted words that almost everyone understands.

3. Because there can be differences in vocabulary, people in one country who have not had contact with other countries will not automatically know their vocabulary.

4. Cities are very important in Hispanic culture, and most people live in large cities. Housing is usually apartment buildings or small houses that are close together. But the houses themselves are quite comfortable, and people like living close to their families and neighbors, proving the value of the extended family and friends in Hispanic cultures.

5. Separate schools for boys and girls are not meant to prevent them from marrying too young. Many schools are Catholic, and nuns or priests have traditionally been in charge of teaching the children. Being with children of the same sex helps them to focus more on their studies and less on relationships, which are the natural focus of family and business activities.

II. Vocabulario y lectura

A. **Encuesta de viviendas estudiantiles.** *Personal answers.*

B. **Para ayudar a un novato.** *Variable answers.* Be sure to spell out the numbers.

C. **Buenos amigos.** *Personal answers*; suggested chores follow.
1. ... limpiar el refrigerador, hacer las camas, ordenar la cómoda, limpiar los dormitorios. **2.** ... cortar el césped, sacar la basura, pasar la aspiradora, pintar las paredes del salón. **3.** ... poner la mesa, lavar la ropa y sacar la basura.

D. **Lectura.** **1.** ... reflejan la sociedad en general. **2.** ... salía de la casa y miraba si había otros niños en la calle... **3.** quería... liberar a las mujeres oprimidas, mostrarles a sus padres la vanidad en sus vidas, salvar el planeta   **4.** a llevar la casa, a ser mamá y tener muchos hijitos   **5.** tiene una tienda muy grande y ahora le enseña a llevar el negocio a su hijo.   **6.** *Personal answer.*

III. Gramática

A. Precisión.   1. eran   **2.** estaba   **3.** estaban   **4.** había   **5.** supe   **6.** podía   **7.** quise   **8.** iba a   **9.** conocía   **10.** era   **11.** eran

B. La vida era más fácil.   *Variable answers,* but should contain preterit or imperfect verbal forms, depending on the context.
1. era..., tenía..., vivía en... Una vez, me dio/ regaló/ invitó/ llevó a...
2. quería... y, además, quería un/a... porque yo creía que era Batman...   **3.** Me gustaba ir a acampar a Tennesee o coleccionar ranas... o montar en bicicleta por... Un verano fuimos a...   **4.** Me sentaba a leer/ a hacer las tareas. Decía que tenía que pensar/ trabajar/ ayudarle a un amigo/ llamar a mi profesora...

C. A travieso, travieso y medio.   1. ¿pintabas...? Yo pintaba...   **2.** ¿dormías...? Yo dormía...   **3.** ¿tenías una...? Yo tenía una...   **4.** ¿recibías...? Yo recibía...   **5.** ¿jugabas a...? Yo jugaba a...   **6.** ¿vendías...? Yo vendía...   **7.** ¿tirabas...? Yo tiraba...   **8.** ¿vivías cerca de...? Yo vivía cerca de...

D. ¡Qué diferentes éramos! *Personal answers;* suggestions follow.
1. estaba enferma/ tenía prueba/ tenía que trabajar/ tenía clases
2. le gusta hacer deportes/ le gustan las montañas/ quiere esquiar mejor   **3.** hablaba mucho/ tenía muchos amigos(as)/ salía con mis tíos/ hermanos   **4.** limpiaba/ aspiraba/ ordenaba la casa, pero ahora no la limpio/ paso la aspiradora/ ordeno nunca.   **5.** peleamos por una muñequita/ nos enojamos porque perdimos un partido/ peleamos por una bicicleta

E. Buen editor.   1. aprendió   **2.** era   **3.** A menudo   **4.** lo   **5.** mayor   **6.** lo   **7.** iba   **8.** dijo   **9.** estuviste   **10.** supieron

IV. Expresión oral

Personal answers; suggestions follow.   **1.** Vi su anuncio y quería saber ¿cuánto vale el/la...? ¿Dónde lo/la compró? ¿Cuántos años tiene?   **2.** Vi su anuncio y quería saber ¿cuánto es el alquiler? ¿Dónde vivía Ud. antes? ¿Dónde trabajó el año pasado? ¿Dónde leyó mi anuncio?   **3.** ¿Dónde quieren vivir Uds.? ¿Cómo era su apartamento en su país? ¿Cuántas habitaciones tenía? ¿Qué servicios tenían?

V. Expresión escrita

Variable answers. Use the vocabulary, strategies, and structures learned. Use verbs on pp. 232-234 to describe activities. Use the pronouns when necessary and the preterit and imperfect tenses of the verbs learned.

PRUEBA: UNIDAD 5

I. Cultura

Variable answers that contain at least the following.

1. Freshness in food is highly valued in Hispanic cultures. Things that are packaged and processed are looked down upon. It is, therefore, better to go to a "smelly" market where things are fresh. Fresh food has aroma and different texture, unlike what Hispanics might call plastic-looking/tasting American food.

2. Even steak, french fries, and a hamburger have different names, aromas and textures in different Spanish-speaking countries. And the variety in food is so great that it would be a shame to miss out and not try different foods. Even though there may be many words for the same food, many times there is a general word that is known almost everywhere.

3. The custom of sitting and talking after a meal is one more testimony of the importance of family and friends in Hispanic culture. People are the important things that one has to "do," and it is considered extremely rude to run off after a meal. Favors and business deals depend a great deal on the time spent with one's counterparts.

4. There are doctors and modern medicine, of course, but many people don't consider it necessary to go to the doctor for common ailments such as colds or upset stomachs. Antibiotics, sulphas and other medicines are considered toxic or too strong in such cases. In contrast, the "doctor" in the marketplace knows the people of a town very well and knows how to listen to them. His/Her prescriptions are inexpensive, individually-mixed, practical and tested, handed down from generation to generation. People know and trust him/her because the prescriptions generally work quite well.

II. Vocabulario y lectura.

A. Encuesta de preferencias alimenticias. *Personal answers.*

B. A precio módico. *Variable answers;* suggestions follow.
1. hamburguesa frita, con mayonesa, mostaza, lechuga, tomate, batido de chocolate o vainilla. Vale unos $3,50 dólares. 2. frito, con salsa de miel y mostaza, con papas fritas, con té frío. Vale unos $4,20 dólares. 3. un taco de carne con lechuga, tomate y queso. Acompañado con arroz con frijoles, salsa picante. Cuesta... 4. una papa asada con tocino, mantequilla, cebolla, queso, ... Cuesta... 5. sopa de vegetales con zanahorias, papas, apio, maíz, trocitos de carne. Cuesta unos... 6. helado de fresas con crema y salsa de chocolate. Además, ... Vale unos...

C. Amigos sabrosos. *Variable answers;* suggestions follow. 1. pescado frito, papas fritas y ensalada de repollo. 2. una tortilla española, ensalada, vino y pan. 3. pollo asado, papas asadas, maíz y ensalada mixta.

D. Lectura. **1.** Porque comemos lo que nos dictan los deseos del cerebro.
2. Porque te vas acostumbrando a lo que comes normalmente y te dan
ganas de seguir comiendo igual. **3.** Porque cualquier comida las
contiene, incluso los huevos y el pan. Todo te da algún efecto. **4.** Si
comes mucho azúcar, el cerebro funciona más lentamente y se te
olvida la prueba. **5.** Porque producen una sensación exquisita y esto
condiciona nuestro deseo de más sensaciones exquisitas. **6.** *Personal
answer.*

III. Gramática

A. Precisión. **1.** estábamos **2.** fuimos **3.** había **4.** querían **5.** he
visto **6.** haber mirado **7.** teníamos **8.** haya hecho **9.** la he
comido/ la como **10.** estaba **11.** pidió **12.** los quiso **13.** estaban
14. se los comió **15.** le pidió

B. Cortesía antes de nada. **1.** haya estado muy alto/ se haya
quemado la casa **2.** hayas comprado los mariscos **3.** hecho otra
salsa **4.** lo hayas quemado **5.** habérmela hecho/ haberla hecho
6. no haber venido

C. Para averiguarlo todo. **1.** ¿Has descubierto...? **2.** ¿Has traído...?
3. ¿Has hecho...? **4.** ¿Has comido...? **5.** ¿Has frito...? **6.** ¿Has
resuelto...? **7.** ¿Has puesto...? **8.** ¿Has roto...?

D. Buen editor. **1.** era **2.** contó **3.** le **4.** hayan limpiado **5.** hervirlo
6. inventó **7.** ha avanzado **8.** hervirla **9.** pasteurizarla
10. uperizada **11.** comprársela

IV. Expresión oral

Personal answers; suggestions follow. **1.** ¿Han llegado los mariscos frescos
ya? ¿Han bajado de precio las naranjas? No creo que hayan bajado...
2. ¿Ha trabajado en...? ¿Ha cocinado langostas/ camarones? Espero que
nunca haya quemado el puré de papas... **3.** ¿Dónde has probado el mejor
pollo frito? ¿Crees que hayan mejorado las cafeterías...? No creo que
haya...

V. Expresión escrita

Variable answers. Use the vocabulary, strategies, and structures learned.
Use a variety of tenses as necessary. For the recipe, you may follow the
model on p. 289 but provide more details. For the thank you note, you
may follow the model on p. 283.

PRUEBA: UNIDAD 6

I. Cultura

Variable answers that contain at least the following.

1. Appearance is very important in Hispanic cultures and can even determine whether or not someone gets a job. Hispanics take more pride in their appearance and value dressing up.

2. Jeans and a T-shirt won't get you far in Hispanic countries. Most people consistently dress up all the time. Their casual dress is never sloppy and is always spruced up with nice shoes, jewelry, etc. Although words for clothes may vary, there are some that almost all Hispanics understand.

3. Because of the high price of clothing and an eye for good quality as well as of an emphasis on industriousness and on attaching special value to what was made or given to them, Hispanics despise waste (throwing away clothing). So rather than buy something new, they fix the old, which can be made like new again. In this way, they avoid wasting what they consider to be perfectly good, expensive and dear clothes.

II. Vocabulario y lectura

A. Encuesta de preferencias en el vestir. *Personal answers.*

B. Asociaciones. *Variable answers;* suggestions follow.
1. impermeable, pantalones, camisa **2.** abrigo, pantalones, bolsa
3. de reparaciones, de moda, de diseño **4.** pantalones, falda, chaqueta
5. cortas, largas, sin mangas **6.** vestido, blusa **7.** prenda, tela,
camisa **8.** vestido, diseño, collar, reloj **9.** zapatos, botas, bolsos,
billeteras, cinturón **10.** chaqueta, vestido, chaleco, pañuelo
11. abrigo, chaqueta, bufanda, gorra **12.** de béisbol, de lana, de tela
13. una prenda, la ropa, un vestido **14.** está a la moda, es finísimo,
es de buena marca, es la talla precisa **15.** *jeans*, camiseta, zapatos,
suéter **16.** reparar, pintar, renovar, cambiar, está gastado/
manchado/ roto

C. Guardarropas. *Variable answers;* suggestions follow. **1.** abrigo de
piel, vestido de Versace impecable, falda de terciopelo nueva, collar de
perlas cultivadas, anillo de brillantes auténticos **2.** abrigo negro de
lana roto, *jeans* rotos, camiseta de manga larga descolorida, ropa
interior abrigada **3.** unas zapatillas blancas, una chaqueta de cuero
con cuello de piel, unos *jeans* **4.** traje gris oscuro, corbata roja,
zapatos negros, camisa fina **5.** vestidos rosados, un anillito, un reloj
de Mickey Mouse, pijama de seda, pulsera de oro, un paraguas blanco
6. *jeans*, collares de oro, gorras de su equipo, chaqueta de su equipo,
chaqueta de cuero, reloj carísimo

D. Por favor, basta. *Personal answers.* Begin: Espero que... nadie me compre... porque ya tengo tres...

E. Lectura. *Variable answers; suggestions follow.* **1.** Trata de telas artificiales. **2.** Me parecen muy útiles las prendas que... **3.** Busco ropa que sea/ tenga/ mantenga la temperatura constante/ me haga sentir elegante... **4.** Los astronautas ya han usado la ropa del futuro. La necesitan porque hace mucho frío y mucho calor allá arriba y, como están estresados, la ropa "relax" los puede ayudar mucho. **5.** Busco una tela/ prenda que sea/ tenga/ valga/ se planche sola/ tenga memoria... **6.** ... se adapta al ambiente o al cliente y se puede usar en cualquier clima. Sus características cambian, en vez de cambiar la ropa.

III. Gramática

A. Precisión. **1.** saquemos **2.** nos organicemos **3.** tengamos **4.** lleve **5.** sepa **6.** haya **7.** pueda **8.** estén **9.** deban/ debamos

B. Cortesía antes de nada. *Variable answers; suggestions follow.*
1. use esas camisas/ ese color ahora, pero te queda original.
2. tengas otro de poliéster para que no tengas que plancharlo ahora.
3. haya tallas grandes como en la tienda XX. **4.** la hayas quemado. ¡Déjame echarle un poco de vinagre para la mancha! **5.** se vean más a la moda, más livianos. **6.** piensen que tengo mal gusto. Prefiero una que tenga unas piedras.

C. Para encontrar lo que quieres. *Variable answers; suggestions follow.* **1.** Busco una blusa que sea... **2.** ¿Tiene un saco que sea de...? **3.** Quiero unos pantalones que tengan... **4.** Busco una cartera que sea de... **5.** ¿Hay un impermeable que sea reversible y que esté bien terminado? **6.** ¿Tiene algún saco que tenga ojales hechos a mano?

D. Me importa la ropa. *Variable answers; suggestions follow.* **1.** la ropa te quede perfecta. **2.** haya otro perfume como éste. **3.** sea elegante, de diseño moderno y de corte impecable. **4.** haga trajes a medida/ por pedido. **5.** pidan uniformes que sean de colores vivos o telas sintéticas.

E. Buen editor. **1.** ponerme **2.** entrevistar **3.** esa **4.** dé **5.** lleve **6.** inspirar **7.** elija **8.** esta **9.** verme **10.** me ponga

IV. Expresión oral

Personal answers; suggestions follow. **1.** ¿Qué ropa es de última moda? ¿Qué telas usan ahora? ¿Hay alguna prenda que sea inteligente? **2.** ¿En qué países voy a trabajar? ¿Venden ropa de algodón o sólo telas sintéticas? ¿Cómo eligen los colores y los diseños? Creo que debemos contratar un diseñador hispano como... **3.** ¿Por qué cree necesario iniciar una revolución en el mundo de la moda? ¿Qué tipo de diseño tiene en mente? ¿Qué telas prefiere y por qué?

V. Expresión escrita

Variable answers. Use the vocabulary, strategies, and structures learned.
1. Use the subjunctive to describe pieces of clothing you like or are looking for. **2.** Use new vocabulary to describe what is wrong with the clothes. Use appropriate, polite expressions to thank the employee in charge.

PRUEBA: UNIDAD 7

I. Cultura

Variable answers that contain at least the following.

1. Reliance on herbal, homeopathic, and natural remedies is a long-honored tradition in several European societies. Most people will combine different medicines and will go to a physician only when the condition looks serious or acute. (Use of natural remedies has grown tremendously in the U.S. as well.)

2. A café, bar or restaurant is the meeting place in every neighborhood or area; it doesn't necessarily mean that people congregate there for drinking, exclusively. These establishments serve food, desserts, drinks and coffee. Different countries do have stringent DUI (DWI) regulations and campaigns.

3. It depends on the country and the area as well as the prevalence of traditional customs among indigeneous or **mestizo** populations.

II. Vocabulario y lectura

A. Encuesta de necesidades de atención de salud. *Personal answers.*

B. ¿Qué pasó? 1. Mal **2.** Bien **3.** Bien **4.** Mal **5.** Mal

C. Asociaciones. *Variable answers;* suggestions follow. **1.** dolor de espalda, infección, transplante **2.** disminuye las grasas, deja de beber **3.** dolor de muelas, cepillarse bien **4.** huesos rotos, pierna, muñeca **5.** sacárselas, levantar una ceja **6.** apoyar bien en la computadora, fracturarse, relajar **7.** tápate/ cuídate las orejas, aretes **8.** ataque al corazón/ al hígado, ataque cardíaco **9.** dedo, mano, cara **10.** fractura, pierna rota, brazo quebrado, me caí, me lastimé **11.** me pica la nariz, me pican los ojos **12.** en la cara, alergia, crema, jabón **13.** escalofríos, para evitar la tos, frótate las manos, influenza, gripe **14.** pulmones, cáncer, te arde la garganta **15.** es malo para el corazón/ la circulación, evita la comida frita, debes bajar de peso **16.** para que duermas bien, para calmar el estómago, insomnio, dolor de estómago

D. Botiquín. *Variable answers;* suggestions follow. **1.** tomar miel con limón/ limonada/ pastillas para la garganta/ antibióticos **2.** ponerse hielo, ponerse una venda/ una curita/ crema con antibiótico, tomar aspirina   **3.** tomar aspirinas o ibuprofeno/ mucho líquido/ limonada/ té, dormir   **4.** tomar jarabe para la tos, tomar caldo de pollo/ taparse el pecho/ ponerse una compresa de mostaza   **5.** tomar un antidiarreico, descansar mucho, evitar la comida cruda, evitar deshidratarse   **6.** tomar un antihistamínico, ponerse hielo en la picadura, evitar las hormigas/ abejas, no ir al campo

E. Puedo hacer un gesto.   *Variable answers*; suggestions follow.
1. cierre bien los ojos   **2.** apunte/ haga gestos con las manos   **3.** no abra la boca   **4.** mueva una mano/ les haga un gesto con la mano

F. Lectura.   *Variable answers*; suggestions follow.   **1.** Tómate una infusión, relájate, tápate los oídos, deja de fumar, deja de beber, no hagas ejercicios violentos, estudia en un lugar tranquilo; es preciso aprender a vivir con el dolor. Hay que salir, divertirse, olvídate del dolor, no sueñes que el dolor se va a acabar, alégrate de estar sano.
2. Me acuesto, duermo, me relajo, tomo dos cápsulas de..., salgo, me divierto, tomo té...   **3.** En la medicina más natural, porque la otra medicina no puede curarle su dolor.   **4.** Porque siempre está con él, vive en la misma casa. Mi hermano es...   **5.** Personal answer. Mira, Ryan, es mejor que dejes de... y que tomes... También piensa en...

III. Gramática

A. Precisión.   **1.** Ayúdame   **2.** Ve   **3.** No lo hagas tú   **4.** Mira   **5.** Llama   **6.** dile   **7.** Cierra   **8.** No me exasperes   **9.** ponte   **10.** no me tomes

B. Chiquita desobediente.   **1.** ¡Tómatelo tú!   **2.** ¡Ciérrala tú!   **3.** ¡Hazlo tú!   **4.** ¡Tráelo tú!   **5.** ¡Contéstalo tú! (¡Levántate tú!)   **6.** ¡Hazlas tú! (¡Anda tú a hacerlas!)

C. Para que no te pase eso.   *Variable answers*; suggestions follow.
1. Deja de trabajar, relájate y estírate cada 30 minutos; levanta los brazos y mueve las manos y los dedos.   **2.** Trata de tener cuidado. Haz ejercicios antes de correr. Precaliéntate.   **3.** Evita jugar cuando tengas los músculos fríos. Trata de comprarte buenas zapatillas. Precaliéntate; relájate.   **4.** Disminuye las grasas; no tomes helados porque tienen crema y azúcar. Toma yogurt descremado/ sin grasa.
5. Toma un histamínico; evita el polvo; trata de aspirar la habitación antes de acostarte; usa una máscara para aspirar; usa tu espray para la nariz.   **6.** Evita los lugares húmedos; trata de usar un espray para los mosquitos; pon un velo sobre tu cama...

D. De veras, lo siento.   **1.** Siento que te hayas quemado...   **2.** Me alegro que no les haya pasado nada.   **3.** Me alegro que ya le hayan sacado el yeso.   **4.** Siento que no tengas qué llevarle a tu amiga.
5. Siento que al médico no le importe que no puedas ir a clases.

E. ¡Ay, doctorcito!   *Variable answers*; suggestions follow.   **1.** déme un remedio para el dolor; examíneme la garganta.   **2.** hágame un masaje en la espalda; déme pastillas para el dolor; tómeme una radiografía   **3.** explíqueme cómo me la agarré...   **4.** déme una nota para mi profesor; recéteme unas pastillas contra la inflamación   **5.** examíneme y explíqueme por qué tengo esta roncha

F. Buen editor.   1. deje   **2.** revelen   **3.** consuman   **4.** ayúdame   **5.** explícales   **6.** adquieran   **7.** experimentar   **8.** siéntete   **9.** coopere   **10.** deje

IV. Expresión oral

Personal answers; suggestions follow.   **1.** ¿Qué vitaminas debo tomar todos los días? ¿Qué minerales me faltan en la dieta de la cafetería? ¿Por qué es bueno que consuma antioxidantes?   **2.** Señora, ¿qué es lo primero que hace cuando sus niños tienen tos/ fiebre? ¿Qué pasa si no tiene dinero y su marido se dobla el tobillo? ¿Cuándo van al hospital?   **3.** ¿Qué puedes hacer para ayudar a un joven drogadicto? ¿Cuándo hay que atacar la drogadicción? Para ti, ¿qué es más peligroso, beber o fumar?

V. Expresión escrita

Variable answers. Use the vocabulary, strategies, and structures learned. Use informal commands to write a routine or to propose courses of action to friends. Use pronouns with the commands whenever necessary.

P R U E B A :   U N I D A D   8

I. Cultura

Variable answers that contain at least the following.

1. This is now a myth since the authoritarian ruler cycle ended in the 80s. Attracting foreign investment has been one of successful present-day democratic leaders' major strategies to upgrade underdeveloped economies into emerging ones.   In turn, international companies welcome the opportunity to expand in countries with non-existent or incomplete environmental laws and cheap labor. Major pollution is caused in this way. More environmental damage is generated by ongoing desertification, defoliation, and erosion processes as well as meteorological catastrophes such as a reversal in the Pacific weather pattern known as **El Niño** (because it hits the South American Pacific coastline around Christmas time).

2. Because most services, educational establishments and jobs are in big cities, Hispanics live in urban areas. A more important reason is the traditional tendency to stay in populated areas to continue cultural behavioral patterns of maintaining regular and close contact with one's circle of family and friends. Only the very wealthy sometimes develop suburb-like communities as weekend residences.

3. Because that's where family and friends, jobs and major manufacturing activities are. Furthermore, since farming and cattleraising is the province of powerful landowners by tradition, there's not much to do for a living in quaint little towns.

4. With NAFTA and global trade standardizing health requirements in the Americas, one runs no more risk of ingesting contaminated food abroad than one can here at home. Domestic hamburger patties contaminated with salmonella or imported strawberries contaminated with cyclospori made the news in 1997 and produced comparable reactions from the public.

II. Vocabulario y lectura

A. Encuesta de vida urbana.   *Personal answers.*

B. Asociaciones.   *Variable answers*; suggestions follow.   **1.** de agua potable, alimentos, combustibles renovables, estacionamiento, fondos, paisajes vírgenes, reservas forestales/ naturales   **2.** de contaminación, impuestos a pagar, delincuencia   **3.** del fracaso de, de los retos, los riesgos, la pobreza, la escasez de   **4.** desamparados, desigualdad, esperanza, cansancio, hambre, desempleados, apoyo a las organizaciones caritativas   **5.** invertir, aumentar, apoyar   **6.** el éxito y el fracaso, la solidaridad y el egoísmo, el amor y el odio   **7.** obras, sucursales de empresas, calles anchas, puentes y carreteras, transporte colectivo, aumentar la tasa de ocupación   **8.** autopistas, carreteras, tráfico atascado, transporte colectivo   **9.** la energía solar o del viento, los parques y zonas verdes, los recursos naturales, los desperdicios   **10.** basura, desperdicios, reciclaje, recoger   **11.** el gobierno, los empleados, disminuir la deuda pública, los servicios públicos   **12.** delfines, extinción, caimanes, tigres, águilas   **3.** reciclar, clasificar, basura, desperdicios   **14.** darse cuenta de, usar energía solar, ahorrar agua/ electricidad   **15.** virgen, defoliado, urbano, cuidar, reducir la deforestación   **16.** letreros, choques de autos, tráfico atascado, calles y aceras, tanto ruido de bocinas

C. Curas dolorosas.   *Variable answers*; suggestions follow.   Ojalá que...
1. que construyeran más ferrocarriles metropolitanos; que exigieran compartir los vehículos   **2.** usaran combustibles renovables/ energía solar o del viento/ ahorraran energía   **3.** redujeran los niveles de CO_2 con nuevas tecnologías, con energía solar   **4.** inventaran otros materiales/ plantaran más árboles   **5.** encontraran otras fuentes de agua potable, ahorraran agua, disminuyeran el mal uso
6. construyeran otras obras/ más centros comunitarios/ para ancianos/ guarderías infantiles, aumentaran las zonas verdes

D. Podría hacer algo.   *Variable answers*; suggestions follow.
1. redujeran la cantidad de industrias nuevas/ desarrollaran nuevas tecnologías/ previnieran los efectos de la combustión de los motores
2. se dieran cuenta que las sierras son pulmones naturales/ prohibieran que la gente construyera más casas/ minas allá
3. protegiéramos a los niños y las madres   **4.** inventaran otros materiales que no usaran celulosa

E. Lectura. *Variable answers*; suggestions follow. **1.** Treinta y cinco mil niños mueren diariamente, la basura y los desperdicios han aumentado, hay mucho ruido. **2.** Recoger la basura; llevar una bolsa de basura a los paseos; clasificar la basura; caminar o montar en bicicleta; enterrar los restos de comida y desperdicios; reutilizar las latas, plásticos y empaques de vidrio, cartón o papel; ocupar menos artículos de papel o reusarlos más; no imprimir nada hasta que esté totalmente terminado; no plantar árboles que exijan demasiada agua; no generar mucho ruido; organizarse para que la industria limpie y recicle también. **3.** *Personal answer.* Creo que sería mejor... **4.** *Personal answer.* Podría ahorrar papel si (no) imprimiera... **5.** *Personal answer.* Sería mejor que... se fijaran metas más posibles...

III. Gramática

A. Precisión. **1.** ahorrar **2.** fuéramos **3.** se da cuenta de **4.** desarrollan **5.** evite **6.** supiera **7.** habría **8.** ando pensando **9.** desarrollará **10.** creciendo **11.** evitaré

B. Ando pensando en el ambiente. *Variable answers*; suggestions follow. **1.** Ojalá que no pusiera insecticida; yo podría limpiarlo **2.** Ojalá que no las tirara; yo podría llevarlas a... **3.** Sería mejor que no tirara el aceite; yo podría... **4.** Ojalá que no metieran...; podríamos... **5.** Ojalá que no fuera tan caro/ no tirara los papeles y...; podríamos... **6.** Sería mejor que no lo tirara...; podríamos...

C. Sensible. *Variable answers*; suggestions follow. **1.** si se extinguieran, sería una gran desgracia porque... **2.** si lo cortaran, sería espantoso porque... **3.** si no los protegieran, se extinguirían los manatíes y los pájaros... **4.** si se agotara, no habría más bisontes ni... **5.** si las quemaran, habría mucho humo y muchos deportistas... **6.** si se extendiera, mucha gente moriría/ se enfermaría...

D. Ni idea. *Variable answers*; suggestions follow. No tengo idea cuándo... **1.** la abrirán **2.** lo construirán **3.** cuándo pagaré/ podré pagar **4.** habrá una estación nueva **5.** tendrán la preferencia

E. Buen editor. **1.** sé **2.** aumente **3.** conduzca **4.** se hiciera **5.** recordando **6.** vuelva **7.** estará **8.** habrá **9.** daría **10.** hubiera

IV. Expresión oral

Personal answers; suggestions follow.

1. Sería mejor que respetara el río porque podría ser peor alterar su curso; ¿por qué no le pide ayuda a...? Debiéramos hacer una campaña para que los industriales ayudaran. ¿No podríamos organizar a la comunidad para que dieran más fondos?

2. ¿Por qué tenemos que usar más terreno en rascacielos/ estacionamientos...? Deberíamos construir estacionamientos subterráneos/ sendas para bicicletas/ sendas para vehículos eléctricos/ zonas verdes...

3. ¿Qué preferirías, más estacionamientos o más...? ¿Qué pasará cuando aumente el número de estudiantes, construiremos más estacionamientos todavía? ¿Por qué no...?

V. Expresión escrita

Variable answers. Use the vocabulary, strategies, and structures learned. Speculate about what could be done about something specific. Use the past subjunctive, the conditional and the future tenses.

1. *Begin:* Soy un joven estudiante sin mucha experiencia, sin embargo, me doy cuenta que... Me gustaría hacer algo y apoyar... Ojalá que alguien me escuchara, así podríamos...

2. *Begin:* Te escribo para ofrecer mi apoyo y mi ayuda para mejorar el uso de los recursos en nuestra universidad... Los estudiantes deberíamos... Si el comité lograra unir a la gente, yo podría... Si fuera necesario, también le pediría a... que ayudaran, porque a ellos les interesa...

Laboratory Manual
Answer Key

LECCIÓN PRELIMINAR

Vocabulario

A. **1.** b   **2.** c   **3.** b   **4.** b   **5.** a   **6.** c   **7.** c   **8.** c

B. **1.** a   **2.** b   **3.** c   **4.** b   **5.** a

C. **1.** p   **2.** p   **3.** n   **4.** p   **5.** p   **6.** n   **7.** n

D. **1.** words on paper   **2.** dictionary   **3.** classmates   **4.** books   **5.** calculator
6. cassettes

Pronunciación

1. ¡Hola! ¿Qué tal? ¿Cómo estás?   **2.** Buenos días. ¿Cómo está usted,
señorita?   **3.** Me llamo Anita López. Y tú, ¿cómo te llamas?
4. Por favor, ¿dónde está la biblioteca? ¿Y el laboratorio?
5. Necesito mi bolígrafo. También necesito mi diccionario. ¿Tienes tus
apuntes?

CAPÍTULO 1

Vocabulario

A. **Paso 1.** Suggested answers: nacionalidad, color de los ojos, características
personales, color del pelo, intereses, gustos

Paso 2. Gilberto: short man, black eyes in bathing suit; Miguel: Tall,
blond man, cooking; Felipe: Blond man, dancing; Gonzalo: Heavy-set man
with camera; Raúl: Short, blond man with computer

B. **Paso 1.** things they like to do
Paso 2. **1.** a   **2.** b   **3.** c   **4.** a   **5.** b   **6.** a

C. **1.** a   **2.** b   **3.** b   **4.** a

Gramática 1

1. c **2.** c **3.** b **4.** b **5.** c **6.** a

Gramática 2

1. b **2.** b **3.** a **4.** a **5.** c **6.** a

Gramática 3

Paso 1. **1.** ir al cine, ir de compras, sacar fotos, estudiar con compañeros

Paso 2. **1.** dos/ir de compras **2.** cuatro/ir de compras **3.** cinco/ir al cine **4.** cinco/estudiar con compañeros

Pronunciación

1. ¿Tienes tu cuaderno y tu diccionario? **2.** Silvia es seria, puntual y un poco impaciente. **3.** Samuel es de piel trigueña y es algo grueso. **4.** Me gusta hacer ejercicio y viajar. **5.** Quiero ser ingeniero o periodista.

C A P Í T U L O 2

Vocabulario

A. Paso 1. sus estudios y metas **Paso 2.** **1.** a **2.** b **3.** b **4.** c **5.** b
Paso 3. Answers will vary.

B. Paso 1. sus planes **Paso 2. 1.** woman at computer **2.** students meeting each other **3.** woman writing check **4.** man with car **5.** interview scene **6.** woman holding paycheck **Paso 3.** 3

C. Paso 1. his spring and summer schedule
Paso 2. el 22 de abril, el 30 de abril, el 15 de mayo, el 23 de mayo, el 1 de junio, el 10 de junio, el 16 de junio, el 19 de agosto, el 30 de agosto
Paso 3. family commitment: el 19 de agosto; career move: el 30 de agosto; academic event: el 23 de mayo; physical challenge: el 10 de junio

D. Paso 1. employees' salaries and length of time with company
Paso 2. Miriam: 24 años, $73,000; Juan Francisco: 11 años, $59,000; Víctor: 14 años, $105,000; Ángela: 13 años, $64,000; Martina: 10 años, $45,000

Gramática

A. Paso 1. por teléfono, en una residencia estudiantil

Paso 2. ir a un baile/ con Margarita y Susana; estudiar; ir de compras; correr/con Antonio; trabajar en el centro estudiantil/con Tomás; ir a la discoteca/con Antonio

Paso 3. (No) Me gusta... ir al cine, ir a un baile, ir al partido de tenis, estudiar, correr, ir de compras, trabajar en el centro estudiantil, ir a la discoteca

B. Paso 1. at a daycare center **Paso 2.** Juanita, crayons; Susanita, tapes; Marcos, computer; Carmen y Elena, books; Ángela, bookbag

C. Paso 1. she and some new classmates
Paso 2. **1.** c **2.** b **3.** a **4.** a **5.** c

Pronunciación

1. ¿Qué intereses tiene, señor López? **2.** Puedo correr rápido. **3.** Además, me gusta ir a los partidos de fútbol. **4.** Quiero un puesto en un hospital.
5. Tengo una entrevista el veintidós de abril.

C A P Í T U L O 3

Vocabulario

A. Paso 1. outdoor **Paso 2.** **1.** otoño **2.** invierno **3.** primavera
Paso 3. Answers will vary.

B. Paso 1. **1.** 2 **2.** 3 **3.** 2
Paso 2. Answers will vary but should include six of the following activities: ir a nadar al río, ir a la piscina, tomar el sol, estudiar, montar a caballo, quedarse en casa, leer, jugar naipes, alquilar una película, llamar a los compañeros, hacer una fiesta, tocar discos compactos, divertirse, salir (con amigos), patinar en el hielo.

C. Paso 1. Errors: lunes: estudiar a las 8:00; jueves: viene a cenar Pedro; miércoles: lavar la ropa a las 8:15; sábado: ir al río a las 7:30; domingo: a las 5:00 los compañeros van a hacer una fiesta en casa de Marilú
Paso 2. Answers will vary.

Gramática 1

Paso 1. **1.** a **2.** b **3.** c **4.** a **5.** a **Paso 2.** Answers will vary.

Gramática 2

Paso 1. A Mariano le gusta el cine español (le gustan las películas). A Yolanda le gustan las novelas de misterio y ciencia ficción. A Gabriela le gustan los discos de Enrique Iglesias y Juan Luis Guerra (le gusta la música de Enrique Iglesias y Juan Luis Guerra). A Verónica le gusta la ropa.

Pronunciación

1. Me gusta esquiar en el agua.   **2.** ¿Cómo está, señora Andrade?   **3.** Voy al parque a acampar.   **4.** Vamos a hacer una fiesta hoy.   **5.** José va a alquilar una película argentina.

C A P Í T U L O   4

Vocabulario

A. Paso 1. 1. universidad **2.** universidad **3.** vacaciones **4.** vacaciones **5.** universidad   **Paso 2.** Answers will vary.

B. Answers may resemble the following: **1.** aburrida **2.** nervioso, estresado, preocupado **3.** contenta, relajada **4.** enojada, furiosa **5.** llena de energía

C. Paso 1. un mensaje telefónico   **Paso 2.** Activities mentioned (all sad faces): ducharse, quejarse de la rutina, despertarse temprano, estudiar para exámenes, acostarse tarde, arreglarse rápido para ir a la universidad, hacer la tarea, trabajar los fines de semana
Paso 3. Answers will vary.

Gramática 1

Paso 1. un viaje al extranjero **Paso 2. 1.** a **2.** c **3.** a **4.** c **5.** b

Gramática 2

Corrected information: llegada a Madrid, 6:22 hrs.; de compras, 16:00 hrs.; salida para Toledo, 10:15 hrs. **Paso 2.** Answers will vary.

Pronunciación

1. Bárbara y Víctor son de Venezuela.   **2.** Vamos a ver los colores de los árboles.   **3.** Tengo que vestirme bien para trabajar.   **4.** El sábado me voy de vacaciones.   **5.** Me divierto en grande con mis nuevos amigos.

C A P Í T U L O   5

Vocabulario

A. Paso 1. Maricarmen, el 16 de marzo, 1957; Blanca, el 12 de febrero, 1960; Olivia, el 24 de diciembre, 1975; Luz Carmen, el 31 de octubre, 1978; Miguel Ángel, el 15 de septiembre, 1981.

Paso 2. Answers may include the following: Maricarmen es la hija mayor, vive en Barcelona, tiene dos hijos; Blanca es la hija menor, vive en Sevilla con su hijo y su tía; Olivia es la nieta favorita, es estudiante de medicina en Madrid; Luz Carmen estudia para veterinaria en Barcelona; Miguel Ángel se parece a su papá.

B. **Paso 1.** **1.** happy **2.** sad **3.** neutral **4.** happy **5.** sad **6.** neutral **7.** sad **8.** happy **9.** happy
Paso 2. **1.** su hermano **2.** su padre **3.** su tío **4.** su hermana **5.** su tía **6.** su madre
Paso 3. Answers may include the following. **1.** Es su hermano menor; los dos se pelearon; es un muchacho egoísta. **2.** Se murió hace dos años en Puerto Rico; Juan Carlos lo extraña mucho. **3.** Vive en casa de Juan Carlos; está divorciado. **4.** Vive en casa de Juan Carlos. **5.** Está divorciada de tío Francisco; los dos no se hablan. **6.** Influyó mucho en Carlos; es cariñosa; Juan Carlos la adora.

Gramática 1

Paso 1. una conversación telefónica **Paso 2.** **1.** pasado **2.** pasado **3.** pasado **4.** habitualmente **5.** todavía no **6.** todavía no **7.** habitualmente **8.** pasado **9.** pasado **10.** todavía no **11.** todavía no

Gramática 2

Paso 1. ¿Cómo fue tu viaje? ¿Trabajaste mucho? ¿Qué hiciste al llegar a San Francisco? ¿Te gustó? ¿Y qué hiciste después de comer? ¿Adónde fuiste después? ¿No te duchaste? ¿Llegaste tarde? ¿Hasta qué hora trabajaste? ¿Te sentiste muy cansado?
Paso 2. **1.** llegó **2.** fue **3.** trabajó, se divirtió **4.** hizo **5.** Fue **6.** fue, se acostó **7.** se olvidó, se despertó **8.** se duchó, se vistió, fue corriendo **9.** Trabajó **10.** se sintió **11.** ganó, consiguió

Pronunciación

1. Adela tiene dieciséis años. **2.** Mi madre creció rodeada de una familia grande. **3.** Mi tía Adriana está casada con un señor divorciado. **4.** Mi tía Dora es viuda; su marido murió el año pasado. **5.** Mi primo Donaldo va a mudarse a otra ciudad el sábado.

C A P Í T U L O 6

Vocabulario

A. **Paso 1.** **1.** el Sr. Castillo **2.** Teresita **4.** Marcos **5.** Luisa **7.** Rolando **8.** Clarita **9.** Rolando **12.** el Sr. Castillo
Paso 2. **1.** maleta, 765 pesos **2.** cajita de música, 326 pesos **5.** juego de vasos de cristal, 1.200 pesos **12.** bolsa de cuero, 480 pesos

B. Paso 1. **1.** joyería **2.** librería **3.** almacén **4.** restaurante **5.** dulcería **6.** ferretería **Paso 2.** un juego de herramientas

Gramática 1

Paso 1. **1.** a **2.** b **3.** a **4.** a **Paso 2.** En el pasado: una cámara fotográfica, camisa de seda, un reloj de oro; Todavía no: vino **Paso 3.** Answers will vary.

Gramática 2

Paso 1. en un almacén **Paso 2.** **1.** el marco pequeño **2.** el pastel de vainilla **3.** el disco compacto simple, no doble **4.** los guantes de lana **5.** la camisa de algodón **Paso 3.** Answers will vary.

Gramática 3

Paso 1. la visita de unos parientes **Paso 2.** **1.** ya ocurrió **2.** ya ocurrió **3.** va a ocurrir **4.** ya ocurrió **5.** ya ocurrió **6.** ya ocurrió **7.** ya ocurrió **8.** va a ocurrir **9.** ya ocurrió **10.** ya ocurrió **11.** va a ocurrir **12.** va a ocurrir

Pronunciación

1. Ya compré mi pasaje a Guatemala. **2.** La señorita Martínez necesita una maleta elegante. **3.** Me mostraron unos aretes de plata. **4.** A mi tía Pati le voy a regalar una botella de su vino preferido. **5.** En esa tienda todo es tan caro; no puedo pagar tanto.

C A P Í T U L O 7

Vocabulario

A. **1.** el jardín (el patio) **2.** la cocina **3.** un dormitorio **4.** el garaje **5.** el sótano **6.** un dormitorio **7.** un dormitorio **8.** el comedor **9.** el salón **10.** el baño

B. **1.** no **2.** sí **3.** no **4.** no **5.** sí **6.** no **7.** no **8.** no **9.** sí

C. Paso 1. una agente de bienes raíces y su cliente
Paso 2. 3 **Paso 3.** muebles, aparatos eléctricos, número de habitaciones, facilidades para lavar ropa, número de baños
Paso 4. Answers will vary.

D. Corrected information:
Calle Tacuba, 454; 328 metros cuadrados; 1927; 184.000 pesos.
Calle Donceles, número 874; precio: 89.000 pesos; año de construcción: 1867.

Calle Río Sena, número 244; 488 metros cuadrados; precio: 205.000 pesos.

Calle Milán, número 576; dos dormitorios; 396 metros cuadrados; año de construcción: 1995; precio: 389.000 pesos.

Gramática 1
1. a **2.** a **3.** c **4.** c **5.** a **6.** c **7.** b **8.** c

Gramática 2
1. 1 **2.** 2 **3.** 2 **4.** 1 **5.** 1 **6.** 2

Pronunciación
1. Quiero alquilar un apartamento grande y moderno. **2.** Mis compañeros Ricardo y Raúl son algo perezosos. **3.** El martes compré un juego de herramientas en la ferretería. **4.** Raquel, ¿quieres sacar a pasear al perro, por favor? **5.** No sé si la estudiante extranjera es de Costa Rica o Nicaragua.

CAPÍTULO 8

Vocabulario

A. Paso 1. Un padre y una madre hablan de sus hijos cuando eran pequeños. **Paso 2. 1.** Daniel **2.** Julia **3.** Julia y Daniel **4.** Daniel y José Miguel **5.** Julia **6.** José Miguel **7.** Daniel

B. 1. e **2.** i **3.** e **4.** i **5.** i **6.** e **7.** i

C. 1. Tenía miedo. **2.** Tenía prisa. **3.** Tenía hambre. **4.** Tenía frío. **5.** Tenía calor. **6.** Tenía razón. **7.** Tenía hambre. **8.** Tenía sueño.

Gramática 1

A. Paso 1. Una nieta habla con su hijo sobre sus nietos.
Paso 2. Bueno(a): María Paz Travieso(a): Jorge, Leonor, Daniel Cruel: Miguelito

B. 1. una ocasión **2.** acciones habituales **3.** acciones habituales **4.** acciones habituales **5.** acciones habituales

Gramática 2

1. viaje reciente **2.** niñez **3.** viaje reciente **4.** viaje reciente **5.** viaje reciente **6.** niñez **7.** viaje reciente

Pronunciación

1. Tengo dos gatos, una tortuga y una lagartija.   **2.** José y su hermano fingían que eran jugadores de béisbol.   **3.** En la guardería me gustaba jugar con mis amigos.   **4.** Me gustaba mirar los dibujos animados los domingos.

C A P Í T U L O   9

Vocabulario

A. Paso 1. Items mentioned: 1, 2, 3, 5, 6, 9, 11-18   **Paso 2.** Answers will vary.

B. Paso 1. una fiesta de cumpleaños **Paso 2.** pollo, camarones, helado, [frutas], almejas, ensalada, bebidas, pastel

C. Paso 1. dos clientes **Paso 2.** Orden núm. 3 **Paso 3.** Answers will vary but should include: pescado, salmón (en salsa de crema), mariscos, gambas (fritas), tortilla española, sopa, ensalada (de legumbres)

Gramática 1

1. a **2.** c **3.** b **4.** a **5.** b

Gramática 2

Paso 1. La dueña de un restaurante entrevista a un mesero.
Paso 2. 1-2, 5-10 **Paso 3. 1.** No sé. **2.** Trabajó en México año y medio.
3. Estudió inglés en el colegio. **4.** No sé. **5.** Tuvo un disgusto con un cliente hace dos meses. El cliente tomó demasiado vino y armó un escándalo con su pareja.

Pronunciación

1. A Lilián le encantan las almejas. **2.** Las tortillas están rellenas con pollo, frijoles y lechuga. **3.** A Samuel le gusta poner mantequilla a las habichuelas. **4.** El restaurante alemán está en la calle Londres.

C A P Í T U L O   1 0

Vocabulario

A. Paso 1. Varias personas leen libros de cocina. **Paso 2. 1.** a **2.** h **3.** f **4.** e **5.** c **Paso 3.** Answers will vary.

B. **1.** sí   **2.** no, porque en España la gente almuerza entre las 2 y 4 de la tarde; cenan entre las 10 y 11 de la noche   **3.** no, porque en el desayuno la gente no come fideos con salsa de tomate; en el almuerzo no se come pan tostado con mermelada   **4.** no, porque hay que pelar las papas antes de freírlas   **5.** no, porque las ensaladas no se sirven bien calientes   **6.** no, porque no se fríe la carne en una taza

C. **Paso 1.** clientes **Paso 2. 1.** c **2.** b **3.** b **4.** a **5.** c **6.** c **7.** b **8.** b
Paso 3. 1. un cuchillo **2.** un tenedor y un cuchillo **3.** un cuchillo
4. un tenedor **5.** una copa **6.** una cuchara **7.** un vaso **8.** una taza
(y una cuchara)

Gramática 1
1. a **2.** b **3.** c **4.** c **5.** c **6.** b

Gramática 2
Paso 1. Dos amigos especulan sobre dónde sus compañeros han ido a comer **Paso 2. 1.** F **2.** C **3.** IS **4.** C **5.** IS **6.** C **7.** F **8.** IS **9.** F
10. F **Paso 3.** Lucrecia e Ignacio comieron en el Gran Muralla; Tomás y Mercedes fueron al Costa del Sol.

Pronunciación
1. Ya hice la reservación para el almuerzo.   **2.** Cecilia me sirvió una porción de arroz blanco en la cocina.   **3.** Necesito media taza de mostaza para esta receta.   **4.** De todas las cervezas, las que más me gustan son las inglesas.

CAPÍTULO 11

Vocabulario

A. **Paso 1.** La sección damas: 1, 2, 3, 9; La sección caballeros: 4, 5, 7; La sección unisex: 8. **Paso 2. 1.** n, m **2.** l **3.** j, k **4.** i **5.** g **6.** f
7. d, e **8.** c **9.** a **Paso 3.** El collar de perlas vale 8.250 pesos; la pulsera de diamantes vale 15.325 pesos. Los paraguas de rayas valen 79 pesos; los de un solo color valen 64 pesos.

B. **Paso 1. 1.** bien **2.** no **3.** bien **4.** no **5.** no
Paso 2.   Answers will vary.

C. **Paso 1.** regalos. **Paso 2.** caja de música (sra.); suéter (sr.); muñeca (sra.); sudadera (sr.); pantalones (sr.); chaqueta de cuero (sra.); los otros regalos (sra.); zapatos de correr (sr.) **Paso 3.** Answers will vary.

Gramática 1

Paso 1. Un joven lee y comenta una carta que acaba de recibir de su novia. **Paso 2. 1.** C **2.** C **3.** SI **4.** F **5.** F **6.** F **7.** F **8.** C **9.** F **10.** F **11.** F **12.** F **Paso 3.** Answers will vary.

Gramática 2

1. a **2.** a **3.** b **4.** a **5.** b **6.** a **7.** c

Pronunciación

1. La falda de algodón me queda mejor. **2.** Me quedan bien los colores blanco y amarillo. **3.** A Marianela le gusta más la pulsera de plata. **4.** Quiero que le regale una blusa de terciopelo azul.

C A P Í T U L O 1 2

Vocabulario

A. Paso 1. en un almacén **Paso 2. 1.** g **2.** c **3.** i **4.** h **5.** b **6.** a
Paso 3. Answers will vary.

B. 1. sí **2.** no **3.** sí **4.** no **5.** no **6.** sí **7.** sí **8.** no **9.** no **10.** sí

Gramática 1

A. Paso 2. 1. empezar **2.** llevar **3.** se organicen **4.** lleven **5.** incluyan
6. hacer **7.** lleguen **8.** durmamos **9.** lleguemos **10.** sugiero
11. consiga **12.** practiquen **13.** tengan **14.** se diviertan

B. Paso 1. una dependienta
Paso 2. 1. a **2.** c **3.** a **4.** c **5.** b **6.** a **7.** c

Gramática 2

A. Paso 1. 1. a **2.** c **3.** b **4.** b **5.** a **6.** b **7.** a
Paso 2. Answers will vary.

B. 1. sí **2.** no **3.** sí **4.** no **5.** sí **6.** no **7.** sí **8.** no

CAPÍTULO 13

Vocabulario

A. **Paso 1.** en la enfermería de una escuela **Paso 2.** Paco, arm; Susana, knee; Juan Antonio, ear; Elena, stomach; Esteban, hand.

B. **Paso 1.** **1.** k **2.** a **3.** f **4.** d **5.** c **6.** j **7.** b **8.** h
Paso 2. Answers may vary: 1, 2, 3, 4, 7, 8

C. **1.** a **2.** c **3.** c **4.** a **5.** d **6.** a

Gramática 1

Paso 1. **1.** O **2.** A **3.** O **4.** A **5.** O **6.** O **7.** O **8.** O **9.** O **10.** A
11. O **12.** O
Paso 2. **1.** positiva **2.** salir a la calle para distraerse, hacer ejercicios todos los días **3.** frutas, verduras **4.** comidas fritas, grasosas

Gramática 2

Paso 1. **1.** un secreto **2.** una tarea **3.** un favor **4.** una viaje **5.** un viaje **6.** salud **7.** ropa, entevista
Paso 2. **1.** d **2.** a **3.** d **4.** b **5.** c or a **6.** a **7.** c

CAPÍTULO 14

Vocabulario

A. **1.** c **2.** a **3.** d **4.** b **5.** b **6.** a **7.** c

B. **Paso 1.** **1.** a **2.** b **3.** d **4.** d **5.** c **6.** a **7.** c **8.** b
Paso 2. Answers will vary.

Gramática 1

A. **Paso 1.** **1.** tú **2.** tú **3.** Ud. **4.** tú **5.** Ud. **6.** Ud. **7.** tú **8.** Ud.
9. Ud. **10.** tú **Paso 2.** 6, 8, 9, 10

B. **1.** buen **2.** buen **3.** buen **4.** buen **5.** buen **6.** buen **7.** mal
8. buen **9.** buen

Gramática 2

Paso 1. **1.** b **2.** f **3.** g **4.** a **5.** e **6.** d **7.** c

Paso 2. **2.** Le dio escalofríos. **3.** Le corrió la nariz. **4.** Le dolió el pecho. **5.** Es alérgico a... **6.** Se dobló el tobillo. **7.** Se tomó medidas...

CAPÍTULO 15

Vocabulario

A. **1.** S **2.** P **3.** X **4.** P **5.** X **6.** S **7.** P **8.** P **9.** P **10.** P

B. **1.** a **2.** a **3.** a **4.** a **5.** e **6.** d **7.** b **8.** c **9.** e **10.** a

Gramática 1

A. **1.** F **2.** PA **3.** PR **4.** F **5.** PR **6.** F **7.** F **8.** F **9.** PA **10.** F

B. **Paso 1.** problemas de la ciudad **Paso 2.** **1.** habitual **2.** futuro **3.** futuro **4.** futuro **5.** habitual **6.** futuro **7.** habitual **8.** futuro

Gramática 2

Paso 1. **1.** en progreso **2.** habitual **3.** en progreso **4.** en progreso **5.** habitual **6.** en progreso **7.** habitual **8.** en progreso
Paso 2. **1.** neutro **2.** positivo **3.** negativo **4.** positivo **5.** negativo **6.** negativo **7.** negativo **8.** positivo

CAPÍTULO 16

Vocabulario

A. **1.** p **2.** p **3.** o **4.** o **5.** p **6.** o **7.** p **8.** o **9.** p

B. **1.** s **2.** s **3.** p **4.** s **5.** p **6.** s **7.** p **8.** s

Gramática 1

1. sí **2.** no **3.** no **4.** sí **5.** sí **6.** no **7.** sí

Gramática 2

1. sí **2.** sí **3.** quizás **4.** sí **5.** quizás **6.** quizás **7.** quizás